Anatomy and Physiology of Speech

ANATOMY AND PHYSIOLOGY
OF SPEECH

Harold M. Kaplan

HEAD, DEPARTMENT OF PHYSIOLOGY
SOUTHERN ILLINOIS UNIVERSITY

McGRAW-HILL BOOK COMPANY, INC.

New York   Toronto   London

1960

ANATOMY AND PHYSIOLOGY OF SPEECH

33278

THE MAPLE PRESS COMPANY, YORK, PA.

PREFACE

[A knowledge of the fundamental structure of the vocal mechanism is essential to an understanding of its over-all functioning.] A sizable body of facts concerning the speech apparatus is available, but it exists in many scattered sources. Unifications of the basic material have been attempted by several writers in the last century. In twentieth-century literature, the biological aspects of speech have been emphasized in the writings of Curry, Judson and Weaver, Berry and Eisenson, Van Riper and Irwin, Moore, and a great many others.

This study attempts to unify the presently known and prominent anatomical and physiological data into an orderly account of the normal sensory and motor aspects of speech. The information is presented for the first time from the standpoint of a physiologist, an approach which seems to the writer to be proper for material that involves an extensive biological knowledge and experience. It is hoped that the text will provide from a new point of view an adequate account of that part of the human structure which is called the speech apparatus. Selected pathophysiological material has been included because of the writer's belief that some knowledge of the applications of anatomy and physiology will better motivate the student to study the more abstract basic subject matter.

The text is directed chiefly to students of speech who are perhaps for the first time encountering a relatively detailed description of the anatomical structures and bodily processes involved. It is also addressed to anatomists and physiologists who are interested in this aspect of human function.

The subject matter is adaptable enough to fit into the needs and limitations of a basic course. No single work that is short of encyclopedic can hope to encompass the information in this field both extensively and intensively. Collateral reading in standardized general textbooks of anatomy and physiology and in current journals is expected.

The biological science of voice furnishes only one means of gaining an understanding of the diverse problems of speech, and it is, in its own right, a specialized kind of knowledge. [The study of phonetics and the physics of sound, among other sciences, are also necessary in the development of a voice science, but even these disciplines are closely bound to structure and function.⏋

A treatise of a fairly pure scientific nature dealing with theories and controversial concepts should work upon a broad base. Any field of biology which can shed light upon the pertinent problems should be brought into the discussion. The practitioner of general medicine studies the theoretical biological sciences for their broad background knowledge, their concepts, and their usefulness in helping him to think about the individual as a whole, even though the subject matter often appears to have no direct clinical application. Disease, however, does not produce any fundamentally different operational system.

Although the detailed presentation of applied subject matter is better appreciated at a more advanced stage in the professional training of the student, a limited attempt has been made in Chapter 8 to bring out a few of the common clinical entities involving the larynx. In the writer's experience this material is readily comprehended at the level of training expected in this study, and it will provide an incentive for further study. It is not expected that this section will be needed by the speech clinician.

A tremendous amount of change is going on in the field of speech to build up a strong basis of theory and facts to support the diverse therapeutic methodologies. Much new instrumentation is involved. For the most part this is still in the experimental stage, and much of it is difficult to present and evaluate in a survey of anatomy and physiology.

The general organization of the material in this text is clearly arbitrary. It has followed the pattern of the course which the author has given for many years to senior college and early graduate students. Some instructors might prefer to begin their courses with Chapter 4, which deals with basic anatomical concepts and bodily organization.

Any arrangement must be more or less arbitrary, but it is the writer's conviction that regulation of the bodily processes must always be kept in mind. For this reason the neural and endocrine regulators are treated at the outset, and neurology is given considerable emphasis. As in the study of general anatomy, which deals with discrete items and isolated regions, the student's comprehension and appreciation of the total vocal mechanism and its interrelated dynamics come into being only with long and diligent study. For the purpose of more rapid motivation, some instructors might like to start their presentation by surveying voice production as a total process and then go into the details of the text from there.

Developmental and comparative anatomy have not been emphasized uniformly for all the structures under discussion. This preferential treatment is based upon the fact that one kind of knowledge explains the functioning and prevalence of anomalies in certain structures better than it does in others. At times the developmental anatomy has not been described under a distinct heading but has been interwoven in the discussion of the organ.

It may be valuable to supplement the course of study with a weekly laboratory session using both the cat and the human cadaver along with selected kymographic and other physiological exercises. There is no substitute for such practical work in helping the student to understand structure and function.

The writer wishes to express his appreciation to several persons. Dr. Chester J. Atkinson in the Department of Speech Correction at Southern Illinois University has given many valuable suggestions about the auditory mechanism described in Chapter 13. Dr. Isaac Brackett and Dr. John Anderson of the same department have been most cooperative and encouraging. Dr. Florence M. Foote in the Department of Physiology has reviewed the anatomy described in Chapter 4 and has offered numerous suggestions. Miss Sally Lou Russler has competently illustrated the text chiefly from materials in this laboratory. Valuable criticism was given by Dr. Vernon Sternberg at the Southern Illinois University Press.

Harold M. Kaplan

CONTENTS

Chapter 1

A SURVEY OF THE SPEECH MECHANISM

PLAN AND SCOPE OF THE STUDY

Some textbooks of physiology have energy as the central theme; others revolve around homeostasis, or the preservation of the dynamic steady state of an organism. The emphasis in this text is more upon the search for correlating structure and function with the acoustical signal. By what operational methods do we transmit information?

The organs which are correlated in vocal activity are not structures primarily formed for speech. They are the inherited products of our ancestral history, and most of the primitive members in this historical sequence were by structural necessity notably silent. The biologist turns to comparative anatomy to shed some light upon the intermediate aspects of this racial story.

In order to produce sound in man, the respiratory and digestive systems in particular have developed regional modifications of their gross and microscopic structure. The anatomical machinery then acquires differentiated functions, and it is these great divisions of function which are discussed in separate chapters of the text.

A nervous system and an adjunctive set of chemical messengers, or hormones, set the speech structures into motion and integrate at one time all the processes involved. The respiratory system generates the air blast, and the vocal folds vibrate with or respond in some fashion to the exhaled stream of air. There is above the folds a series of resonating chambers which serve to modulate the vibrations. Structures for articulation mold the resonated waves into meaningful speech sounds. Finally, there is the auditory mechanism which provides for reception, transmission, and even crude analysis of the incident sound. The degree of auditory perception has much to do with the ability to form and modulate sounds correctly.

Neural Control. A primary cerebral motor area may initiate and immediately direct the action of the discrete groups of skeletal muscles which energize the speech structures. Since no meaningful series of

1

sounds seems possible simply as a result of many isolated although delicate movements, other areas of the brain appear to be necessary for an over-all command. Thus we note the action of the premotor cortex and secondary cerebral motor areas.

The cerebellum is also necessary as a distribution and timing center. It monitors the cerebral impulses and fires them into the muscles much as the distributor of an auto engine sends high-voltage electric current from the spark coil into the separate spark plugs just at the right time.

The basal ganglia, which are islands of cells lying principally within the white matter of the cerebral hemispheres and downstream from the cerebral cortex, come into play adjunctively with the cerebellum to regulate the tone, rhythm, and directiveness of the nerve impulses which are firing into the muscles as a consequence of cerebral activation. Lower centers in the brain stem and in the core of the brain, called the reticular formation, are similarly kept busy correcting the nature of the stream of neural impulses which are funneling into the effectors. The muscles, by self-contained devices called stretch receptors, feed information back into the central nervous system concerning what has happened to them with respect to tension, tone, position in space, etc. This is truly automation, and it permits the whole circuit to be hypothetically subject to considerable mathematical analysis by the methods of cybernetics.

Great association areas are additional elements of the regulatory apparatus. They are needed for the synthesis of the ideas to be expressed and for the automatic selection of the words to be used in syntax. In the localization theory, Broca's area, which is one of the association areas, is necessary to integrate the speech musculature. If destroyed on both cerebral hemispheres, the individual speech muscles may not be paralyzed but they cannot be coordinated.

Respiration. The energy for sound originates in the lungs, and the intensity of the sound is related to the force of contraction of the chest muscles. At this stage we are dealing in generalizations. For example, intensity is a physical determinant of loudness, and the latter is related to the amplitude of excursion of the vocal folds and to any amplification of tone by the resonators.

Although it is possible to produce sounds upon inhalation, it is the exhalation which normally drives air up through the glottal opening between the vocal folds. The vocal folds, in consequence, respond in many different ways, depending upon many factors.

While the lung pressure is increasing, the vocal folds tend to be approximated, and they remain so until they are forced apart directly or indirectly by the pressure of the exhaled air. When the streams of air arrive in the spaces above the larynx, they produce the characteristic noise, or fricative properties, of many consonants, and still higher they provide the pressures essential to give the sounds which are articulated.

The Vocal Folds. The true cords or folds are the essential parts of the larynx or voice box. The larynx is a system of cartilages so acted upon by voluntary muscles that it moves as a whole or in localized internal areas. The true folds are mobile structures whose length, mass, position, and tension are readily altered. Although the intensity of sound is importantly related to chest muscles and pulmonary pressures, the pitch and to a certain extent the quality or timbre are related to the vocal folds, particularly to their tension and length. Thus, breathy, harsh, and hoarse qualities refer to defects of the tone produced by the folds (Fairbanks, 1940).

The Resonators. The original tone produced by the activity of the vocal folds is called the glottal tone. The complex waveform contains the fundamental and the overtones whose frequencies are multiples of the fundamental frequency. The tone is monotonous and quite unlike the final speech sounds. All the spaces above the larynx are capable of physically modifying the transmitted sound vibrations so that the quality of the voice is eventually changed. Some of the waves are weakened and others are reinforced. The distribution of energy has been changed, and cavity resonance is said to have occurred. The nasal quality of a tone involves resonance in variable degrees.

The pharynx, mouth, and nose are the important but not the only resonators. Jackson (1953) states that the vocal cavities form a linear system which has several damped resonances. The excitation is produced by the larynx as a repetitive series of impulsive shocks, and also by turbulent airflow through narrow passages.

The Articulators. The exhaled air eventually reaches structures which act as valves to stop the air stream completely or to narrow the spaces for its passage. The sounds are shaped, fused, and separated. The articulators give quality to the consonants and assist in forming some of the vowel-sound families. Articulators include the lips, tongue, mandible, velum, posterior pharyngeal wall, hyoid bone, and the inner edges of the vocal folds. The hard palate and teeth belong in this category in that they act as walls against which the articulators move.

The Ear. Since speech is transmitted by sound waves, much can be learned by examining the physical properties of sound waves and by studying the ear as an organ for the reception and analysis of sound waves. Sound, itself, acts like a feed-back mechanism, which significantly influences voice and articulation.

Chapter 2

NERVOUS REGULATION OF SPEECH

Animals and man express their "states of mind" by a pattern of behavior or language that takes many diverse forms in the various phylogenetic groups. In man the articulate sounds emitted in the form of vowels and consonants are shaped into words, each of which is an expression or symbol of a thought or idea. In the development of speech the units, or words, are each progressively associated with all possible stimuli arising in the external and internal environment, both in receiving the sound message and in responding to it. An enormously complicated associating structure, the brain, is developed to receive, channelize, and interpret the incoming messages and to form concepts by which meaningful expressive sounds may be adaptively produced at will. In the speech function the nature of the associations between the incoming impulses from tactile, visual, auditory, and other receptors and the manner of response to these by adequate control of the effective devices is important. On the expressive side alone of sound an enormous integrative faculty is needed to articulate a single idea, since many bodily structures and processes have to be activated in coordination at one time.

The control of speech by the nervous system was emphasized a century ago by Broca (1861) and Wernicke (1874), but these investigators were concerned with cortical localization. Although their ideas were later disputed by Pierre Marie (1906), Head (1926), and Goldstein (1926), the involvement of the nervous system was conclusively demonstrated.

The neural regulators of speech are divided into (1) the central nervous system, consisting of the brain and spinal cord; (2) the peripheral nervous system, including the cranial and spinal nerves; and (3) the autonomic nervous system innervating organs not under voluntary control, such as smooth muscles and glands. The autonomic system is treated separately in Chapter 3.

THE STRUCTURAL UNIT OF BEHAVIOR

The neurons are the basic units of which the entire nervous system is composed. These are specialized nerve cells that come from the outermost embryonic tissue called the ectoderm. The neuron assumes an elongated form best adapted to its function of conducting impulses by the sprouting out of various processes from its centralized cell body.

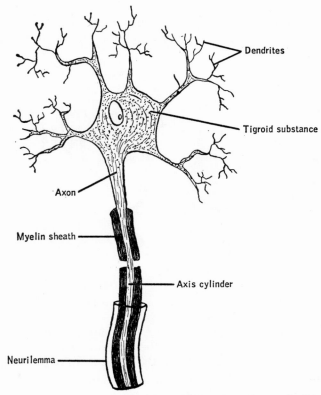

Fig. 2–1. A single multipolar neuron showing axon, dendrites, and cell body.

Any single process may become enormously attenuated on one side of its parent cell body, thus forming the axon or nerve fiber. In man one nerve fiber may extend from the lower spinal cord to the tip of the toe, a span of about three feet. On the opposite side of the cell body the processes called dendrites are considerably shorter and more numerous, and they serve to collect impulses from the axon of the preceding neuron.

The region of interneuronal contact called a synapse is not one of actual fusion, but rather one of microscopically close contact that nevertheless allows the passage of nerve impulses. Any disruption of this functional linkage interferes with the operation of the pool of neurons involved in a given activity. One of the older but unlikely explanations of unconsciousness and sleep is the supposedly temporary separation of synaptic junctions through fatigue products. The synapses act as valves to ensure a forced polarity in conduction from dendrite to cell body to axon and thence to the next neuron.

The core, or axis cylinder, of a neuron appears to contain neurofibrils which extend the length of the neuron and which are probably concerned in the transmission of nerve impulses. The Nissl bodies, which

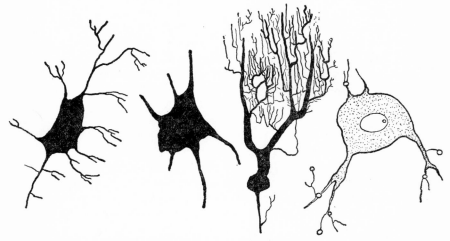

Fig. 2–2. Some representative neurons to show variations in form.

are granules of chromatin-like material that may play a part in neuron metabolism, are distributed around the nucleus and in the dendrites. These bodies may be fragments of the nuclear substance. Since they decrease in size during conduction it has been claimed that they contribute material for the conduction process. In some diseases they disappear, a process called chromatolysis, and there is a concomitant loss in neuron conductivity.

Nerve fibers differ in their coverings. Fibers without sheaths are found in the gray matter of the central nervous system. The typical cranial or spinal nerve contains a fatty myelin (medullated) sheath within a neurilemma (Schwann's sheath). The myelin sheath is periodically constricted by nodes of Ranvier, and each internode is associated with a single neurilemma cell. The neurilemma invests the myelin sheath with a thin, nonjointed living membrane, and it is necessary for regeneration if a nerve is injured. Unmyelinated fibers found in certain varieties of peripheral nerves have only a neurilemma, while the fibers of the white matter of the central nervous system contain only myelin.

The typical neuron, which has one axon and several dendrites, is called multipolar. It is characteristic of the efferent cranial and spinal nerves. In distinction, the afferent fiber of the peripheral nerves is bipolar. It has a centripetal dendrite and a centrifugal axon, both arising from a cell body that helps form a dorsal-root ganglion.

THE NERVE IMPULSE

Neurons are uniquely adapted to control and direct the activity spreading through them as a reaction to a stimulus. The propagated disturbance is the nerve impulse. The activity is expressed by such manifestations as oxygen and carbon dioxide interchange, heat production, and the flow of electric currents. In the classical theory the nerve impulse was thought to be identical with a wave of axon potential called the action current inasmuch as the velocities of the nerve impulse and the action current were identical. The velocity in medullated fibers varies from 100 to 125 meters per second and in nonmedullated fibers from 65 to 100 meters per second. With the discovery that specific chemicals are liberated along the trunks of active nerve fibers, diffusing across synapses and entering the cells of the final effectors, the nerve impulse has come to be considered as electrochemical. Each cell or segment receives the impulse and transmits it in an all-or-none fashion to the next segment of the fiber, the energy for transmission coming from the fiber itself.

In the resting nerve fiber the selectively permeable surface membrane separates positive ions on the outer surface from negative ions on the inner surface; the membrane is therefore polarized, with a resting potential of 60 to 90 millivolts. One of the marked effects of a stimulus is to depolarize the membrane, which permits a rapid movement of sodium ions inward; this so reverses the potential that the external surface becomes negative to the interior. The alteration in potential difference is expressed as the spike potential of an action current that once begun spreads automatically along the fibers. Immediately after the passage of the nerve impulse the excitability of the nerve drops to zero and then rises, producing absolute and relative refractory periods. The impulses thus cannot be transmitted continuously like a stream of water from a hose, but they resemble more the discontinuous yet repetitive volley of bullets from a machine gun.

The action currents occurring during conduction in peripheral fibers can be visibly recorded by the cathode-ray oscilloscope. In the central nervous system the action currents are recorded as an electroencephalogram or EEG. This kind of visualization is a useful tool in speech, since the reproducible brain waves of an individual may vary in a characteristic and predictable direction in a given speech disorder involving organic brain damage.

THE FUNCTIONAL UNIT OF BEHAVIOR

The actual response to a stimulus or reflex arc requires at least two neurons, situated between receptor and effector. The arc is the unit of function. It consists of a receptor, an afferent nerve, a center of adjustment, an efferent nerve, and an effector such as a muscle or gland.

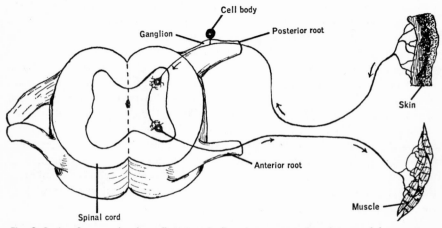

Fig. 2–3. A reflex arc showing afferent and efferent neurons and an internuncial connector.

Reflexes involving only two neurons are rare; the knee kick is considered an example. In most arcs one or more association neurons, always located within the central nervous system, link the afferent and efferent fibers. Through such connectors many afferent neurons may converge upon one efferent neuron, or one afferent fiber may send impulses to several efferent fibers. The afferent fibers enter the central nervous system only through the dorsal (posterior) roots, while the efferent fibers leave only through the ventral (anterior) roots. If the entering impulses are not confined to their segmental level but ascend to reach the cerebrum or any other brain area in which they can attain consciousness, the afferent neuron or impulse is called sensory. Impulses not producing consciousness are nonsensory. If the outgoing impulses energize a muscle, the efferent neuron is motor. Using this terminology, secretory fibers activate glands, vasomotor fibers regulate the caliber of blood vessels, and so on.

Reflexes intermediated through centers in the spinal cord are relatively fixed in character, and they function as though an operational groove or "path of least resistance" between the receptor and effector had been laid down constitutionally in the cord. Such reflexes are unlearned or unconditioned. They are not completely fixed, since they may be reinforced (facilitated) or inhibited (suppressed) with circumstances. Inhibition is an important property of reflex or central conduction, especially reciprocal inhibition in which the afferent neurons so dichotomize (divide) that they may excite certain motor neurons while inhibiting their immediate antagonists. In this way purposeful behavior is obtained. If we energize the elevator muscles of the mandible or of the hyoid bone, we should inhibit the antagonistic depressors. If we abduct (open) the vocal folds, we should inhibit the adductor (closing) action. If the stimulation of an afferent nerve promotes limb flexion on the same side (flexor reflex), it usually produces limb extension on the opposite side (crossed extensor reflex).

There is ordinarily a balance between muscle agonists and their antagonists, or between excitation and inhibition, so that all muscles continuously exist in variable degrees of partial tension or tone. Tone implies that few fibers are reacting when the muscle is at rest. Those which react, however, do so maximally. This is called the all-or-none principle.

Cates and Basmajian (1955) say that the state of resting tone does not exist in man and that all voluntary muscles can be completely relaxed. The evidence is from electromyography. This view is not commonly encountered in present textbooks. We shall assume that tone exists and more or less follow the definition that tone is a state of excitability of the nervous system, regulating or affecting voluntary muscle.

The above facts are applied to the analysis of an important speech activity called the stretch reflex, which is an unconditioned response, characteristically involving two neurons. In this reflex the stimulation of specialized receptors called proprioceptors, located in a muscle or tendon, sends impulses into a localized segment of the central nervous system, and the impulses returning through the motor neurons increase the tone of the same muscle. By this action a muscle responds adaptively to any force which tends to stretch it or to change its shape. When one stands up, the extensors of the limbs increase their tension by this machinery in order to resist gravity. The tension so imparted to the muscles through their segmental spinal nerve centers is ordinarily moderated and regulated by central fibers that come down from higher centers to synapse upon the cell bodies of the motor neurons (final common path).

The muscles are able to send back to the central nervous system from their proprioceptors information concerning their tensions and positions in space. This is the principle of feedback whose essential machinery is the stretch reflex and whose governing centers are, to an appreciable extent, below the cerebrum, making these reflexes basically unconscious. The speech muscles are examples of such reflex machines, and they employ the same method of operation. Much of speech is automatic or self-regulating, although always susceptible to diversional or antagonistic influences from many sources. Thus, speech is readily subject to interruptions and breakdowns, particularly in central disturbances of an emotional nature.

The kinesthetic sensibility, which expresses for the stretch reflex the quantitative consciousness of the movement, position, and tension of muscles, has been investigated in the speech literature. Fairbanks and Bebout (1950) studied the amount of error in trying to duplicate a tongue position. College students with superior and inferior articulation showed no real differences. On the contrary, Patton (1942) studied general bodily muscles and concluded that speech defectives have an inferior kinesthetic sensibility.

The stretch reflex is involved in the neurology of spasticity. Many cerebral-palsied individuals are spastic because the higher centers no longer brake the relatively intense activity of the segmental stretch reflexes. Antagonists do not relax when the agonists are active. A spastic muscle responds to any kind and strength of stimulus, with stretching as the usual stimulus. If a spastic muscle is stretched, it gives a hyperactive response.

In the inherited-reflex pathways certain structural conditions act as facilitation, inhibition, and other properties do to prevent invariability in the reflex response. For instance, if a single strong stimulus is applied with the expectation that a muscle will respond with one strong contraction, the muscle may, on the contrary, continue to contract, a phenomenon called afterdischarge. There are two reasonable explanations. For one thing, the branching of the afferent fibers may allow the impulses to travel at different times through paths containing many internuncial neurons. As a second possibility, it has been convincingly demonstrated that some of the association or internuncial neurons form closed or reverberating circuits so that the impulses travel circularly through such neuron pools, firing at intervals into the motor neuron even after the afferent impulses have ceased to enter the cord. These reverberating or cybernetic circuits characterize every level of the central nervous system, and they are considered to be important in the analysis of all kinds of behavior. Memory is an illustration of this in that we recall the same thought over and over again, implying that the nerve impulses traverse the same neuronal circuits repeatedly. Impulses confined to localized circular neuron pools will lead to similar thoughts or behavior.

Many of the reflexes concerned in speech are not of the simple inherited type but are conditioned or developed through associations. The conditioned reflexes involve the cerebrum primarily but not exclusively, since they have been produced in decorticate animals. These responses occur when an indifferent stimulus is given for a period of time along with the stimulus that ordinarily evokes a fixed response. The indifferent stimulus then becomes adequate to elicit the same response. Thus the ringing of a bell while placing food in the mouth soon causes salivation even when the bell is sounded in the absence of food. Man or animals may be progressively conditioned to respond only to a certain note. This selectivity requires an internal inhibition which is very slowly developed in the cortical and perhaps the subcortical regions.

All learning involves the conditioning of reflexes, and this includes the development of speech. In the historical origin of speech there are views implying that speech is primitively an unconditioned response, in that man and animals spontaneously produce sounds through irregularities in their respiratory movements when they are excited by violent external stimuli. The conditioning of speech is illustrated in man when he begins to make sounds for directive purposes, as in meaningful speech. Given environmental symbols become associated with specific sounds.

The early cultural development of conditioned speech is associated with social imitation. In the development of a single individual, the random or aimless activities occurring in the speech apparatus progressively drop out. The child can express what it wishes, using the neuromuscular machinery with increasing efficiency until all the essential reflexes become automatic and subconscious. The random unconditioned responses that first elicit the sounds occur in the tongue, lips, jaws, throat, and respiratory system. Such chance sounds come to be associated with success in the fulfillment of needs. If the sound when given alone also obtains a successful result, the stage is set to use it independently of the other generalized bodily activity previously employed. Conditioning or associative behavior has occurred, and speech becomes a volitional act.

CENTRAL LEVELS FOR SPEECH REGULATION

Stimuli arising in the external and internal environments of the individual excite specific receptors that discharge nerve impulses into the afferent nerve fibers. These impulses at specific levels enter the spinal cord through the spinal nerves or enter the brain through the cranial nerves. Reflex responses in the cord may occur segmentally at the level of entry, or the impulses may simultaneously ascend through definite tracts and end in various levels of the brain. Through the sense organs and entering-fiber systems we are made aware of those stimuli that influence and activate many bodily processes, including speech. The impulses do not cease at the upper arrival levels of the brain to which they are projected, but they are associated with previous experiences stored subconsciously as memory. From the results of such associations meaningful speech is produced.

All levels of the central nervous system do not equally receive the impulses for speech or equally control the expressive machinery of

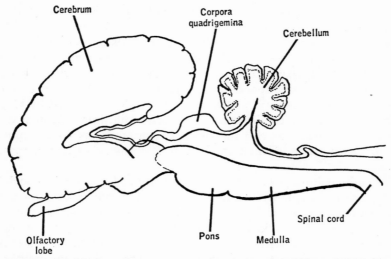

Fig. 2–4. Sagittal diagrammatic representation of the major divisions of the brain.

speech. The centers of greatest importance are in the highest level or cerebrum, but there are diverse adjunctive subcortical regions of considerable regulatory importance. The divisions of the central nervous system will be described with this in mind.

The brain develops as three expansions, or vesicles, that form the forebrain, midbrain, and hindbrain. The forebrain includes such structures as the cerebrum, corpus striatum, thalamus, and hypothalamus. The midbrain is the smallest of the original vesicles and includes among its important bodies the corpora quadrigemina, red nuclei, substantia nigra, and peduncles. The hindbrain contains in its anterior section the cerebellum above and the pons below; it contains in its posterior section the medulla, or bulb, which is a continuation of the spinal cord within the skull. All of these structures will be treated in more detail below.

The Cerebrum. This is the major derivative of the telencephalon, or anterior portion of the forebrain. It arises as lateral outgrowths that form the paired cerebral hemispheres. These become larger than all other parts of the brain, practically enclosing the other structures. Each hemisphere differentiates to a corpus striatum, olfactory lobe, and pallium. The corpus striatum is in the anterolateral region of the hemisphere. The olfactory lobe is an outgrowth of the floor in front of the corpus striatum, and it forms the smell brain, or rhinencephalon. The pallium constitutes the great remainder of the hemisphere, which differentiates to an outer cellular or gray layer called the cerebral cortex and an inner white or medullated nerve-fiber core called the medulla. The white fibers of the medulla form a complex network that connects various regions of the cortex with one another and with other parts of the brain, providing for intercommunication and association. Some white fibers form great crossbands, or commissures, that interconnect the paired hemispheres. Thus, the corpus callosum connects the paired non-olfactory regions called the neocortex, and the anterior commissure connects the paired olfactory regions called the archipallium.

Penfield and Rasmussen (1950) cite literature to the effect that the transcortical association fibers are less important than once thought. The fibers of the human corpus callosum have been surgically sectioned with no significant effects. Brain (1955) says that speech involves coordinated bilateral movements of the muscles of articulation, and this coordination is brought about by corpus callosum fibers traveling from the lower part of the left frontal lobe to the corresponding area of the right hemisphere. Through another band of white fibers called the external capsule, other associations are effected. Thus the posterior half of the left cerebral hemisphere, which helps elaborate meanings in response to auditory and visual stimuli, is linked by the external capsule to the lowest part of the precentral convolution, which regulates articulatory movements. In this way articulated speech becomes the expression of meanings. The external capsule extends from the tip of the temporal lobe, beneath the cortex of the island of Reil, to the lower portion of the precentral convolution and to the posterior section of the second and third frontal convolutions.

The surface of the cortex is increased by the formation of folds, or convolutions, that appear as hills, or gyri, and valleys, or sulci. The deep sulci are called fissures; the paired cerebral hemispheres are divided by the great longitudinal fissure. The fissures also subdivide each hemisphere into regions called lobes, which are useful in the rough localization of structures and functions. The frontal lobe is anterior to the fissure of Rolando (central sulcus) and superior to the fissure of Sylvius (lateral cerebral fissure). The parietal lobe is above the Sylvian fissure and between the Rolandic and parieto-occipital fissures. The temporal lobe is below the Sylvian fissure and in front of the parieto-occipital fissure. The occipital lobe is behind the parieto-occipital fissure. The lobes correspond roughly to the cranial bones that overlie them.

There are hollow spaces inside the hemispheres which are confluent with a centralized canal that extends through the entire central nervous system. This longitudinal canal is called the ventricles within the brain and the central canal within the cord. The central canal is small and of about uniform size along its entire length, but the ventricles differ in capacity in different brain regions.

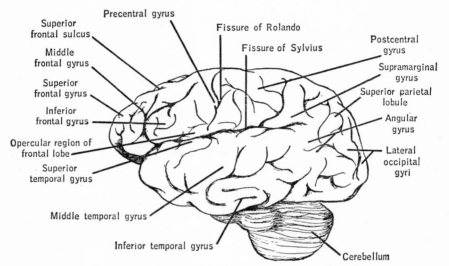

Fig. 2—5. The major divisions of the cerebrum.

The fourth ventricle of the hindbrain runs forward to an aqueduct of Sylvius under the midbrain. This aqueduct extends to the third ventricle, which is the hollow core of the diencephalon. The third ventricle, or cavity, of the posterior forebrain, also runs forward to form the hollow core of the anterior forebrain, or telencephalon. The paired cerebral hemispheres, growing laterally from the telencephalon, enclose a pair of lateral ventricles. Each lateral ventricle joins the telencephalic part of the third ventricle by an opening called the foramen of Monro.

The cerebrospinal fluid flows within the entire neural canal system. The fluid is secreted ultimately from the blood which gains access to the ventricles by transudation across specialized blood vessels called choroid plexuses. The material circulates from the lateral ventricles to the third ventricle, where it penetrates the walls and enters a space in the coverings (meninges) of the brain and cord called the subarachnoid space. Active circulation ensues in this space around the brain and spinal cord. Eventually the excess fluid is drained back to the blood stream by leaving the subarachnoid space through specialized arachnoid tufts and entering spaces called the dural venous sinuses, located in the outermost brain covering (dura mater). The fluid within these dural sinuses continuously drains downward and out of the skull and eventually returns to the right side of the heart. The force behind the cerebral circulation is a continuous gradient of pressure between the capillaries at the formation and absorption sites.

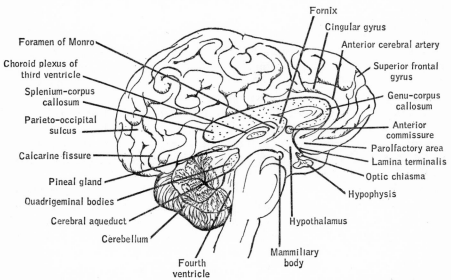

Fig. 2—6. Internal view of the cerebrum showing major structures and the ventricles.

The cerebrospinal circulation is intimately related to a variety of brain damage caused by fluid-pressure alterations or by fluid-volume and chemistry changes following infectious diseases. The consequence of such damage could be manifested as a disorder of symbolization or the general capacity to use language.

Cerebral dominance has been a concept of considerable importance and controversy in speech pathology. In the course of evolution many important functions have shifted to the cerebrum, a process called encephalization. The cerebrum has become more complex in structure and function, and the areas within it that are needed for associations have been greatly increased. The differentiation of speech has come to be linked with the development of the highest cerebral centers and with an increasing importance of the descending tracts controlling the speech effectors.

In man encephalization has even produced the dominance of a single cerebral hemisphere. At birth the hemispheres seem, controversially, to have about equal potentialities. The angular gyrus, located close to the junction of the parietal, occipital, and temporal lobes, appears to be bilaterally functional. This gyrus is an area in which the brain synthesizes many diverse impulses to integrated concepts. Many sensations are simultaneously associated within it, and the composite meaning of such sensations is lost if a sizable lesion develops in the angular gyrus of the dominant hemisphere. The patient, for example, may become aphasic in that he fails to comprehend the meaning of the written or the spoken word.

The reasons for one hemisphere to take control are obscure, but it may be difficult or impossible to synthesize meaningful concepts about the same stimulus simultaneously in both hemispheres, and therefore one side somehow gains ascendancy. Berry and Eisenson (1956) state that the mid-line organs subserving speech, such as the jaw, lips, tongue, and larynx, have a bilateral cortical representation but that only the neurons in the primary motor-projection area in one hemisphere are essential for speech. Although the mechanisms of voice are bilaterally present, the skills needed to organize and express speech are restricted to a dominant hemisphere.

As evidenced by present tests, the left hemisphere of the cerebrum is dominant in approximately 90 per cent of the population, and the left angular gyrus is the more important integrative center. Guyton (1956) states that the nondominant angular gyrus becomes so inhibited that its surgical removal causes no appreciable decrease in the intelligence quotient but that the removal of the dominant angular gyrus usually reduces the intelligence to that of an idiot. The time of removal is important. When the dominant angular gyrus is excised in the young child the other side takes over almost completely, and this implies a potentially functional ambivalence. Irreversibility eventually sets in, since the removal of the dominant gyrus in an adult produces a permanent impairment in general comprehension. However, a partial recovery is possible.

Other cerebral areas are also unilateralized. The premotor cortex, which is anterior to the motor area, is generally dominant on the same side as the angular gyrus. The speech areas located in the premotor region which control the larynx, jaw, and tongue are strongly left-dominant. There is an ideomotor area just in front of the angular gyrus that is more functional on the generally dominant hemisphere. This area initiates the habitual motor activities that are in the subconscious; it can, for example, quickly and automatically select the appropriate sequence of words necessary to the pursuit of a logical conversation.

Another lateralized function is that of hearing. Although the auditory tract projects to both temporal cortices, a right-handed individual undoubtedly recognizes the sound in the left hemisphere, and the reverse may hold true for the left-handed person.

Dominance usually implies that most or all functions will be governed by one hemisphere, but this is not always so. The premotor and parietal functions may be mutually contralateral (on opposite sides). The ambidextrous and left-handed individuals may show right dominance in the premotor cortex and left dominance in the angular-gyrus and ideomotor areas. Such facts may be disturbing in mapping out speech therapy or in rehabilitation after neurosurgery.

Cerebral localization was suggested a century ago when the anatomists Goll and Spurzheim associated specific functions in man with definite cortical areas. Since then the existence of localization has been abundantly demonstrated in the laboratory and clinic. An early proof of a specific motor area was that of Fritsch and Hitzig in 1870. They applied a galvanic current to the exposed cerebrum of a wounded soldier and then observed a strictly localized muscular response. Much of the later work has been based upon observations of responses in the electrically stimulated cortex and upon the bodily effects of artificial and natural cortical lesions.

There have been many objections. Subcortical regions have yet to be thoroughly examined. The cause-and-effect relations among a bodily defect, a cortical lesion, and the assumptions as to the normal function of that part of the cortex suffer upon logical analysis of the argument. Speech as a function is not analyzable into motion or sensation but is based upon integrated processes involving the entire brain, and its disturbance is expressed in terms of the highest psychic activities. In spite of this, the results obtained on the assumption of localization have greatly expanded the literature, and for the physiologist the theory has provided a tangible working basis for the analysis of cerebral function.

The cortex is no longer considered in terms of its lobes, but it is divided into functional areas. The original system of Brodmann had nine general areas in the neocortex subdivided into perhaps fifty secondary areas, each designated by a numeral. Over 200 secondary areas are now numbered.

There are several cerebral motor areas. The principal motor area, 4, is in the precentral convolution of the frontal lobe, just in front of the fissure of Rolando. This contains the pyramidal neurons that control the voluntary muscles, such as those of the lips, jaw, tongue, pharynx, and larynx.

Lassek (1939; 1940) dissected the human pyramidal tract and showed that the histological units called Betz cells are not the only neurons making up the pyramidal system. Of approximately one million pyramidal fibers, there are only 25,000 to 30,000 Betz cells on each side. The majority of the fibers are myelinated, and these originate on the cortex, but the origin of the numerous unmyelinated pyramidal fibers is obscure.

Different parts of the body are represented in specific regions of the precentral convolution. Motor reactions occurring in order from toe to head are controlled by discrete centers running from the Rolandic fissure down into the Sylvian fissure. The movements are isolated and delicate. The response with prolonged stimulation spreads. This is seen in Jacksonian epilepsy where there is a "march" of the symptoms.

Rasmussen and Penfield (1947) describe the bodily representation as follows. Centers for laryngeal and pharyngeal movement are located at the inferior end of the precentral convolution. When one cortex is stimulated the pharynx is bilaterally contracted and both vocal folds are adducted. Above these cerebral centers there are motor nuclei for the palate, mandible, and tongue in successive order. Above in succession there are centers for movements of the lower face, neck muscles, thumb and fingers, wrist, forearm, arm, shoulder, and the upper and lower trunk. Anterior to the upper trunk is a center for the diaphragm. Above the centers for the lower-trunk muscles there are centers for the thigh, leg, foot, and toes. However, the precentral convolution is not the same as the motor cortex inasmuch as other cortical centers produce bodily movements.

Area 4 is not purely motor since lesions there weaken muscular sensibility. Either the motor and sensory areas overlap or they are connected by association tracts. Actually, all areas are activated in behavior. Area 4 has a relatively great cellular representation for the speech muscles, which is out of proportion to the size of the muscles involved.

There are several secondary motor areas. Area 8 in the frontal lobe and area 19 in the parietal lobe can produce eye movements independently of area 4. There are areas, such as 4-S just in front of the motor area, called suppressor areas in that they inhibit motor activity. Other areas in the parietal lobe act similarly.

Some secondary regions such as area 6 of the premotor cortex control voluntary motion. Area 6 works in part through the motor cortex, but it also projects downward into relay systems called the basal ganglia. Stimulation of the premotor cortex has a greater influence over the mass movements of groups of muscles than it does over the delicate movements of single muscles. The mass movements, like the swinging of a limb in walking, are postural, and they relate the individual to his position in space.

The motor areas for controlling speech are well developed in both the premotor and motor cortex. Area 44 (Peele, 1954), located in the frontal lobe in the left inferior frontal convolution above the union of the fissures of Rolando and Sylvius, controls the formation of words, and it shows marked unilateral dominance. This is called Broca's area after a French surgeon, Paul Broca (1861). It has connections to and from every part of the cortex so that all varieties of conscious experiences are potentially associated with speech. Broca's area acts as a special correlation center which funnels impulses to that part of the motor cortex which will in turn control the bodily effectors of speech. The impulses are transmitted down to the motor nuclei of cranial and spinal nerves. In 1861 Broca first read his now-famous paper on speech loss from pathological disturbance of the cerebral cortex before the Académie de la Société d'Anthropologie. Bastian (1880) found still other localized areas, and he related cerebral lesions with language defects.

Although the existence of Broca's area seems well established, other speech areas, such as area 7B along Rolando's fissure in the frontal lobe and area 7A behind and beneath the great sensory areas of the parietal lobe, have been proposed. Area 7C in the frontal-orbital region is said to associate the emotional components of speech, originating in a lower center, the thalamus, with ordinary muscular speech movements. Penfield and Rasmussen (1950) speak of at least three areas that control the formation of words; one is frontal, one parietal, and one temporal.

Investigators such as Von Monakow, Head, and many others have denied that there are any strict centers for speech (Wepman, 1951). One argument is that various areas of cortical damage can effectively destroy the speech function. The localization concept is important in the speech literature, and it will be discussed later in this chapter.

The prefrontal cortex, areas 9, 10, 11, and 12, at the anterior-apical end of the frontal lobe, is important in speech and in general intellectual activities. Prefrontal-lobe lesions and prefrontal destruction subsequent to bilateral section called lobotomy are not followed by distinct defects. Personality changes such as disinterest, change in social attitudes, and intellectual deterioration occur. The prefrontal cortex has been called an ideational association area in which the bases of abstract thinking are evolved. In this sense it is a significant determinant for speech, which depends upon memory and abstractions.

Oddly enough, much work on this region was begun in the last century when a man named Phineas Gage had a crowbar blown through his head by an explosion. The motor cortex was not penetrated but the prefrontal areas were destroyed. The patient recovered but displayed obvious personality changes. Such alterations in behavior eventually suggested the possibility of prefrontal lobotomy.

There seems to be little or no dominance in the prefrontal areas. These areas connect to an ideomotor center which is in the supramarginal gyrus of the predominant parietal lobe. When the ideomotor area receives impulses, it consciously and automatically decides upon a course of action; in this sense it reflexly selects the words and sentences of a conversation.

The ideomotor area is inhibited by the prefrontal cortex so that the rapid reflex activity of the former may be subjected to censor. This monitoring and selection of ideas now appear to be a definite function of the prefrontal cortex. The pattern is illustrated in speech. The prefrontal area plans the speech in its own time by calling upon memory and associations, and then the ideomotor area decides upon the sequence of the words. The ideomotor area in turn sends this information to Broca's area or other motor areas, after which the laryngeal and associated organ patterns are placed into integrated motion.

We have so far described the correlating and expressive areas of the cerebral cortex, but we have not yet considered the afferent or receptive areas that receive the impulses. Information is received from any of the bodily receptors and ascending tracts, and it is also received as a feedback from the very muscles that have been activated.

The parietal cortex, including areas 3, 1, 2, 5, and 7, is called the somesthetic area. It receives and integrates general senses such as pressure, pain, hot, cold, and muscle sensations. The bodily periphery is represented spatially on the contralateral somesthetic cortex. Areas 5 and 7 allow tridimensional reasoning about the projected sensations. Thus we recognize form, texture, weight, etc., a faculty called stereognosis. Speech is an example of such stereognostic activity. The proprioceptive muscle impulses from the speech muscles and elsewhere, which are fed back into the post-Rolandic region, reflexly stimulate a continuous and orderly pattern of behavior in the very same muscles. Cutaneous as well as deep pressure impulses can by association initiate a flow of responsive speech.

The temporal cortex and perhaps a portion of the parietal lobe are concerned with auditory sensations. The auditory projection endings in the temporal cortex are in Heschl's convolution, which is in the superior temporal gyrus. About one-half of the impulses from each ear end in each superior temporal gyrus so that the total removal of one temporal lobe hardly impairs hearing. Removal of the temporal lobe on the dominant side, however, decreases the meaning of sounds. This results from loss of the auditory association areas, 41 and 42, located in the hind part of the superior temporal convolution. Speech responses are greatly dependent upon the meaning of sounds.

Speech is also related to impulses arriving in other sensory cortical areas, such as those dealing with vision, taste, or smell; but these relationships are more indirect, and the cortical areas in question will not be described.

The concept of sensory centers of speech historically followed the localization views for the motor cortex. Wernicke (1873) in Germany described an auditory center in the temporal convolution. This is now called Wernicke's area. It includes a region in the left superior temporal gyrus called area 22. This is directly behind areas 41 and 42, and it also includes the adjacent part of the middle temporal gyrus. Its destruction is followed by the failure to understand the spoken word (acoustic verbal agnosia) and occasionally by inability to comprehend the written word (visual verbal agnosia). This is Wernicke's aphasia, or sensory aphasia.

A writing center was postulated by a Frenchman named Charcot (1883). He also described a center for *ideation*, and he proposed a concept of visual- and auditory-minded individuals. Mills (1904) spoke of motor centers, a visual center, a graphic center, and an auditory center.

Dejerine (1901; 1906) described a sensory aphasia which is a word blindness, or alexia, resulting from impairment of that part of the left cortex in which the angular gyrus and the parietal, temporal, and occipital lobes meet.

Electrical stimulation of certain cortical areas has produced vocalization in which the individual does not produce words but utters a sound which is usually a vowel. Penfield (1950) has produced vocalization by stimulating the precentral or postcentral "face" field in either hemisphere and by stimulating the medial aspect of the superior frontal convolution in either hemisphere in front of the central fissure. By stimulating these Rolandic and superior frontal areas, speech has also been arrested.

The Basal Ganglia. Many subcortical centers, or nuclei, cooperate with the cerebrum to control the voluntary muscles, including those of speech. Basal ganglia is a collective term for several subcortical nuclear masses located in the forebrain and midbrain. These masses connect directly or indirectly to the premotor cortex above and project down to a midbrain structure called the red nucleus. The latter has decussating fibers traveling down the spinal cord so that the basal ganglia have a contralateral control over the muscles.

The term basal ganglia is used variably by different writers. Peele (1954) says that it includes the caudate, putamen, globus pallidus, and the amygdaloid nuclei. It would secondarily embrace other nuclei in the diencephalon, midbrain, pons, and medulla. These would include the subthalamus, red nuclei, substantia nigra, and certain nuclei of the brain tegmentum and reticular formation. The thalamus and hypothalamus are only remotely included in that they connect as the others with parts of the extrapyramidal system. West (1957) definitely classifies the thalamus as a basal ganglion, although he agrees with conventional views in excluding the hypothalamus.

For convenience in the present discussion, the basal ganglia, or at least the extrapyramidal fibers, are discussed as including the corpus striatum, thalamus, hypothalamus, red nucleus, lateral geniculate bodies, body of Luys, substantia nigra, claustrum, and amygdala. The corpus striatum is divided to a caudate and lenticular nucleus, and the latter is subdivided to the putamen and globus pallidus.

The basal ganglia seem to have originated as motor areas, but they have become primarily suppressor over motor function. Inhibitory circuits lead from the cortex to the basal ganglia, and there are suppressor fibers returning to the cortex. Lesions in such circuits may produce continual writhing. The latter is exemplified in athetoid movements, particularly in the limbs. Such movements are normally inhibited by the premotor cortex working through the basal ganglia. The speech may be feeble and slurred.

The basal ganglia, except for the thalamus, help to control muscle tone. If they are destroyed, then certain facilitative structures such as the motor cortex, as well as the bulboreticular centers of the brain stem, become more excitable. This produces muscular hypertonicity and rigidity.

In sequential motor acts initiated by the motor cortex, it is necessary to inhibit active muscles while exciting other muscle groups. In this activity the suppressor circuits involving the basal ganglia and the cerebrum may play a role. If such inhibition is lacking, then unsuppressed oscillations, as in athetosis, could occur.

There is a damping function of the basal ganglia which prevents oscillations between muscle agonists and antagonists when the muscles are at rest. This prevents the muscles from abruptly changing their state and entering into oscillatory contractions. Basal ganglia lesions remove the damping mechanism and tremors may result. This may be the basis of the resting tremors seen in Parkinson's disease.

The disturbances in muscle tone or other activities resulting from basal ganglia disease are usually considered to be release phenomena. These include tremors, tics, and also choreiform and athetoid movements.

It is difficult to ascertain which of the basal ganglia are responsible for a specific function or dysfunction. Most of the earlier work overemphasized the cerebrum and neglected the adjunctive subcortical regions. The striate bodies, including the caudate, lenticular, and amygdaloid nuclei, have descending axons that synapse with brain stem nuclei. The latter in turn innervate the muscles of the face, tongue, pharynx, and larynx. The athetoid patient shows disorders of articulation, facial grimaces, and other symptoms indicating trouble somewhere in the complex striate circuits.

The red nucleus and substantia nigra, which lie in the midbrain, are circularly connected with the corpus striatum and the premotor cortex. The cerebellum sends many of its impulses to the muscles by way of the red nucleus. Muscular rigidity and tremor can result from lesions in these bodies.

In the dorsal segment of the midbrain there are four bodies called the corpora quadrigemina. The more cranial pair of these are the superior colliculi, or centers for unconscious visual reflexes. The more caudal pair are the inferior colliculi, or centers for auditory reflexes.

The thalamus, which lies on either side of the median third ventricle of the forebrain and medial to the striate bodies, is often excluded from the basal ganglia because it primarily receives ascending impulses whereas the others are way stations on the descending trails. The structures called the medial and lateral geniculate bodies are found as paired structures in the thalamic wings.

The thalamus perhaps plays some part in every cortical activity, since it sends many tracts up to the cortex and in turn receives some cortical tracts. In its own right it is an organ of crude consciousness. It has a high threshold of stimulation, however, and an exaggerated capacity to respond when this threshold is exceeded. The thalamus deals with the affective qualities of a sensation, i.e., the pleasant or unpleasant qualities associated with the stimulus. Emotional experiences are constructed in this organ and then brought to full consciousness probably in the prefrontal cortex. The physiological manifestations of the emotion are expressed through the hypothalamus, which is the center of the sympathetic sector of the autonomic nervous system. The hypothalamus lies directly below the central mass of the thalamus.

The emotional parameters of speech are probably synthesized in the thalamus as affects of the diverse stimuli entering it from many sources. Facial expression and the quality of the voice have thalamic as well as cerebral components in their organization.

The Lower Brain Stem. The midbrain, hindbrain, and medulla comprise the brain stem. The cerebellum is excluded in most descriptions.

In the midbrain region where the cerebral hemispheres join the brain stem, there are structures belonging to the phylogenetically older parts of the brain. These structures produce a limbic system, which controls such emotional behavior as sleep and the waking state, activity and rest, eating, and reproductive activities. The limbic system is still a vaguely limited group of structures.

The pons is an important part of the hindbrain. It lies ventral to the cerebellum and forms a bridge between the midbrain and the medulla. Its dorsal section is a continuation of the reticular formation of the medulla.

The pons contains gray matter and interlacing transverse and longitudinal white fibers. The transverse fibers form a union between both halves of the cerebellum. The longitudinal fibers allow the pons to be a bridge between the medulla and the cerebrum. The pons contains the nuclei of cranial nerves, V, VI, VII, and VIII. It also contains the tracts of ascending and descending nerve fibers which connect the spinal cord and the brain.

The relation of the pons to speech lies in its connections with the basal ganglia and the cerebellum. In this sense it forms a part of the extrapyramidal system which controls the muscles. It also contains breathing centers for regulating the respiratory rhythm essential to phonation.

The most posterior part of the hindbrain is the myelencephalon of the embryo. This forms the medulla oblongata.

The medulla is pyramidal in shape. It is thought to be an embryological expansion of the spinal cord, but its internal structure and its functions are unlike those of the cord. This region contains all the ascending and descending tracts and fibrous systems.

The nerve cells in the medulla form nuclei, some of which produce the cranial nerves IX, X, XI, and XII. Others produce such vital centers as the cardiac, respiratory, and vasomotor. Still other nuclei act as relay stations for sensory tracts traveling from the spinal cord to the brain.

A small lesion in the medulla may impair many functions. The integrity of the muscles of speech depends upon the vitality of medullary centers and cranial nerves. This is illustrated in bulbar poliomyelitis in which speech disturbances may be marked.

The reticular formation is the central core of the brain stem. It is a continuous network of nerve cells and fibers which extends from the corpus striatum all through the brain stem and into the spinal cord. O'Leary and Coben (1958) stress the point that the conceptual importance of the reticular core has so increased that the cerebral cortex is on the brink of becoming a dependency. They present an extensive review of the brain stem literature, bringing up a newer dynamics that minimizes specific neural centers and emphasizes over-all integration and multimodal activation of units.

The reticular formation is a key area in man, since the vital centers of breathing as well as the cardiovascular centers are in its caudal sector. The long ascending tracts of the cord send collaterals (branches) into it as they pass forward to the thalamus. In turn the reticular formation connects with the cerebral cortex. It is said to help produce consciousness by bombarding the cerebrum with impulses to keep it stimulated. The cerebrum returns impulses to it, thus producing a reverberating circuit. The chief motor tract of the reticular formation is the reticulospinal tract. This is considered to be an important extrapyramidal system.

The reticular formation is fed by the basal ganglia and the cerebellum. Through this reticular way station the premotor cortex and the cerebellum project down to the motor nuclei of the muscles. It appears that most or perhaps all of the suppressor areas of the cerebrum and cerebellum act through an inhibitory mechanism which is located in the bulbar reticular formation. Even the inhibition of spinal activity, which is due to the corpus striatum suppressors, may be mediated in the same way. This bulbospinal machinery for inhibition is not automatic but depends upon inflows from higher parts of the brain.

The reticular formation also contains a facilitative mechanism acting with the cerebellum. Similar influences come from the motor cortex via the pyramidal tracts. Pathological spasticity of muscles may be maintained chiefly by the excessive facilitation of spinal stretch reflexes, which is brought about by impulses descending from the brain stem facilitative mechanism and the reticulospinal tract. This is at variance with the view that spasticity is mostly related to pyramidal disturbances.

Tremors, as well as rigidity, may originate in disturbances of the reticular core. There is considerable evidence for brain stem tremorogenesis (O'Leary and Coben, 1958).

There is an activation theory of emotion (Lindsley, 1951) which holds that extremes of emotion, e.g., great excitement and rage as opposed to relaxation and sleep, are dependent upon activity in the reticular core.

The Cerebellum. The cerebellum lies in the dorsal part of the metencephalon (anterior hindbrain) surrounding the anterior section of the fourth ventricle. The structure is divided to an outer cortex and to an inner white matter which contains subcortical nuclei. The surface of the gray matter is increased by leaf-like folds called folia.

The organ contains (1) the flocculonodular lobe, or archicerebellum; and (2) the corpus, which is subdivided into a segmented anterior lobe, or vermis, and a large posterior lobe. The latter is in turn divided to the hemispheres, or neocerebellum, and to the pyramis and uvula which with the vermis form the paleocerebellum.

The cerebellum connects with other brain regions through its paired stalks or peduncles. The superior stalks are chiefly efferent to the thalamus or red nucleus. The middle ones are afferent from the pons. The inferior pair are afferent and efferent with the medulla.

The cerebrum connects with the cerebellum through the corticoponto-cerebellar tract. The latter is a crossed motor pathway from the frontal or temporal lobes of the cerebral cortex, traveling by way of the pons and the middle peduncle.

The cerebellum sends a cerebellorubral tract out through the superior peduncles to the red nucleus, and this tract is interrupted in the cerebellar subcortical relay nuclei. The path continues down to the spinal cord from the red nucleus through the rubrospinal tract or, more im-

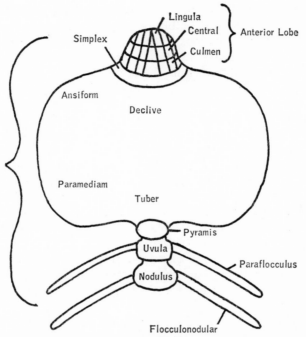

Fig. 2—7. The cerebellum extended to a plane to show its major divisions.

portantly, through the rubroreticular system into the reticular formation of the brain stem. Thence it descends through the reticulospinal tract into the cord, where it synapses with the motor nuclei of the skeletal muscles at every spinal level. The cerebellar neurons decussate to the red nucleus, but the lower neurons decussate back again so that the cerebellar muscle control is ipsilateral (on the same side).

Some efferent neurons of the superior cerebellar stalk rise to the thalamus. This organ in turn sends fibers to the cerebral cortex, thus providing a closed circuit between the cerebrum and the cerebellum. The superior stalk also receives proprioceptive muscle impulses from Gower's tract of the cord.

The cerebellum receives through its inferior stalks proprioceptive impulses from Flechsig's tract and from the columns of Goll and Burdach of the spinal cord. It accepts impulses through the inferior stalks from the vestibulocerebellar and olivocerebellar tracts and from cranial nerves V, VII, IX, and X. Impulses travel out of this stalk through the cerebellovestibular and cerebello-olivary tracts. These descending tracts first terminate in brain stem relay nuclei. These nuclei in turn send extrapyramidal tracts down the cord to synapse with the nuclei of the anterior horn cells.

The cerebellum is involved in voluntary muscle coordination and in the timing of muscles impulses. It thus coordinates breathing and

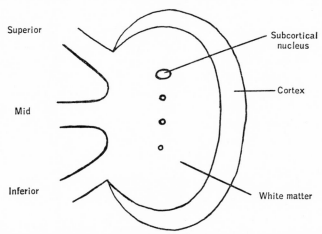

Fig. 2—8. Lateral diagrammatic view of the cerebellum to show its subcortical nuclei and its peduncles.

speaking, gestures, and facial expression. It regulates the strength of the voice and the inspiratory speech pauses to correspond with the meaning of the spoken words. This structure moderates and improves tone and strengthens neuromuscular activity. In an afferent sense it is the head ganglion of the proprioceptive system. The cerebellum is an assistant to the cerebrum. The latter initiates the discharges while the cerebellum distributes them by exciting or inhibiting lower centers. The cerebellar action is ipsilateral and devoid of consciousness.

In human cerebellar lesions, coordination but not sensation is lost. The primary ill effects decrease perhaps because the premotor cerebral cortex takes over. Certain symptoms are retained. One is asthenia, or loss of muscle force; another is atonia, or loss of tone. Still another is ataxia, or asynergia, which is the loss of the direction and regularity of a movement. Precise movement is impossible as seen in past pointing in which the patient cannot bring a finger to a predesignated point such as his nose. There is astasia, or loss of steadiness, so that the individual develops an intention tremor when he tries to perform a movement. Alternate acts such as rapidly thrusting out and retracting the tongue become difficult. This failure of timing is called adiadochokinesis.

The cerebellum is extremely important for normal speech. The ataxic individual has an unmodulated and cluttered speech since the timing of alternate movements necessary for modulation and integration is lacking. The over-all rhythm fails and speech occurs in sudden starts. In severe cerebellar injury speech is explosive. The voice apparatus may lose its dominance over respiration. The patient starts to talk with normal intensity, but the voice is soon expended.

There is a cerebellar localization. The flocculonodular lobes (archicerebellum) deal primarily with information from the postural areas of the internal ear. The adjusted impulses are sent into the facilitative and inhibitory regions of the brain stem through which they regulate extensor muscle tone.

The paleocerebellum receives chiefly the tracts of Flechsig and of Gower, and it sends out responses to the reticular formation, the red nucleus, and the thalamus. It may be primarily an inhibitory center. The impulses from both archi- and paleocerebellum, which travel into the reticular formation, maintain equilibrium even while the muscles are in rapid movement.

The neocerebellum controls rapid, skilled movements. It facilitates by tonic (continuous) feedback the action of the motor and premotor cortex. This quickly increases or decreases the tone in muscle agonists or antagonists according to the need. The basal ganglia differ in that they control the muscles by inhibition and not by excitation. The neocerebellum is able to judge the status of peripheral movements through its extensive proprioceptive reception. It can give this information to the cerebrum which can then modify its own action adaptively. The neocerebellum is said to be able to predict the result of a movement in space and to brake the action at the appropriate time, thus, for example, preventing past pointing or tremors.

THE SPINAL CORD

The spinal cord is a center of reflex activity and also a region for the transmission of impulses to and from the brain. The true nervous part of the cord extends from the foramen magnum at the base of the skull to the first lumbar vertebra at the small of the back, a distance of about 18 inches. Although the cord is so shortened that it does not extend through the whole length of the vertebral column, the spinal nerves maintain their intervertebral exit positions so that the lowest nerves continue vertically inside the neural canal for some distance before emerging. This produces a horsetail appearance called the cauda equina at the hind end of the cord. Only the upper nerves leave the cord at right angles; the lower one exit at increasingly acute angles. The nonnervous continuation of the cord, which ties it down to the lowest vertebrae, or coccyx, is called the filum terminale.

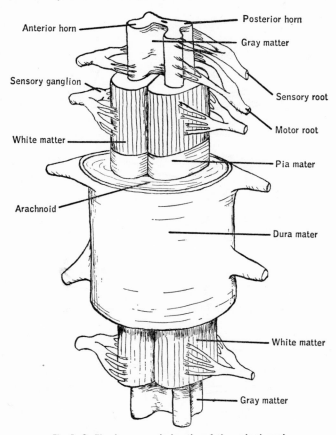

Fig 2–9. The layers and sheaths of the spinal cord.

The cord has the same sheaths as the brain. These are the outer dura mater, the middle arachnoid membrane, and the inner pia mater. Cerebrospinal fluid flows within the subarachnoid spaces.

There is a gross swelling at the level of the arms and of the legs. These cervicobrachial and lumbosacral enlargements are associated with the increased nerve supply to the limbs. In these regions the ventral roots of the segmental nerves form an interlacing network, or plexus, so that the nerves which exit have a complex composition. The respiratory and some other muscles active in speech are energized from branches of the cervical and brachial plexuses.

A transverse section at any level of the spinal cord shows its internal structure. The gray or nuclear matter is internal and arranged like the letter H with a dorsal and a ventral horn in each half of the cord. Each horn is cross-connected by a transverse gray band. The center of this

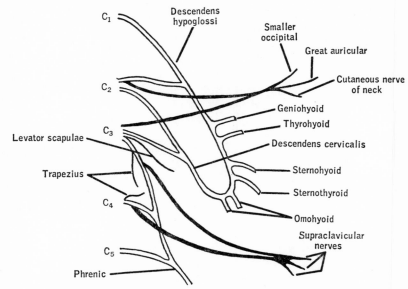

Fig. 2—10. The uppermost or cervical plexus of the spinal cord.

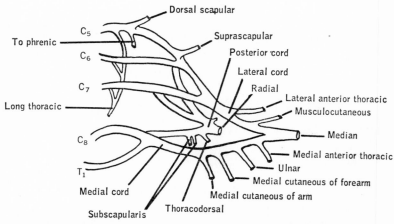

Fig. 2—11. The brachial plexus and its nerves of distribution.

band contains a central canal which is continuous with the brain ventricles. The white matter forms columns, or funiculi, which are dorsal (posterior), lateral, and ventral (anterior). Within each funiculus there are tracts whose fibers have the same origin and ending and fasciculi which contain fibers belonging to two or more tracts.

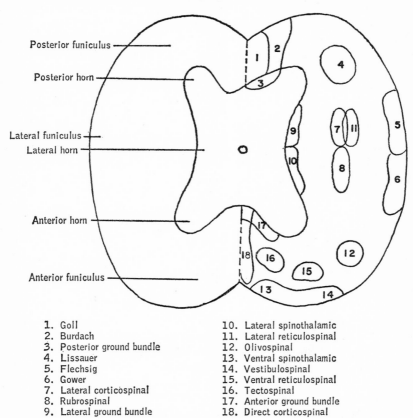

Fig. 2–12. Diagrammatic section of the spinal cord showing the major ascending and descending tracts.

1. Goll
2. Burdach
3. Posterior ground bundle
4. Lissauer
5. Flechsig
6. Gower
7. Lateral corticospinal
8. Rubrospinal
9. Lateral ground bundle
10. Lateral spinothalamic
11. Lateral reticulospinal
12. Olivospinal
13. Ventral spinothalamic
14. Vestibulospinal
15. Ventral reticulospinal
16. Tectospinal
17. Anterior ground bundle
18. Direct corticospinal

The tracts are ascending or descending, and they may be long or short. The short tracts begin and end in the cord, and they may be ascending, descending, or mixed. The short tracts connect the activities of one spinal segment with another, and they are association tracts, or ground bundles. The long tracts connect the brain and the cord, but they also contain individual fibers which are actually short association neurons.

Sensory Tract Systems. The sensations synthesized in the brain are either general or special. General sensations include such modalities as pain, heat, cold, touch, and proprioception. Special sensations include vision, hearing, taste, and smell. Each modality is carried from its own distinct peripheral sense organ through specific pathways in the spinal cord and brain stem up to its cortical terminus.

There are various levels of termination so that all impulses generated from the receptors do not reach consciousness but establish lower reflex connections for essential but unconscious bodily reactions to the stimulus. Many reflexes operate only through a localized segmental level of the cord, as do the ungoverned proprioceptive stretch reflexes.

The receptors are exteroceptors or cutaneous, proprioceptors or deep, and interoceptors or internal. These discharge intermittently in an all-or-none manner. They adapt to a uniform stimulus by a progressive decrease in response.

The dorsal columns of Goll and Burdach in the cord carry several kinds of impulses. One variety is deep pressure or muscular sensibility in which we recognize the position of our muscles and the extent of their movements. Stereognosis is the sensation that results when the tridimensional qualities of a stimulus are perceived. This sensation is also described as conscious proprioception.

The dorsal columns mediate still other sensations. We perceive the rapid oscillations of a tuning fork (vibration sense) through these fibers. Most of the cutaneous touch and pressure sensations use the same columns. These include general touch sensations, two-point discrimination (of compass points), and touch localization.

Deep receptors called proprioceptors are the end organs for muscular sensibility. They include muscle spindles, Golgi tendon spindles, and the Pacinian corpuscles located between muscles and around the joints. These receptors respond to stretch or deformation.

Exteroceptors are the cutaneous touch and pressure receptors. There are several varieties including Meissner's corpuscles, hair end organs, and hederiform terminations.

The first-order neurons from all these receptors end in the medulla, whereupon second-order neurons decussate and travel up as the internal arcuate fibers of the medial lemniscus. The lemniscus terminates in the thalamus. From there, third-order neurons reach the somesthetic (parietal) cortex.

Cruder impulses for touch and pressure are sent up a few segments by the tract of Lissauer in the posterolateral funiculus, then pass across the cord to the ventral spinothalamic tract. This tract intermingles with the medial lemniscus and reaches the thalamus. The thalamic radiations in turn pass to the somesthetic cortex.

Pain, heat, and cold impulses are transmitted a few segments up the tract of Lissauer. Then they decussate to enter the lateral spinothalamic tract. This tract also joins the medial lemniscus and reaches the thalamus. The final thalamic radiation goes to the somesthetic cortex.

The exteroceptors for pain are free nerve endings. The receptor for heat is Ruffini's end organ, and that for cold is Krause's end bulb. All the exteroceptive sensations are localized accurately.

Some of the muscle impulses from the proprioceptive end organs, including some impulses from the speech musculature, travel in a different path and go primarily to the cerebellum. Information concerning these impulses is then sent by the cerebellum to the cerebrum. These nonsensory afferent impulses travel ipsilaterally to the cerebellum in the tracts of Flechsig and of Gower (dorsal and ventral spinocerebellar tracts). Some of the nonsensory afferent impulses ascend to the cerebellum in a different way; they travel in the external arcuate system, which contains ipsilateral fibers originating in the columns of Burdach and of Goll. The cerebellar activity, which is described as unconscious proprioception, may serve to regulate the rapid and rhythmic movements of the skeletal muscles.

The special senses, which may now be briefly treated, are not all of equal importance to speech. The auditory tract has a special significance. The visual tract is next in importance.

The visual fibers originate in the retina of each eye, and they travel toward the brain in the paired optic nerves. At a region called the optic chiasm the fibers from the nasal half of each retina cross over to become a part of the opposite tract. This allows two retinal images, formed on corresponding retinal points, to be fused to a single stereoscopic sensation in one cerebral hemisphere.

The first-order neurons end in lower visual centers, mainly the lateral geniculate bodies. The second-order neurons travel in the geniculocalcarine tract to the occipital cortex.

The auditory tract begins in the organ of Corti in the cochlea of the internal ear. This tract will be considered in Chapter 13.

Response through the Descending Tracts. We have already anticipated some of the discussion to follow. The material is treated here, not with emphasis upon cortical or higher central processes, but from the standpoint of the descending fibrous systems and the associated activities involved.

The sensory impulses which are integrated in cerebral association areas of various levels of significance are eventually processed by a master center of correlation located in the angular gyrus. This is situated at the approximate center of the more elementary association areas belonging to each of the general and special senses.

Impulses for the adaptive responses are sent from the angular centers to the ideomotor area just in front of it in the supramarginal gyrus of the dominant parietal lobe. This area quickly selects the course of action, although it is under the inhibitory influence of decisions formulated in the prefrontal lobe. The ideomotor area once fully activated works through the motor and premotor cortex. Broca's area of speech is controlled from this region, and it in turn feeds into the projection areas of the cortex.

The motor cortex (area 4) works through the corticospinal and corticobulbar tracts. These fibers form a bundle running through an area called the internal capsule that is surrounded by the corpus striatum. At the upper end of the midbrain the corticobulbar fibers begin to separate from the internal capsule, and they synapse with the nuclei of the cranial nerves III, IV, and VI to the eyeball muscles. The remainder of the corticobulbar fibers pass through the ventral, or motor, aspect of the crura and pons, and they course into the medulla where they synapse with nuclei of cranial nerves V, VII, IX, X, XI, and XII. These fibers decussate to a variable extent at the level of the nuclei they supply. The corticobulbar tract has an important control over the speech muscles of the head and neck through the intermediation of the cranial nerves.

The greater corticospinal tract descends to the pyramids of the medulla where 70 per cent or more of the fibers decussate to form the lateral corticospinal tract. The remaining fibers continue ipsilaterally down the anterior funiculus of the cord as the anterior corticospinal tract. There is considerable decussation even in the ipsilateral tract so that for the most part one side of the brain controls the other side of the body. The anterior tract does not seem to pass below the thoracic cord. At every level of the cord the fibers of the lateral tract synapse upon internuncial neurons and to a lesser extent upon the anterior horn cells. The pyramidal (corticospinal) fibers constitute the upper motor neuron whereas the anterior horn cell and its axonal nerve fiber form the lower motor neuron. It takes two neurons in this total path to innervate the muscle effectors.

The pyramidal fibers give the energy for contraction. This is expressed in the form of isolated, delicate, and graded movements. If the upper motor pyramidal neuron is interrupted, the muscles go into flaccid (atonic) paralysis. These pyramidal fibers must normally have a tonic or facilitative effect upon the spinal centers. This facilitation is not powerful; if area 4 is destroyed along with suppressor area 4-S, the muscles become spastic. A flaccid paralysis is also produced when the lower motor neuron circuit is interrupted. This is caused by the loss of nerve impulses from the nutritive central motor nuclei. A progressing peripheral or Wallerian degeneration follows.

The premotor cortex works chiefly through the basal ganglia and the extrapyramidal tracts. It also sends into the motor area impulses which excite the Betz cells and the associated nuclei. In this way it influences or controls the motor area. Both premotor and motor cortex are necessary in skilled movements. The premotor area establishes the background for activity in the muscles by putting them into a correct postural pattern, and the motor cortex provides the delicate adaptive movements. The premotor cortex controls groups rather than individual muscles. Such suppressor areas as 4-S, 8-S, and others in the premotor cortex inhibit muscles. In this way activity such as respiratory movements may be suppressed with demand during phonation.

There are many descending routes from the premotor cortex and basal ganglia, and any estimate of their relative importance is still questionable. All the tracts taking part in this system are called extrapyramidal. Until recently the rubrospinal tract was thought to be of considerable significance. This tract originates in the red nucleus into which impulses funnel from the cerebellum and upper basal ganglia. It then crosses over in the pons and descends through the lateral cord to the sacrum, and it synapses at every level with the anterior horn cells.

The reticular formation of the brain stem and the reticulospinal tract have assumed an increasing importance. A considerable number of frontal cortex fibers end in the reticular formation. There is an uncrossed reticulospinal tract in the anterior funiculus and a crossed one in the lateral funiculus. Before the motor cortex energizes a muscle, inhibitory impulses are sent down through the reticular substance to the cord to suppress the segmental facilitation which could disturb the proposed motion. It is to be reemphasized that the reticular formation also contains centers for facilitation which, on occasion, increase the excitability of the anterior horn cells. The red nucleus may work chiefly through the reticular formation by way of the rubroreticular tract.

The vestibulospinal tract lies chiefly in the anterior cord, and it runs ipsilaterally from the vestibular nucleus down into the sacrum. It adjusts the body muscles to postural changes first occurring in the head.

The tectospinal tract runs contralaterally from the midbrain to the thoracic region in the anterior cord. It is a path from the retina and the auditory receptors to the muscles of the head and neck.

The olivospinal tract in the lateral cord runs from the inferior olivary nucleus to the cervical cord. It is of uncertain function.

Just as there is a corticobulbar separation from the corticospinal fiber system, so the extrapyramidal tracts tend to project to the motor neurons of the brain stem as well as to those of the spinal cord.

The discussion above, which seems to dichotomize the pyramidal and extrapyramidal systems, may need some reevaluation. Peele (1954) says that many cerebral cortical areas are probably associated in part with extrapyramidal activity.

Meyers (1955) has questioned the conventional view that voluntary movements are the unique function of the pyramidal system. In an operation which he termed crusotomy, the pyramidal tracts were interrupted bilaterally in the intermediate three-fifths of the midbrain crura in order to decrease the severe hyperkinesia and disorder of striated muscle tonus found in certain patients with cerebral palsy. In those people whose abnormal movements were lost contralaterally after a first-stage crusotomy was done on one side, there was also a significant decrease of such movements on the ipsilateral side even prior to the second stage operation. In time many crude movements returned which were definitely voluntary. It thus appears that volitional acts may involve something other than a purely pyramidal control. A bilateral projection of corticofugal impulses, especially to the limbs, may exist.

Meyers (1956) challenged the concept of the dichotomy of the pyramidal and extrapyramidal tracts, stating that their separateness has never been operationally demonstrable. He also stated that the composition of the pyramidal tract or system is for the most part unknown. Moreover, he objects to equating voluntary phasic activities with the pyramidal tract and involuntary tonic-postural behavior with the extrapyramidal system.

We are approaching an era of revolutionary thought in neurology. Bucy (1957) asserts that there is no single pyramidal tract arising in the precentral gyrus which is responsible for the control of voluntary muscular activity. The origin of many of the pyramidal fibers is in doubt, and probably not all of the fibers originate in the cerebral cortex. Bucy urges that the term pyramidal tract and the concept which it represents should both be discarded. Instead of a pyramidal system there are fibers of diverse origin passing from the brain to the spinal cord. He seems to be even more opposed to the concept of the existence of an extrapyramidal system. This is said to have no unity whatsoever except that it is not a part of the pyramidal system. Even the term premotor cortex may have to be discarded. There is some evidence that it does not give the cumbersome mass movements described in the literature. If we regard the above statements as true, then we have the task of discovering the neural mechanisms responsible for voluntary motion.

In order to coordinate the movements of various cranial nerves with upper cervical nerves, a bilateral association tract called the medial longitudinal fasciculus is laid down between the midbrain and the upper cervical cord. This tract has ascending and descending fibers on each side to associate the motor nuclei.

THE PERIPHERAL NERVES

All speech behavior is made possible by impulses flowing through selected cranial and spinal nerves. Nearly all nerves contain both afferent and efferent fibers so that they conduct impulses toward as well as away from the centers. We not only produce motion, secretion, or changed blood supply in our speech effectors, but we in turn receive considerable information from these very organs concerning their general status and vitality.

There are typically in man thirty-one pairs of spinal nerves differentiated to eight cervical, twelve thoracic, five lumbar, five sacral, and one caudal (coccygeal). Each pair, except for the cervicals, is named from the vertebra above its exit.

The spinal nerves, as well as the cranial, constitute the lower motor neurons, or final common paths, into which impulses are funneled from both the pyramidal and extrapyramidal systems. The muscles of speech which are innervated by the spinal neurons are in the neck, thorax, and abdomen. These muscles receive their innervation through cervical and thoracic nerves.

The anterior divisions of the upper four cervical nerves intertwine to form a cervical plexus. Nerves going out from this plexus are the chief source of innervation for the muscles of the neck which are concerned in speech.

The last four cervical plus the first and usually the second thoracic nerves produce a brachial plexus. Nerves branch out from this plexus to innervate the upper extremity and the upper muscles of respiration.

The nerves leaving the thoracic sector of the spinal cord below T-2 do not intermix to form a plexus. They leave the cord as individual pairs of nerve trunks. These nerves innervate thoracic and abdominal structures, including the respiratory muscles in these regions.

Most of the largest peripheral nerves contain fibers which have originated from several spinal nerve roots. The phrenic nerve to the diaphragmatic muscle of breathing originates typically from three roots in the cervical plexus. A lesion in a single peripheral nerve trunk may thus involve fibers belonging to more than one spinal nerve.

The cranial nerves arise from the brain as twelve pairs. Unlike the spinal nerves they originate at irregular intervals. The cranial nerves are not all concerned with speech; all, however, will be briefly characterized. They are conventionally designated by Roman numerals I to XII.

I. *Olfactory Nerve.* It arises in the mucous membranes of the upper nasal cavity, and it ends in the olfactory bulb. From there the olfactory tract passes to the rhinencephalon. The nerve is purely sensory and serves for smell.

II. *Optic Nerve.* It arises in the retina of the eye, and it ends in the lower visual centers. From there the geniculocalcarine tract passes to the occipital lobe of the cerebral cortex. The nerve is sensory and serves for vision. It could be involved in word blindness. Because of its importance the optic tract is diagrammatized herein.

III. *Oculomotor Nerve.* It passes as a motor nerve from the midbrain to several eyeball muscles.

IV. *Trochlear Nerve.* It passes as a motor nerve from the midbrain to a single eyeball muscle.

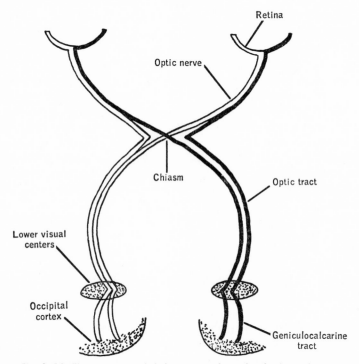

Fig. 2–13. The neurons and their manner of crossing in the optic tract.

V. *Trigeminal Nerve.* This is important to speech. It is sensory to the muscles of the face and tongue, and it is motor to the muscles of chewing. It has three great divisions, the ophthalmic, maxillary, and mandibular. The sensory ophthalmic innervates the nose, orbit, forehead, and cranium. The sensory maxillary innervates the upper row of teeth, the upper lips, and the cheek. The mandibular is sensory from the teeth and skin of the lower jaw and also from the skin on the side of the cranium; it sends motor fibers to the muscles of mastication while it receives proprioceptive impulses of movement from these muscles.

VI. *Abducens Nerve.* It passes as a motor nerve from the pons to a single eyeball muscle.

VII. *Facial Nerve.* It travels as a mixed nerve from the medulla; its sensory fibers innervate the taste buds of the anterior two-thirds of the tongue. Its main distribution is motor to the facial muscles of expression situated about the scalp, forehead, eyes, nose, and mouth. Lesions produce ipsilateral facial paralysis involving disorders of facial expression and movement. There may be faulty control of jaw movements in a motor-root involvement.

VIII. *Auditory Nerve.* This goes between the auditory and non-auditory labyrinth of the internal ear and the medulla. It has cochlear and vestibular divisions, and both sections are sensory. The former is for hearing, and the latter for postural reactions of the head. Lesions of the cochlear division lead to hearing defects. Lesions of the vestibular division lead to disturbances in bodily equilibrium and orientation in space.

IX. *Glossopharyngeal Nerve.* This is a mixed nerve of the medulla. Its motor branches innervate pharyngeal muscles. Lesions of these fibers produce variable degrees of paralysis of the palate, pharynx, and larynx. Its sensory branches include taste fibers from the root of the tongue as well as from the mucous membranes of the mouth and pharynx. Paralysis of sensory fibers affects taste and also proprioception of movements in the tongue root.

X. *Vagus Nerve.* This will be described in detail under laryngeal innervation. It is a mixed nerve from the medulla, supplying sensory and motor fibers to the vocal organs, pharynx, lungs, esophagus, alimentary canal, and the heart. The terminal branches to the larynx have crossed and uncrossed fibers. There are two great divisions which are pertinent to phonation, the superior and inferior laryngeal nerves. Lesions of either trunk will produce specific phonatory disorders, to be discussed later.

XI. *Spinal Accessory Nerve.* This is a motor nerve from the medulla to the palate, neck muscles, and trapezius. It has a cranial branch which joins the superior laryngeal and pharyngeal branches of the vagus. It also has a spinal branch to the sternocleidomastoid muscle, and this branch joins with cervical nerves. Impairment of muscle action following lesions in this nerve leads to faulty articulation and to difficulty with gutteral sounds.

XII. *Hypoglossal Nerve.* This is a motor nerve from the medulla to the muscles of the tongue. The upper motor neurons are chiefly crossed. The nerve also innervates muscles connecting the tongue with the mandible and hyoid bone. In lesions of the nerve the tongue deviates, and it may become paralyzed and atrophied. With failure to control the tongue many sounds are slurred.

APPLIED ANATOMY AND PHYSIOLOGY

The increasing body of theory and facts now known about speech disturbances of nervous system origin or involvement are most properly discussed in specialized clinical treatises. Certain selected conditions are brought to attention here as elsewhere through this text because they emphasize the correlative significance of the functional anatomy. A formal scheme for the examination of the higher cerebral functions including speech is given by Merrit et al. (1947).

The importance of cerebral dominance is illustrated by the defects following lesions in the major hemisphere. The aphasias are examples. In a motor aphasia the individual may not be able to speak, and if lesions should occur they are often found in the dominant Broca's area. There are several varieties of the expressive types of aphasia, and all are correlated by variable evidence with some area of the motor or premotor cortex. A pathological inability to decide what to do, such as to choose meaningful words in speech, has been correlated with lesions in the ideomotor area and classified with the aphasias.

Merrit et al. (1947) state that the upper part of Broca's speech area allows association between the cortical-visual and cortical-manual areas, and that patients with motor aphasia usually have a writing defect, or agraphia. Just as speech deteriorates without auditory reinforcement, so writing deteriorates without visual reinforcement.

The importance of dominance is also illustrated in the sensory aphasias. The failure to recognize spoken words (word deafness) is usually associated with lesions in the dominant superior temporal gyrus. Lesions in the dominant visual-association areas may be associated with failure to recognize written words (alexia) or objects in general (visual agnosia). Wepman (1951) suggests that aphasia may result from cerebral damage on the left side alone, and that only the left cerebral hemisphere in all people is concerned with language on the symbolic level. On the articulatory or dysarthric level, language disturbances may result from damage of either hemisphere.

It is said that aphasics retain lower language functions, such as emotional expressions and memorized language content. This occurs supposedly because these faculties are mediated by the nondominant cortex (Eisenson, 1957).

Penfield and Rasmussen (1950) have shown that perceptual auditory illusions and receptive auditory aphasia, involving alteration of judgment and of interpretation of sounds, may result from lesions in the superior part of the first temporal gyrus. Solomon (1957) says that the angular gyrus, dealing with the recognition of the visual image of words, and Wernicke's area, dealing with the recognition and interpretation of language sounds, are mutually dependent for correct association of words and sound; the usual clinical picture of a major lesion between both of these areas is a total receptive aphasia characterized by incorrect speech and writing and the inability to understand speech and writing. Solomon notes the existence of a hypothetical relationship between these areas which allows an internal language that is a necessary step to rational speaking or writing.

Among its characteristics, dominance may be pure or mixed; the latter is common in the same person. It need not be all-or-none, as exemplified by ambidexterity. There is always the problem of whether it is congenital or acquired.

Penfield and Rasmussen (1950) state that there is an extraordinary degree of specialization of speech representation in the dominant hemisphere. It contains three distinct areas where electrical stimulation produces aphasia. There is neurosurgical evidence that the sensorimotor cortex between the frontal and parietal speech areas can be removed without aphasia. This also seems to be the case for the anterior and inferior portions of the dominant temporal lobe. In contrast to the demonstrated lateralizations there is no hemispheric preference for the sensory and motor elements concerned with word articulation and vocalization. A surprisingly large amount of the cortex is dispensable, which does not imply absence of major function but rather shows that much of the cortex is employed on an optional basis.

Aphasia is associated with many cortical disturbances; the most frequent are hemorrhages, stationary clots (thrombi), and moving clots (emboli). Wounds, tumors, and infectious diseases such as encephalitis and meningitis are occasionally involved as are epilepsy and some of the degenerative diseases of the brain. Such pathological processes do not necessarily give evidence for the doctrine of localization.

Aphasias are not always associated with organic lesions in localized cortical areas. Hughlings Jackson (1834–1911) refused to accept the doctrine of localization and stated that the aphasic suffers from a change in the whole personality. He wrote his first paper on speech disorders in 1864. His view became important because he introduced a dynamic concept of aphasia. He distinguished propositional or meaningful speech from emotional speech, and he recognized the failure of propositional speech in aphasia. Henry Head (1926) proposed a functional approach in which aphasic disorders must not be viewed as isolated affections of speaking, reading, and writing. Each clinical type is an affection of symbolic formulation and expression. Head recognized four forms of such disturbance and called these verbal, nominal, syntactical, and semantic.

Verbal aphasia is a disorder in using words singly or in combination, and in severe cases the patient may be almost speechless. There may be associated lesions found in the region anterior to the motor area for the head and neck.

Nominal aphasia involves the lack of ability to comprehend specific words and particularly names, letters, and numbers. Lesions may occur in the angular gyrus.

Syntactical aphasia implies the inability to place words in an intelligible sequence, resulting in jargon. There may be lesions in the center of the first temporal gyrus.

Semantic aphasia is of the highest order and involves a failure to recognize the true meaning of language. Although a word or phrase is understood, a story is not comprehended nor can it be repeated in its true sense. There are views that there may be associated lesions in or posterior to the supramarginal gyrus (Krieg, 1942).

Among other investigators after Head, Kurt Goldstein (1942; 1948) emphasized the gestalt theory in which localization is denied but integration as a unit is disturbed. The language difficulty is only one symptom of aphasia. Wepman (1951) stated that better prognosis is possible for aphasics through a nonlocalizationist standpoint in which recovery follows reintegration of residual cortical tissue into a functioning whole. Strict proponents of the opposing localization school include Henschen (1926), Nielson (1941), and many others.

The contrasting opinions on localization obviously determine the therapeutic approach. Weisenberg and McBride (1935) have emphasized that there is the negative problem of what the patient is unable to do because of a lesion, or the positive view of what he is able to do through the function of the undamaged brain, and that the first aspect has received greater consideration. In both normal and damaged structures physiological processes, including language, are dependent upon the functioning of the anatomical parts. In aphasia it is possible to produce only what the intact structures are capable of producing.

The failure of or interference with an established dominance has been a prominent tenet in the neurological theories of the cause of stuttering. Bryngelson (1935) explains stuttering as a failure of unilateral dominance along with persistent ambilaterality. The theory of stuttering associated with conflict between two sides of the brain is not new (Barbara, 1954). The speech and writing areas are closely associated in the dominant hemisphere, and the dissociation of the writing area from the speech area, by, for instance, retraining a left-handed person to use his right hand, has been widely considered in the past to be sufficient cause to provoke stuttering. In cerebral palsy a technic has been used to establish a dominance by a maneuver such as binding one hand for some months.

Stuttering has also been explained neurologically on the basis of a failure in the timing action of the integrative centers located in the cortical or subcortical regions. This results in distorted rhythms.

There is the hypothesis (Karlin, 1950) that stuttering is associated with a delay in the acquisition of the myelin sheaths which ordinarily cover spinal nerve fibers and which also cover the fibers comprising the white matter of the brain. Girls are said to develop the necessary cortical myelin earlier than boys, and they show a lesser incidence of stuttering.

Actually, stuttering is an obscure disorder, and any attempt to explain or manage it through pure neurophysiology could meet with failure. The organicists themselves have changed the choice of organ to which they have referred the causative factor. Aristotle thought the tongue was too hard and thick. Hippocrates applied medications to the neck and throat. Celsus emphasized the respiratory aspect.

The views involving a psychogenic origin have gradually gained favor (Hahn, 1943; Barbara, 1954). Studies with physiological variables including heart rate, blood pressure, and basal metabolism have not led to the discovery of significant differences between stutterers and non-stutterers, so that physiological activities are not necessarily involved unfavorably (Trumper, 1928; Ritzman, 1942; Williams, 1955; Mc-Croskey, 1957). Williams used electromyography, which involved the testing of action potentials from the masseter muscle, and he reached the conclusion that there is no evidence for a basic or neurophysiological difference between the two groups.

In the psychological views stuttering is explained as a symptom of an emotional difficulty, as a pathological social response, as an inhibition before the conditioned reflex is firmly established, as a symptom of certain psychoneuroses, and in many other ways that are beyond the scope of this text. The functional approach to causation is sharply expressed in the view of Gottlober (1953); who prefers the term blocking to either stuttering (repetitious speech) or stammering (hesitant speech). He defines blocking as a disorder in the way the speech mechanism is constructed to operate. The somatic speech mechanism is said to be only an instrument through which the psyche expresses itself.

Among the neurological disturbances, those related to the control of voluntary movements are of importance. The basal ganglia can play a significant part in such disorders. The function of the basal ganglia in preventing oscillations between agonist and antagonist muscles in the resting individual has already been noted in the release phenomena following lesions. If any of the suppressor nuclei of this group is seriously affected by lesions in it or in the afferent and efferent tracts connecting such nuclei with the suppressor parts of the cerebral cortex, the excessive undamped activity in other cortical regions, probably the premotor cortex, is initiated. Athetoid oscillations, or the choreiform movements seen typically in St. Vitus's dance, may arise following an incomplete interruption of the suppressor systems. The tremor of Parkinson's disease also indicates that the normal basal nuclei possess a damping action over muscle activity.

Similar kinds of abnormal movements are found in cerebral palsy, which is a condition of motor dysfunction expressed as a paralysis or lack of coordination in the motor system. In many ways the disease transcends the limited definition of a neuromuscular disorder.

Opinions vary about the etiology of cerebral palsy. Heredity does not seem to be important. The most common cause of the brain damage is hypoxia (oxygen lack) before, during, or after birth.

There are several forms of the disease. These express the effects of varying and diffuse pathological processes upon different parts of the brain. At one time all the manifestations of such palsies were classified as Little's disease.

The types of involvement in cerebral palsy include spasticity, athetosis, ataxia, tremors, rigidity, and atonia. The first three varieties are the most frequent.

The spastics may have damage at any level of the extrapyramidal system so that cortical inhibition from the upper premotor neuron is cut off. The muscles of the tongue, larynx, and respiration may be affected, which makes speech slow, labored, and jerky. Pitch and volume may be abruptly altered.

The athetoids show purposeless, slow writhing movements, which may cease in sleep; and their speech is slow, labored, and arrhythmic. The lesions are somewhere in the extrapyramidal system. Athetosis affects mainly the small muscles of the hands and feet, resulting in irregular flexion and extension of the fingers and toes. Grimacing, laughing, crying, chewing, and breathing are all impaired in addition to speech. Athetoid movements are to be distinguished from choreic movements, the latter being brief, sudden, rapid, irregular, and purposeless.

The ataxics usually show cerebellar dysfunction or else extrapyramidal involvement somewhere downstream from the cerebellum. These patients find it difficult to coordinate the speech muscles and articulation may be slurred.

The term rigidity generally implies an increase in muscle tone, and it is a fairly universal indication of pathology in the corpus striatum. It is a release phenomenon in that the striate inhibition over lower centers is cut off. Rigidity fluctuates in the course of time, and it is not as intense as the pyramidal type of spasticity.

A tremor when present and of basal ganglion origin varies from fine to coarse, and it shows rhythmicity with a rate of 5 to 8 oscillations per second. It implies an improper distribution of tone to the muscles, and it is probably a release phenomenon.

In closing the chapter some reference may now be made to the brain stem. The importance of the brain stem is brought out in bulbar palsy (poliomyelitis) in which the motor nerve cells of the brain stem and the spinal cord are attacked by a virus. Any of the cranial nuclei in the medulla may be destroyed with subsequent atrophy of their axons. The breathing centers of the reticular formation may be damaged with resulting paralysis of the diaphragm and intercostal muscles. When the vagus nerve nuclei are attacked, weakness or paralysis of the pharynx, soft palate, and vocal folds may result.

When the muscles controlling the soft palate are paralyzed, an adequate nasopharyngeal port closure is lacking, and nasality becomes chronically sustained.

Damage to the medullary nuclei involving speech or an injury to both corticobulbar tracts can produce a thick speech, in which the patient seems to have a mouthful of soft food while he is talking.

The age of incidence of bulbar palsy is highest in the first ten years, and the onset of symptoms is more abrupt in children. A fatal peripheral respiratory failure is common.

SUMMARY

The speech apparatus is regulated by the nervous system through the continual operation of adaptive reflexes. Many of these reflexes have arisen by association, and such conditioning is at the basis of learning.

The cerebrum is the highest level of regulation, and preferential control or dominance appears to exist, usually in the left hemisphere. There is considerable evidence both for and against localization of cerebral function.

Lower areas of the brain are of considerable importance in speech. The basal ganglia, which send impulses to the skeletal muscles through an extrapyramidal system of tracts, are concerned with postural tone. The cerebellum and the brain stem also contribute to the development of the final qualities of the muscle contraction.

Many impulses are received into the spinal cord, which can act both as a reflex center of adjustment and as a conductor of impulses to and from the brain. The brain can receive and send back impulses not only by way of the cord but also by its own peripheral system of cranial nerves.

Chapter 3

AUTONOMIC AND ENDOCRINE
REGULATORS OF SPEECH

We have seen that the central nervous system functions in part for the reception and storage of information with the capacity to associate the information into complex concepts. The action of the centers upon the peripheral effectors such as muscles and glands is volitional, rapid, and usually precise.

The autonomic and endocrine regulators play a supporting role, which is none the less important. The endocrines come into action relatively slowly, but their effect is strong and sustained, unlike the quick although fleeting responses elicited through reflex nervous control. The autonomic and endocrine agencies help establish the background conditions of speech, and they are especially significant in determining the individuality or emotional coloring of the voice.

The autonomic nervous system and the endocrine glands are closely associated in function. This is especially true for the thoracolumbar, or sympathetic, section of the autonomics which acts functionally with the medulla of the adrenal gland to form a *sympatho-adrenal* system. The linkage of these two great agencies is seen in the fact that the hypothalamus in the forebrain is the head center of the sympathetic autonomic nerves and is also the organ in which emotional reactions gain expression. Such behavior intimately involves the activity of both autonomic nerves and endocrine glands.

EMOTIONS AND NEUROENDOCRINE INVOLVEMENT

Much of the motivation for speech is emotional. Although phonation appears first as purposeless sounds, it comes to be used in struggle situations, as in hunger, pain, or anger.

The voice is the medium for expressing the emotions, and it is linked with such emotional aspects of personality as stability, friendliness, sympathy, and aggressiveness. The machinery of the emotional responses is located primarily in the hypothalamus. This is evidenced by the sympathetic nervous concomitants of an emotion. Stage fright, for example, produces not only speech aberration but also occasional sympatho-adrenal responses, including a rapid pulse, cold sweat, and muscle trembling. Although stage fright is considered to be a fear response, traceable in its expression to autonomic hyperactivity, there are other theories.

General neural coordination appears to break down in strong emotional experiences, and vocal tremors and abnormal muscular rhythms can be produced. The sequelae of the alterations in muscle tone may be reflected in throat tensions and a harsh, strained voice. The autonomic changes have an influence upon breathing. An increased rate and depth of breathing can lead to a lack of reserve breath and the disruption of smooth speech flow. Not only do emotions affect respiration, but even the recollections of emotions do so.

Holmes (1946), has an interesting and provocative hypothesis concerning the role of emotions in poor phonation. Efficient voice production is said to require the matching of an optimal pressure by the breath stream with an optimal resistance by the laryngeal valve. The laryngeal musculature is claimed to operate first for struggle reactions, and such behavior involves a maximum resistance of the laryngeal valve to the passage of the breath stream. This conflict presents the greatest single problem influencing good voice sounds. The conflict is exaggerated in strong emotional states in which the voluntary muscles may enter a generalized hypertonic condition. If the emotional changes persist, the approximated vocal folds may become too resistant for good phonation.

Emotional behavior is linked with changes in thyroid gland function. Anxiety may be a symptom of both hypothyroidism and hyperthyroidism. It appears also in dysfunction of other endocrine glands. Thyroid gland disorders may be associated with vocal fatigue, hoarseness, oral dryness, pressure sensations in the throat, and difficulty in projecting the voice.

ENDOCRINES AND THE LARYNX

Although the larynx is usually thought of as a structure regulated by the vagus and cervical sympathetic nerves, it should also be looked upon as a secondary sexual organ which is changeable at puberty and thus subject to complex endocrine control. Similarly, the status of the nasal mucosa and its subsequent contribution to voice resonance are under endocrine control. In this sense the voice may be thought of as a barometer of psychic function.

At puberty gonadotropic hormones help shape the voice registers. In the male and female climacteric, which is under strong endocrine control, the characteristics of the voice are again subject to change.

Much of our behavior is endocrine-controlled, although this factor can be overemphasized. Before birth the endocrines partly determine growth and differentiation. The prenatal influence of the endocrines in the development of the vocal mechanisms is obscure.

ANATOMY OF THE AUTONOMIC NERVOUS SYSTEM

The autonomic nervous system innervates all the smooth muscles, glands, and the cardiac muscle. It controls vital functions not under voluntary control. The system is not causative but regulative for functions that are essentially automatic.

Usually only the efferent autonomic (visceral) nerves are described because of their high degree of anatomical organization. The visceral afferents are difficult to consider as an integral unit because they arise from voluntary (somatic) as well as autonomic receptors, and they are not necessarily an exclusive part of the autonomic system.

The autonomic system is relatively independent of the central nervous system in its functioning, although always subject to the results of affective experiences mediated in the cerebrum and basal ganglia. The system is embryologically derived from the central system by the proliferation of neuroblast cells, which maintain contact through nerve fibers with the brain or spinal cord. The typical connections and outflows involve at least two neurons; the first called preganglionic connects the central nervous system with the autonomic ganglion (group of cells outside the brain or cord), and the second called postganglionic travels from the ganglion to the visceral effector. The preganglionic or white ramus has a myelin sheath which is not present in the postganglionic or gray ramus.

Whereas the cells producing cerebrospinal fibers are found at every segmental level of the spinal cord and also at twelve levels in the brain for the cranial nerve outflow, the entire autonomic preganglionic outflow involves four general areas or levels: the midbrain and hindbrain, and the thoracolumbar and sacral segments of the spinal cord.

The thoracolumbar efferents comprise the sympathetic nervous system, while the two cranial plus the one sacral outflows constitute the parasympathetic system. The entire efferent mass is collectively termed the autonomic nervous system. A brief survey of the segmental outflows follows.

Sympathetic Nerves. The preganglionics leave the spinal cord in the anterior roots of all twelve thoracic segments and in those of the first two or three lumbar segments. The postganglionic fibers eventually supply almost every region of the body.

The paired preganglionics terminate just in front of the cord in the sympathetic cell bodies or ganglia. When seen through the exposed abdomen this system forms a kind of stepladder or paired chain of perhaps twenty-two so-called vertebral ganglia anterior to the cord. Each ganglion is cross-connected to its mate like the horizontal rung of a ladder. In this structure each ganglion extends fibers to the ganglia

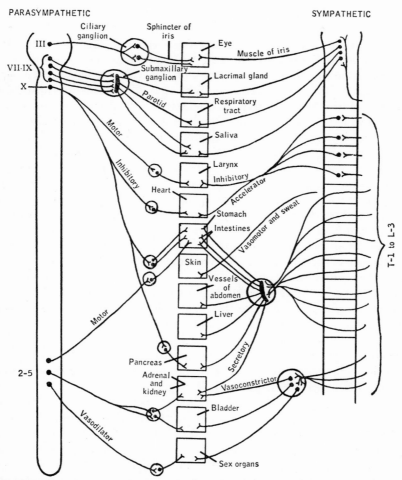

Fig. 3–1. Diagrammatic representation of the parasympathetic and sympathetic outflows.

above and below it like the vertical runners of the ladder. The postganglionics leaving each ganglion run peripherally toward the autonomic effector. The uppermost part of the ganglionic chain is in the neck at the level of the thyroid cartilage angle, and this cervical portion contains the paired superior, middle, and inferior cervical ganglia.

The superior cervical ganglion, which is at the level of the second cervical vertebra, gives off several branches. The most superior, or internal carotid nerve, constitutes the cephalic sector of the system. It enters the cranial cavity with the internal carotid artery. The great cardiac nerve is a second branch and goes to the deep and superficial cardiac plexuses of the heart. The ganglion also gives off rami which travel with the first four cervical nerves.

The middle cervical ganglion sends postganglionic fibers to 5-C and 6-C, and it also gives off the middle cardiac nerve. The inferior cervical ganglion sends fibers into 7-C and 8-C, and it is the origin of the inferior cardiac nerve. The three pairs of cervical ganglia have no direct connection to the cervical cord by white rami, but they are upward extensions of the thoracic part of the stepladder-like chain and receive their preganglionics by upward proliferation of fibers from this chain. By means of the efferent postganglionic outflows from the three pairs of cervical ganglia, a sympathetic control is afforded for all secretory and vasomotor phenomena in the head and neck regions. The organs of phonation, resonance, and articulation are significantly involved.

The thoracic sympathetics are typically one pair to each spinal segment. The first cervical fuses with the inferior cervical ganglion to produce the stellate ganglion. This ganglion is important, since it may be reached by injection of anesthetics for blocking sympathetic impulses from localized bodily areas. Every thoracic ganglion is connected to the cord by a white ramus.

The upper five gray or postganglionic rami supply the thoracic aorta and its branches. If there are three splanchnic nerves, 5 to 8-T form the great splanchnic, 9 to 10-T the middle splanchnic, and 11 to 12-T the least splanchnic. These penetrate the abdomen behind the crura of the diaphragm, and they enter the celiac plexus or its branches at 1-L.

In the abdomen there are four lumbar ganglia; the first three are connected to the cord by white rami, and the fourth is an inferior extension of the straight chain. The postganglionics travel into the superior mesenteric, aortic, and hypogastric plexuses from which additional sympathetic fibers go to the abdominal and pelvic visceral effectors.

The lowest extensions of the chain are four or five sacral ganglia which have no direct white rami connections to the cord. Their gray postganglionic fibers go to the pelvic plexus and to the coccygeal ganglion.

Plexuses. Within the thorax, abdomen, and pelvis there are several great collections of ganglia, or plexuses (also called prevertebral ganglia). These are outlying way stations for the readjustment of impulses, and they receive fibers not only from sympathetic but also from parasympathetic fibers. The nerve trunks that leave any plexus on their way to the final effectors are thus heterogeneous in their composition.

The cardiac plexuses, superficial and deep, lie at the base of the heart. They collect from the three cervical sympathetic ganglia and from the superior and inferior cardiac branches of the vagus nerve.

The celiac (solar or epigastric) plexus is composed of right and left celiac ganglia behind the stomach. It receives the right vagus and the splanchnic nerves. It in turn sends out branches which follow the celiac artery to its visceral endings. The celiac plexus also sends fibers down the surface of the great descending aorta. These fibers help form lower plexuses which receive reinforcing fibers from lumbar and sacral segments and afterward supply the abdominal and pelvic viscera.

Parasympathetic Nerves. The preganglionics do not go to a straight chain as in the sympathetic system, but they travel greater distances to terminate in outlying plexuses or ganglia, some of which lie upon the visceral effector and require only a short postganglionic terminal trunk.

The tectal or midbrain outflow includes autonomic nuclei belonging to the oculomotor cranial nerve. It controls the sphincter of the iris and the ciliary muscle of accommodation.

The bulbar or hindbrain outflow is involved in speech and other functions, and it includes several cranial nerves. The facial nerve carries vasodilator and secretory impulses. Some of these impulses travel from the superior salivatory nucleus through the chorda tympani to the tongue and salivary glands. Other fibers pass through the greater superficial petrosal and vidian nerve via the sphenopalatine ganglion to the palate, nasopharynx, and parotid and orbital glands. Similar impulses travel in fibers belonging to the glossopharyngeal nerve. Such impulses go from the inferior salivatory nucleus through the lesser superficial petrosal nerve via the otic ganglion to the parotid gland and oral regions. Another nerve carrying similar impulses is the vagus to the thoracic and abdominal viscera; this nerve will be considered in more detail in subsequent chapters.

AUTONOMIC FUNCTIONS

The entire autonomic system deals with adaptations to the environment. It innervates structures that are automatic but need only to be regulated by a relatively simple control.

Most bodily organs have a double autonomic innervation with few exceptions, such as the sweat glands which appear to have only a thoracolumbar supply. The two kinds of nerves are in one sense mutually antagonistic, e.g., excitatory versus inhibitory, but in another sense they are complementary. Each division may excite or inhibit depending upon the end organ in question. Thus the vagus may cause active secretion in the vocal folds, but it inhibits or slows down the heart. The autonomic system is not essential to life. In the early experiments of

Cannon, a totally sympathectomized cat was kept alive for three and one-half years, although it lost its power of adaptation to external changes and had to be kept under uniform environmental conditions.

The thoracolumbar system is, in a limited sense, considered to act as an emergency device to prepare an organism for severe muscular effort. It is involved in heightened neuromuscular irritability, raised blood pressure and pulse rate, increased secretion of sweat glands, and similar stress activities, responding adaptively to preserve the steady state.

The medulla of the adrenal gland is an embryological derivative of the sympathetic nervous system, being a modified postganglionic structure, and thus it receives only preganglionic fibers. The nature of sympathetic impulses is therefore similar to that of the adrenal medullary hormone, epinephrine, and the unitary concept of the sympatho-adrenal system is a logical construct.

AUTONOMIC CONTROL CENTERS

The hypothalamus is said to control the sympathetic nerve outflow. Lesions in the hypothalamic region indicate that a set of descending fibers runs down from it to the visceral nuclei of the spinal cord. The hypothalamus is connected to the cerebrum so that it is influenced by states of consciousness. Thus, any affective experience can have an autonomic effect.

The head centers of the parasympathetic system are more obscure, although evidence points to other bodies in the diencephalon.

In regard to control over effective experiences such as the emotions, it has been emphasized (Dunbar and Rowntree, 1943) that the thalamus or hypothalamus should not be considered the "seat" of the emotions, since the cerebral cortex plays an essential part in such processes. In this view an emotion is not an attribute of a specific organ but rather the bodily expression of a flow of energy which permeates the whole organism.

Perhaps the reader should be cautioned early against regarding any localized area as the seat or center of a complex vital function. Certainly, an emotion is not a clear-cut phenomenon to be described in terms of anatomical parts and physiological correlates. The impression should not be gained that the thalamus or hypothalamus can be equated with an emotional experience. It must be stated, however, that an anatomist or physiologist may feel compelled to analyze bodily structure in terms of function and to attribute to a given structure on the basis of adequate experimentation one or more specialized functions. This provides a working basis for further experiments, but the limitations of such knowledge should be recognized.

West (1957) writes that the innate emotional automatisms are controlled by the basal ganglia, and he envisages each organ in this system as being arranged in a linear series from input to output. In this scheme the thalamus is first in line, and the next organ is the caudate nucleus which produces a crude and unconscious interpretation of the thalamic sensations. Then the impulses reach the putamen which stores innate patterns for effective responses following caudate nucleus interpretations. Finally, the globus pallidus sets off the motor impulses which result in appropriate behavioral responses.

West is aware of the danger of oversimplification; he notes additional connections of the basal ganglia to the motor cortex of the cerebrum, to the hypothalamus whereby autonomic behavior is activated, and to the lower motor neurons innervating speech effectors. Because of the diversity of the interconnections, the automatisms may go into conflict. When an individual attempts to express something with deep emotional implications, both speech and the emotional reactions occur together, and there may be associative conflicts.

CHEMICAL MEDIATORS

The differences in the effects of sympathetic and parasympathetic nerves are explainable by the fact that unlike chemical substances are liberated through the postganglionic terminals into the end organs. The actual substances were originally investigated in detail by Cannon and by Loewi, and subsequently, Dale classified parasympathetic fibers as cholinergic and sympathetic fibers as adrenergic.

The parasympathetic postganglionics release acetylcholine (ACh) or its derivatives whereas the sympathetic postganglionics release adrenalin-like substances. All preganglionics release ACh. These extracts of nerves give the same effects as stimulation of the nerves themselves. In this regard the vagus slows the heart by sending ACh into the cardiac cells, and the sympathetics accelerate the heart through transmission of adrenalin-like substances. Cannon originally called the latter sympathin E or I to explain differential excitation or inhibition, but the nature of sympathin has been subjected to various interpretations. Sympathin E had been thought to be nor-adrenalin and sympathin I has been called adrenalin (or sympathin A). Sympathetic stimulation has been demonstrated to release a mixture of adrenalin and nor-adrenalin in varying proportions.

Certain drugs mimic each system and others paralyze one of the two systems. Adrenalin is sympathomimetic but ACh, pilocarpine, and physostigmine are parasympathomimetic. Atropine paralyzes parasympathetic postganglionics and is parasympatholytic. Ergotoxine paralyzes limited varieties of sympathetic postganglionics and is sympatholytic. In general, the autonomic blocking agents do not prevent the release of ACh or other derivatives, but they prevent these substances from entering cells and reaching the receptive compounds of these cells. Cells contain cholinesterase, which destroys ACh quickly, and there are other similar compounds which inactivate the adrenalin derivatives.

THE ENDOCRINE GLANDS

The endocrines are specialized glands without a duct system for carrying out their secretory products or hormones. The secretions must

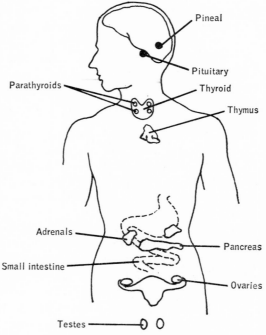

Fig. 3–2. Endocrine glands.

therefore be liberated into the surrounding hemal or lymph drainage systems for transportation throughout the body. These glands do not always accelerate a reaction but they may prevent it. Hormones usually excite target organs that are situated at a distance from the site of the hormonal production. The target may be a specific area or process or, as in the case of the thyroid, the target may be every cell of the body. A hormone in speech should be looked upon as a drug, potent in minute blood concentration, either permeating speech muscle tissue and influencing its activity, or else permeating and affecting the nerves to the muscles.

Some of the glands producing hormones have both an external (duct) secretion as well as an internal (ductless) secretion. In a few cases the endocrines may be found not as discrete organs but as areas within an organ serving other purposes. This is seen in the pancreas, the small intestine, and the kidney.

The influence of the endocrines upon speech is perhaps most vividly seen in speech under tension. The highly irregular rhythm of breathing, the arrhythmic pulse, and the tremors in the voice are some of the

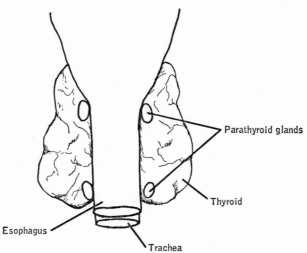

Fig. 3–3. The thyroid gland viewed from behind to show the positions of the embedded parathyroid glands.

indicators of excess hormone output. The regulatory substances are secreted from more than one gland, and they act in synergism with the sympathetic nervous system.

Thyroid Gland. This consists of two lateral lobes and an inconstant inferior connecting portion called the isthmus. All the parts are situated upon the anterior surface of the trachea and loosely attached thereto. The nerve supply is autonomic, consisting of the parasympathetic thyroid branch of the superior laryngeal division of the vagus and sympathetic nerves from the superior and middle cervical ganglia. These nerves are vasomotor rather than secretory, and the gland is normally regulated by the thyrotropic hormone from the anterior lobe of the pituitary gland.

A note is inserted here about the usage of tropin instead of trophin as a suffix. Trophin implies a nutritional state, as in atrophic or hyper-trophic. Tropin means a substance which has a specific functional affinity for given tissues, and it is the proper suffix to use for thyrotropin.

The thyroid is interrelated with glands other than the pituitary. There is a relationship with the gonads. Thus, the thyroid enlarges at puberty, menstruation, and pregnancy, whereas its activity is depressed upon castration. The thyroid is inhibited by the activity of both the adrenal cortex and the medulla.

There are several hormones secreted into the central lumen or colloid of the acini, which are the histophysiological units of function. The major inorganic component of all the secretions is iodine, and this is essential to the endocrine function.

Controversially, the active hormone is thyroxine, which is a cyclic amino acid built from tyrosine; this hormone has been synthesized. Free thyroxine may not in itself be the true thyroid hormone, but perhaps it builds up to a more active polypeptide. The stages of thyroxine synthesis have been found with a tracer called radioactive iodine, which is I-131. Tyrosine is first built to the relatively inactive di-iodo-tyrosine, which is the principal precursor of thyroxine.

Thyroglobulin, which is the specific material of the colloid, has also been thought to be the true hormone. It may be a storage form in which thyroxine conjugates with a protein.

Radioactive iodine compounds in the gland have been separated by chromatography, and by this means another active and possibly very important compound has been discovered called tri-iodo-thyronine.

The physiological action of the active principle is to increase tissue oxidation and the standard metabolism (BMR). Accessory actions involve increase in the mental activity, heart rate, blood circulation, heat production, and sweat gland function.

In thyroid pathology certain upsets in metabolism follow. Deficiency or hypothyroidism takes many forms. If iodine is lacking in the diet, the gland swells to compensate, and this produces a simple goiter which is amenable to iodine replacement. Deficiency or absence of the secretion in the infant produces infantile myxedema or cretinism in which growth is slowed and dwarfism results. There is concomitant depression of the metabolism, sluggish mentality, and arrested somatic and sexual development. In the adult type of myxedema similar but less severe symptomatology occurs. By early and judicious use of thyroid extracts these conditions are improved.

Hypometabolism of endocrine origin, ascribable basically to hypothyroidism, is a common clinical condition. It produces many nonspecific symptoms, such as fatigability and intolerance to cold.

The skeletal muscles in hypothyroidism often become torpid and relaxed. Berry and Eisenson (1956) speak of a husky, unmodulated voice and slow, clumsy speech in myxedema. Cecil and Loeb (1955) describe a thick speech resulting from an enlarged tongue and swollen lips.

In cretinism there may be inner ear deafness, and in myxedema there may be a hearing loss. The external ear is sometimes dry and itching because of reduced ceruminous gland activity. Thyroid medication is rational in such cases (Hilger, 1956).

In excessive secretion the body is flooded with hormone, although the thyroid becomes depleted. In general, the symptoms include raised metabolism, tachycardia, sweating, hypertension, tenseness, nervousness, and exophthalmos (protruding eyeballs).

The skeletal muscles in hyperthyroidism may develop a tenseness which leads to an unpleasant, high-pitched, rapid voice displaying breathiness, fine tremors, and irregularities in pitch (Berry and Eisenson, 1956). Modern medical treatment has turned to the possibilities of radioactive iodine in general treatment.

The processes of development, which include both growth and differentiation, are upset in hyper- and hypothyroidism. Speech, however, need not be significantly disturbed in an endocrine disorder. This is a problem of the individual case.

Parathyroid Glands. These glands are less directly related to normal speech functions, and they will be only briefly considered. There are generally two small glands on each side, very close to or imbedded within the thyroid glands. Their total excision leads to death. In an experimental animal, total extirpation produces, after a day or more, involuntary muscle twitching which becomes coarser and more severe until it terminates in convulsions. Death occurs from respiratory failure through spasms of the muscles of breathing. The condition is called parathyroid tetany, and it is a result of a decrease in the calcium concentration of the blood. The parathyroids maintain the blood calcium level, as well as that of phosphorus, by releasing parathormone. This hormone draws calcium into the blood from its storage reservoirs such as the bones. Too little secretion results in decreased serum calcium, but excessive hormone raises the serum calcium concentration. A balance is preserved between the blood calcium, the calcium in the bones, and the total excretion of calcium from the body.

The blood calcium is related to neuromuscular irritability, and in this regard the vocal mechanism becomes involved. When calcium decreases excessively, nerve and muscle irritability increases, but when calcium increases, irritability is decreased. In the pathological state of decreased blood calcium, a rapid and overly nervous speech may be observable.

A by-product of these facts involves the possibility of a real basis for blood-chemistry studies in speech disorders. This line of endeavor

has already been pursued in the study of certain psychoses. Such in-
vestigations have indicated, for example, that there are biochemical
differences in the blood between stutterers and nonstutterers (Starr,
1928; Kopp, 1933; 1934; Karlin and Sobel, 1940). There have been
studies on the acidity of the saliva as a means of differentiating normal
individuals from stutterers (Starr, 1922; Hafford, 1941). It has also been
found that the application of the parasympathetic drug, acetylcholine, to
the cerebral cortex of the rat changes the hemispheric dominance where
the drug is applied with a subsequent effect upon handedness (Peterson, 1949).

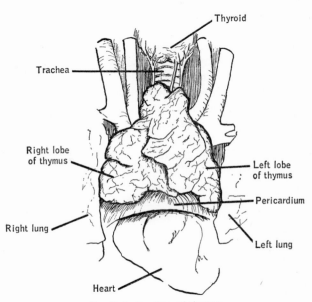

Fig. 3–4. Location of thymus.

Caution is advised in overemphasizing this line of attack. Speech is
an extremely complex function involving the whole psychic as well as the
biological machinery of behavior. Deviation in the serum concentrations
of given substances may be only remotely related to the diagnosis of a
given disturbance or to the proper way of treatment.

Thymus Gland. This organ lies in the neck, anterior and lateral to the
trachea, and deep to the sternohyoid and sternothyroid muscles. It
descends into the superior mediastinal area of the thorax behind the
sternum and in front of the great vessels of the heart. It is composed of
two lobes supplied with blood from the internal mammary and superior
thyroid arteries. The vagus and sympathetic autonomics comprise its in-

nervation. The structure is prominent in the infant and grows in size and weight to eleven or twelve years of age. At about fifteen years it begins to involute, and in old age it is hardly recognizable as a structure.

There are numerous hypotheses concerning thymus function, and many of the views are contradictory. Its control over growth and secondary sexual characters, as well as its capacity to produce lymphocytes, has been frequently emphasized. Its role in speech is purely one of pathology. If the thymus does not regress, it exerts undue pressure upon the structures of the throat neighboring it. Speech may become infantile and mechanically clumsy. Fortunately, the gland is susceptible

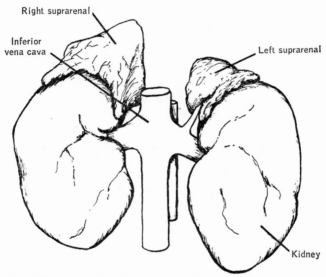

Fig. 3–5. Relationships of the suprarenal glands to other structures.

to X rays, which act directly to produce shrinkage. In thymus hypertrophy or tumor formation, irradiation or thymectomy has in many instances improved the status of the affected individual. An enlarged thymus with excessively developed lymphoid tissue occurs in status lymphaticus.

Adrenal Glands. These lie above the kidney and consist of a central medulla and peripheral cortex. Both parts are independent functional units joined together in development.

Medulla. The actions of this part resemble those caused by stimulation of the sympathetic sector of the autonomic nervous system. In this sense the gland is important in helping to shape the emotional tone of the voice and the autonomic background conditions for speech. The speech of stage fright and of other fear responses is analyzable on an organic basis by endocrine changes, especially those involving the sympatho-adrenal system.

Histologically, the medulla consists of neuroblasts which are identical with the ganglion cells of the sympathetic nervous system. The medulla is innervated only by preganglionic fibers from the splanchnic nerves, while its secreting cells are morphologically homologous with post-ganglionic fibers of the sympathetic nervous system. This again emphasizes the logical use of the term sympatho-adrenal system.

The active hormone is epinephrine (adrenalin, suprarenin, adrenin), which is built from the amino acid called phenylalanine. Epinephrine has been isolated in crystalline form. Its effects are fast but transitory. It acts directly upon effector cells, and even if the neural connections to an organ are severed, the same effect is obtained as through stimulation of sympathetic (adrenergic) nerves. The general function of epinephrine is to aid in the adaptation to conditions demanding vigorous neuro-muscular activity. In other words, it comes into play during stress. Ordinarily, the amount of circulating hormone is very small, but it increases demonstrably during emergency states of stress. Epinephrine secretion is increased by sympathetic (chiefly splanchnic) stimulation, but denervation of the adrenal glands does not entirely inhibit the secretion.

Epinephrine has several specific bodily effects in addition to diverse therapeutic uses. It increases the rate and force of the heart. It constricts cutaneous vessels and those of the splanchnic region while dilating the arterioles of the coronary vessels and those of the skeletal muscles; the constrictor effect predominates, and this maintains the level of the blood pressure. Epinephrine contracts the spleen, dilates the pupil, and relaxes smooth muscles. It produces liver glycogenolysis and thus raises the blood sugar to prevent fatigue.

The vasomotor and secretory activities of the vocal mechanism are simply localized counterparts of the general bodily effects produced by sympatho-adrenal stimulation. Some nor-adrenalin (arterenol, sympathin E) is involved with adrenalin in the effector responses.

Cortex. The adrenal cortex is vital to life but the medulla is not. The cortex has almost thirty hormones. All are called steroids, and they have the same basic structural nucleus as cholesterol. They are chemically related to the sex hormones, some of which are synthesized in the adrenal cortex as well as in the sex glands.

The active adrenal steroids fall into three groups according to physiological activity. The mineralocorticoids are in group 1 and they have no oxygen on the carbon-11 position. These steroids bring about the reabsorption of sodium and chloride from the kidney to the blood. Important examples are desoxycorticosterone and aldosterone. Electrolyte balance of the blood is preserved.

The glucocorticoids are in group 2. The oxygen atom is typically in the C-11 position but may also be in the C-17 position. These steroids do not markedly affect electrolyte balance, but they produce sugar breakdown in carbohydrate metabolism. Important examples are compound E, or cortisone, and compound F, or hydrocortisone. These have the capacity of being anti-inflammatory drugs, and they have had considerable use in rheumatoid arthritis.

The hormones of group 3 are of great interest in vocal physiology. They include the androgens, estrogens, and progesterone. They are variably involved in secondary sexual development. In tumor formation they are excessively secreted, and masculinizing effects occur. Rarely are there feminizing tumors. One may see precocious sexual and somatic development in children, or virilism and hirsutism in females (as with the bearded lady of the circus). The effects can be exerted upon or expressed through the qualities of the voice.

The steroids eventually are sent into the urine as 17-ketosteroids, some of which come from the sex glands. The ketosteroid concentration in the urine is used to evaluate cortical activity.

The voice in many ways expresses the general bodily status, and it is involved in the general adaptation to the environment. The adrenal cortex facilitates such adaptation. Hans Selye has postulated the nature of the machinery used by pointing up what occurs upon exposure to stress. He calls the forces *stressors* and the reactions the *adaptation syndrome*. The schema of Selye's concept follows. Any alarming stimulus, or stressor, excites the central nervous system, particularly the hypothalamus, which then stimulates a secretion of epinephrine from the adrenal medulla. This causes the anterior lobe of the pituitary gland to liberate adrenocorticotropic hormone, or ACTH. This in turn specifically influences the adrenal cortex to liberate hormones of adaptation, which underlie the bodily effects. One of the practical indices of the adrenal cortex involvement is a reduction in the eosinophile count (eosinopenia), and there is also a lymphopenia.

Note that corticoadrenal function is controlled by the anterior pituitary. ACTH is said to be beneficial in treating arthritis by stimulating compound E or F which then alters the bodily resistance.

The concept of Selye has been challenged. It is denied, for example, that the nonspecific mechanism described above can account for the evolvement of a given specific reaction.

Pituitary Gland (Hypophysis). This gland sits in the sella turcica, or saddle-like depression in the body of the sphenoid bone, located in the central part of the floor of the skull. It consists of anterior and posterior lobes which are unlike each other in origin and in function. Neither lobe is vital, and a total hypophysectomy can be survived. There is an intermediate lobe having the same origin as the anterior lobe. It secretes a hormone which regulates skin pigmentation. The control of pituitary secretions is obscure; it may be neural.

The posterior lobe has no apparent relation to the vocal mechanism. It secretes pitocin, which is involved in the contraction of the muscles of the uterus, and pitressin, which (1) constricts smooth muscles of all arterioles and (2) increases the renal absorption of water.

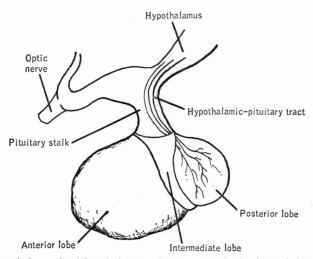

Fig. 3—6. The pituitary gland in relation to other structures in the floor of the diencephalon.

The anterior lobe is a master gland which controls many other endocrine glands and bodily processes through a number of hormones. It controls several kinds of activity, but not all of its hormones are known or capable of being correlated with specific activities. Only selected hormones are briefly touched upon below.

The somatotropic or growth hormone acts directly upon tissue cells. It has been crystallized and identified. If early in life there is marked somatotropic deficiency, dwarfism results. This is usually amenable to early treatment by pituitary extracts. There may be lack of development of the bony and cartilaginous structures comprising the speech machinery. The voice may be weak and the speech infantile.

Hyperpituitarism, involving particularly the growth hormone, can cause giantism if the overactivity occurs in youth. In an adult, overall growth is not the problem, but there is excessive bone thickening, swelling, and deformation called acromegaly. The mandible and skull bones are involved. Other structures, including the tongue, hyoid bone, larynx, and vocal folds overgrow. The use of X rays to shrink a causative tumor of the pituitary region or the final resort to surgical excision are not very satisfactory.

Speech disorders may be associated with changes in bony and cartilaginous structures. Speech can be altered by too long a mandible. The male larynx may simulate the high-pitched vocal quality of the female. The motor patterns of gesture, vocal inflection, and facial expression may resemble those of the opposite sex. Berry and Eisenson (1956) speak of the indistinct articulation and the hoarse quality of the voice in acromegaly.

The thyrotropic hormone has already been discussed. Thyrotropin has been prepared but only in fairly pure state. The pituitary stimulates the thyroid by secreting thyrotropin. The thyroid gland in turn produces its characteristic effects upon the general metabolism of the body.

The adrenocorticotropic hormone of the pituitary has been discussed. ACTH has been isolated in pure state, and it stimulates the adrenal cortex to produce its characteristic effects.

The pituitary gonadotropic hormones are important in speech. They act only indirectly by stimulating the gonads to produce sex hormones. Thus, they have no effect in castrates. There are three gonadotropins. These include follicle-stimulating hormone (FSH), luteinizing hormone or interstitial-cell-stimulating hormone (LH or ICSH), and prolactin (luteotropin).

In the male, FSH is gametogenic, and it induces sperm production and the development of the semen-carrying tubules. ICSH stimulates the production of testosterone in the testis. The pituitary hormones are essential in sexual development. Thus, after experimental hypophysectomy the male does not attain sexual maturity and acts like a castrate. This condition is amenable to anterior pituitary-extract therapy.

In the female, FSH stimulates maturation of the follicles and growth of the ova. LH converts the ripened follicles into a corpus luteum. Prolactin maintains the corpus luteum and stimulates it to secrete the hormone called progesterone. Prolactin initiates milk secretion in developed mammary glands. After childbirth it depresses the maternal sexual cycles and their associated estrogenic-hormone secretion. In hypophysectomy before puberty, the sexual cycles and sexual maturity fail to occur. In hypophysectomy after puberty, the cycles are abolished, and the secondary sexual characteristics are weakened. Anterior pituitary extracts reverse the changes.

The Gonads. *The Male.* The male sex hormones, or androgens, are derived in the gonads from the interstitial cells of the testis, under the influence of the pituitary ICSH. Although several compounds with activity have been isolated, testosterone is the true testis hormone. There are also adrenal cortex androgens and synthetic androgens.

Some testosterone is secreted in the embryo, and it produces early initial differentiation of secondary sexual characters. This is seen in the descent of the testes. At puberty, ICSH produces permanent growth of the interstitial cells and maintains testosterone secretion. The latter hormone has many actions; it stimulates spermatogenesis, develops the reproductive organs, and expresses the secondary sexual characteristics, including the vocal mechanism.

The voice changes or fails to mature in eunuchism, or total castration, and eunuchoidism, or testicular insufficiency. Castration before puberty causes the most marked disturbances. Testosterone is palliative in adult castrates for most of the bodily changes except spermatogenesis, but the drug must be given throughout life. The gonadotropic hormones of the pituitary or placenta are useless in castrates, since these drugs work through the intact testis. Hypogonadism, or testicular insufficiency, and an associated involvement of the larynx may be produced by changes in the testes or in the anterior pituitary. The opposite condition of hypergonadism, which leads to precocious puberty and voice changes, is often ascribed to tumors of the interstitial cells or of the anterior pituitary. In the hypogonadism of the male climacteric, therapy with natural or synthetic androgens is often effective.

The Female. The sex hormones are produced in the ovaries. By acting in conjunction with the pituitary gonadotropins, they regulate reproductive activities, especially from puberty to the menopause. Ovarian function includes (1) growth and differentiation of the reproductive tract; (2) oogenesis; (3) development of secondary sexual characters; (4) control of the menstrual and ovarian cycles; (5) implantation of the ovum in the uterus and the development of the placenta; and (6) control of growth and milk secretion in the mammary glands.

In ovariectomy before puberty all maturation, gametogenesis, and sexual cycles stop, and the secondary sexual characters fail to develop. Genital-tract atrophy, no cycles, sterility, obesity, and considerable emotional disturbance occur in postpuberal ovariectomy. However, the voice, as a secondary sexual activity, need not be markedly disturbed.

The ovum develops within a follicle that produces estrogens. These are hormones belonging to the steroids. Among the active estrogenic hormones are estrone and the more powerful estradiol. The chief function of the estrogens is to stimulate the development of the sexual tract and mammary glands. They also maintain cyclic processes and help express the secondary sexual characteristics. The voice mirrors these changes in a limited area.

Disorders of the gonads in the male or female produce profound changes in the personality. Such changes may be directly or more remotely reflected in the qualities of the voice.

There is some evidence that the pineal gland in the cranium is an endocrine organ, and that it acts as a brake upon maturation and development of the child before puberty. Where there is a pineal tumor in the child, physical and sexual maturation are precocious and speech is disturbed. Ordinarily, the pineal becomes inactive by puberty.

SUMMARY

The autonomic nervous system and the endocrine glands adaptively control much of our unconscious behavior. The relationship of these two regulatory agencies is indicated by the fact that the medulla of the adrenal glands originates from the sympathetic part of the autonomic system.

The activity of nerves and endocrine glands, which is often synergistic, establishes the background conditions of speech, such as the individuality and emotional aspects of the voice. Neural and endocrine agencies control the blood supply and the secretions to any organ, and they stimulate the differentiation of structure necessary for proper bodily functioning.

Chapter 4

ANATOMICAL CONCEPTS AND BODILY ORGANIZATION

The discussion of the neuroendocrine regulation of speech has emphasized the high degree of biological organization evolved for accomplishing meaningful sounds. A markedly diversified series of bodily structures involved in the speech mechanism is still to be described. For the worker whose field is not primarily biological, the pertinent anatomical concepts and terminology and the over-all operational plan of the human organism may be difficult to comprehend. The anatomical information in the present chapter is generalized, but it should provide a basis for a better understanding of the vocal apparatus.

THE ARCHITECTURAL PLAN OF THE BODY

Vertebrate animals, including man, develop as a tube within a tube; the outer one is the framework of the body wall, and the inner one is the digestive tube. The space between the two tubes is the body cavity, or coelom. The primitive nervous system runs longitudinally down the entire body, just dorsal to the coelom.

The coelom in mammals becomes a ventral cavity enclosed by the body wall. In development it is divided into the thoracic and abdominal cavities by a partition called the diaphragm. The thoracic cavity is subdivided into two lateral or pleural cavities between which there is a central region, or mediastinum; the pericardial cavity which encloses the heart takes up a sizable portion of the central mediastinum.

The abdominal cavity is only arbitrarily but not actually subdivided into an upper abdominal and a lower pelvic cavity. The abdominal cavity acquires a lining which is called the peritoneum. The space and all the soft organs lying within the lining are said to be in the peritoneal cavity. Some organs lie behind the peritoneum. An organ such as the kidney may lie behind the peritoneum (or be retroperitoneal) but still lie within the greater abdominal cavity. The pelvic chamber is that portion of the adbominal cavity located inferior to an imaginary line stretched across the crests of the hip bones.

The different body cavities hold the soft internal organs called the viscera. We shall discuss such organs in the thoracic cavity as the lungs, heart, trachea, thymus gland, and certain large blood and lymph vessels.

The terminology adopted in anatomy is called the BNA (*Basle Nomina Anatomica*), which is a result of a series of international meetings in Basle, Switzerland. The meetings were begun by anatomists in 1895 to adopt a universal anatomical language. It is often confusing to the beginner to find that certain structures, such as muscles, are named both in Latin and English. The student who will become a professional worker in speech pathology is advised to consult sourcebooks of Greek and Latin roots (Henderson and Henderson, 1949; Robbins, 1951; Hough, 1953).

TERMINOLOGY OF SPATIAL RELATIONS

Because of man's erect position, confusion arises at times in the usage of terms that describe corresponding structures in man and animals. In man, the anatomical position is one in which the individual stands erect with his face toward the observer, his arms hanging at the sides, and the palms of his hands turned forward. All references to parts are based upon this arbitrary posture.

In man, the terms dorsal and posterior are synonyms for the region of the body toward the back, whereas ventral and anterior refer to the front or belly side. The terms superior and cranial refer to the uppermost region in the standing position, but, on the contrary, inferior and caudal refer to the lowest region. In comparative or animal anatomy, the head end is said to be anterior and the tail end posterior; the region toward the back is dorsal and the belly side is ventral. A part above another part is superior in man and cranial in animals; a part below another is inferior in man and caudal in animals. The term cephalic means cranial in all cases.

Median is toward the mid-line, and lateral is away from the midline. Internal means the center of mass of the structure described, and external is the opposite. These terms are used most frequently in describing the walls of cavities and hollow, soft organs (viscera). Cutaneous vs. deep is used to refer to the body surface in contrast to that region just within the surface. Proximal means nearer the point of attachment, and distal means farther away. Thus, the wrist is distal to the elbow. Adverbs are formed from these adjectives by substituting for the ending -al, the ending -ad or -ally, e.g., proximad or proximally. Central is a term referring to the principal part found internally, but peripheral indicates an extension toward the surface. The central and peripheral nervous systems are examples. Parietal describes the walls enclosing the body cavity or surrounding the organs, whereas visceral refers to the organs within the body cavities.

In addition to the foregoing terms, several planes of reference are used. The median longitudinal or sagittal plane passes anteroposteriorly only through the center of the body, and it divides the body into right and left halves. Any other similarly directed cut produces a longitudinal plane that is off center, and it is thus not a median or sagittal plane. Some writers disagree and use the term sagittal for any plane parallel to the sagittal suture of the skull. A vertical cut at right angles to the sagittal, passing in a transverse or right to left direction through the body, divides the body into anterior, or ventral, and posterior, or dorsal, parts, and is called a frontal plane. A transverse plane is a crosscut at any level that divides the body into cranial and caudal parts.

PROTOPLASM

An analysis of the construction of a complex multicellular vertebrate animal shows that it is highly organized into progressively complex building blocks called cells, tissues, organs, and systems, in that order. The ultimate structural and functional unit is the cell. The science of the cell is cytology.

Protoplasm is the living material of which cells are composed. In the living state the ground structure of protoplasm may not be clearly outlined, but upon fixation and staining it is characteristically granular, fibrillar, or alveolar. Its living secrets are unknown because chemical analysis makes it lifeless.

The elementary analysis of protoplasm shows a predominance of carbon, hydrogen, oxygen, and nitrogen, but there are several other protoplasmic elements. These may also be found in inorganic matter, indicating that the materials alone of protoplasm do not endow it with the properties of life. These properties are a result of the integrative pattern in which the elements are brought together.

The elements combine to characteristic compounds so that protoplasm contains about three-fourths water, many inorganic salts, and organic compounds classified as proteins, fats, and carbohydrates. The inorganic salts are remarkably similar in concentrations to those of the same salts in sea water, and these relative concentrations stay fairly constant among diverse organisms in the face of widely different environmental conditions.

Protoplasm presents the picture of a colorless, viscous, slimy substance or colloidal mass that may change with activity from a fluid or sol state to a viscous or gel state. For example, muscle contraction may represent a reversible gelation of the colloids of protoplasm. Sol-gel changes are generally reversible processes, and life ceases with any tendency toward irreversibility.

The vital attributes of protoplasm include irritability, growth, metabolism, contractility, conductivity, and reproduction. Irritability denotes the power to respond to stimuli. Growth means an increase in size by multiplication of cells. Metabolism implies all the energy exchanges within the organism at a given time. Contractility refers to the power of motion and locomotion. Conductivity implies the propagation of impulses, which are usually nervous. Reproduction is based on the capacity to produce new protoplasm.

THE CELL

The cell is an organized mass of protoplasm surrounded by a limiting membrane. The cell typically contains a central nucleus and the outer cytoplasm. The ground substance, or nucleoplasm, is within the nuclear

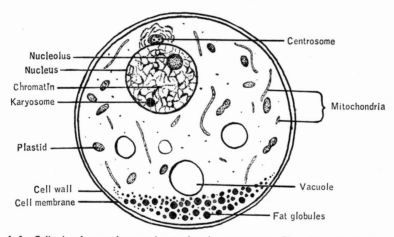

Fig. 4–1. Cell showing nuclear and cytoplasmic components. The shape is diagrammatic.

membrane and is traversed by fine threads, or linin. The fibrils appear to hold the material called chromatin in the form of granules. One or more sharply demarcated spherical bodies, or nucleoli (karyosomes), also lie within the nucleus. The nucleus is thought to be the controlling or informational center for the entire cell. It is necessary for normal cell division, which occurs by an orderly process called mitosis. In this cell fission the chromatin strands condense to discrete elongated bodies called chromosomes. These bodies carry the genes that are needed for transmitting the parental characters to the offspring.

The cytoplasm similarly possesses many organized protoplasmic structures. Living structures called mitochondria appear as rods, granules, or filaments. The functions of these bodies are primary. The Golgi apparatus is typically a fibrillar network close to the nucleus, and it may function in cell secretion. Vacuoles appear as single spaces, droplets, or a fine canal system. Associated with cell division is a centrosome, which consists of a granule or centriole surrounded by a centrosphere. There are also many kinds of cytoplasmic granular inclusions which are derived from cellular metabolism. These bodies represent food, pigment, and secretory granules.

Cells are usually microscopic and are measured in microns, the order of which is a thousandth of a millimeter. The largest single cell in the human body is the ovum, or egg cell, whose diameter is 130 to 140 microns. In the protozoans the entire organism is one cell, but in the multicellular organisms there are billions of cells.

All cells have a life span varying with their position and function. The human red blood cell lives four months, but the white blood cell lives only a few weeks or less. A nerve cell may live as long as the individual. Cells of glands and skin are continually perishing and always being replaced. Many kinds of changes indicate cell senescence, including enlargement or shrinkage, opacity, fragmentation, and loss of function. There are mechanisms, such as chemical solution or ingestion by other phagocytic scavenging cells, to clear the resulting cellular debris.

TISSUES

When groups of similar cells and their intercellular products combine for particular functions, they form a tissue. The science dealing with the microscopic anatomy of tissues is called histology.

Tissues may be classified by embryological origin, such as from one of the three primary germ layers of the embryo called ectoderm, mesoderm, or entoderm. They may also be classified more commonly by function, in which case there are four fundamental types called the epithelial, connective, muscular, and nervous tissues.

Epithelium. This covers the outer surface of the body, and it lines the walls of internal cavities. It also forms glands and parts of the sense organs. It guards the underlying structures against dehydration, chemical assaults, and pathogenic organisms. In the alimentary canal, for example, it acts as a selectively permeable membrane which controls the directional flow of water and other substances.

Epithelial cells are closely packed to form a continuous sheet, or membrane, with very little intercellular material acting as a cement.

Blood vessels are absent. The epithelial cells come from any of the germinal layers of the embryo. The ectoderm produces outer coverings, such as the epidermis of the skin or the linings of the nose, mouth, and anus. The entoderm forms inner linings, such as those of the digestive and respiratory tracts. The mesoderm produces the linings of the heart, blood vessels, lymph vessels, and ducts of a great part of the urogenital system as well as the linings of the peritoneal, pleural, and pericardial cavities.

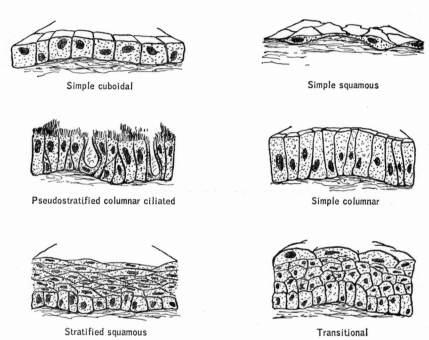

Simple cuboidal   Simple squamous

Pseudostratified columnar ciliated   Simple columnar

Stratified squamous   Transitional

Fig. 4–2. The shapes of epithelial cells.

The term epithelium is a general one, and specialized terms are also used. For example, the endothelium refers to the single layer of cells which forms the internal wall (intima) of blood and lymph vessels as well as the internal wall (endocardium) of the heart. The surface covering of the peritoneum, pleura, and pericardium is called mesothelium. The single layer of cells lining the spaces of the brain and cord sheaths is called mesenchymal epithelium.

Epithelium is of three kinds, depending upon the shape of the cells. It may be squamous (flat), columnar (in which the height exceeds the width), or cuboidal (in which the height and width are about equal).

There may be one or more layers of cells in a given type of epithelium and this differentiates it as simple or stratified. The layers are correlated with function, e.g., a blood capillary requires only a one-layered wall to permit maximum interchange of substances across it, but the skin needs several cell layers for mechanical and antibacterial protection. For similar reasons the epithelium may need many glands to lubricate it against mechanical injury, as in the digestive tract, and it may need to have the power to push out foreign bodies, as in the respiratory tract. In the latter region the cells contain hair-like processes, or cilia, which move in synchronism to expel unidirectionally any mucous film or foreign particle.

Some epithelia, as in the respiratory tract, contain cells which falsely appear to be stratified. These are said to be pseudostratified. A transitional epithelium exists, whose appearance is between that of stratified squamous and stratified columnar. It appears characteristically in the urinary bladder, where the shape and number of cells change with the degree of distention of the bladder. The empty bladder has many cell layers but the filled organ has very few.

Glands are specialized epithelial structures which produce and discharge fluids. If the material discharged is useful, it is called a secretion; otherwise it is an excretion. The gland may in some respects resemble a tube with an opening or duct, in which case it is an exocrine gland. It may have other shapes and no duct so that its products are delivered to the surrounding blood or lymph capillaries. In this instance it is an endocrine gland, and its products are hormones.

Unicellular glands found on mucous membranes are goblet cells, and they secrete a gelatinous substance called mucus. This is to be distinguished from a watery or serous fluid put out by serous glands. Mixed glands secrete both fluids and thus are seromucinous.

The mucous membranes and their glands form the linings of the digestive, respiratory, and genitourinary tracts. They have one or several layers of epithelial cells resting upon a foundation of connective tissue called the submucosa. Although a certain proportion of the epithelial cells produce mucus continually, secretion increases with infections or irritations, as in the running nose of the common cold and the accumulation of mucus in tracheal or bronchial infections. The protein or mucin component of the mucus develops in the cytoplasm of the goblet type of epithelial cell, and such cells when filled burst to discharge their contents. The mucus is a protection against irritants, and it traps minute foreign substances.

The typical gland is multicellular. Its cells do not lie upon the epithelial surface but invaginate (sink below the surface) like a recessed test tube into whose lumen they discharge their secretions. The secretion reaches the surface through a pore. In the simple glands there is one

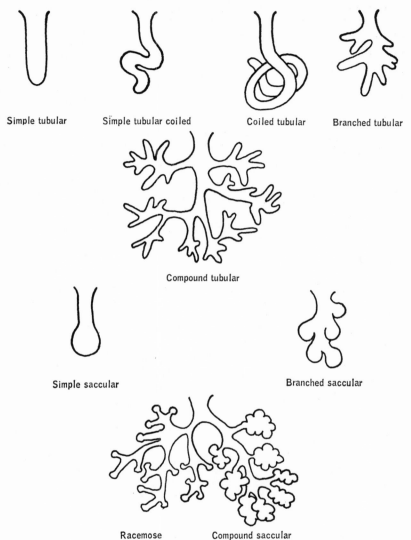

Simple tubular   Simple tubular coiled   Coiled tubular   Branched tubular

Compound tubular

Simple saccular   Branched saccular

Racemose   Compound saccular

Fig. 4—3. Simple and compound exocrine glands.

test-tube-like sac. In the compound tubular or alveolar (round) glands there are many sacs which eventually deliver their secretion to a common stem.

Connective Tissues. These tissues serve to connect or bind structures, to support the body, and to aid in bodily defense, repair, nutrition, and regeneration. Their origin is from mesenchyme, which is embryonic connective tissue, or that part of the mesoderm which forms the connective tissues and also the blood and lymph vessels.

The three main components of connective tissue are cells, fibers, and a matrix. In general, connective tissue has relatively few cells compared with other tissues, but it has a large amount of intercellular substance, or matrix. There is generally a rich blood supply. The matrix looks different in each variety of connective tissue. This difference is correlated with the special functions of the tissue, as in cartilage or bone. Connective tissue is the most widely distributed of all tissues.

Considerable attention is now being given to the matrix of connective tissues in certain regions. For example, the permeabilities and spreading activities of ground substance have been correlated with nasal infections (Hopp and Burns, 1958; Weisskopf and Burns, 1958).

The matrix, or ground substance, may be a liquid like blood and lymph, or a solid like cartilage and bone. The fibers are embedded in the matrix and are elastic (yellow), nonelastic (white or collagenous), and reticular.

Collagenous fibers are typical of all kinds of connective tissue, and they yield a gelatinous substance called collagen upon boiling. The fibers are long, flexible, wavy threads, and they form bundles which travel in any direction through the intercellular framework. Although the bundles are strong and pliable, they lack extensibility. This group includes the strong but not particularly stretchable muscle tendons, and the ligaments, which show a more irregular fiber arrangement. Sometimes the dense white fibers are arranged into broad sheets called aponeuroses. Their presence will be considered later in structures such as the palatine aponeurosis, or framework of the soft palate, and in the abdominal aponeurosis, or framework of the anterior abdominal wall.

The elastic type of fiber, unlike the collagenous type, contains elastin. It shows a high degree of elasticity which decreases with age, as in the blood vessels. Elastic fibers are not so numerous as collagenous fibers, and they appear as delicate threads which may branch repeatedly to form a network. Hollow organs subject to internal pressure variations contain membranes built of elastic tissue. This is characteristic of such speech structures as the trachea, bronchioles, and larynx.

Reticular fibers contain a scleroprotein known as reticulin. These fibers are immature structures which form the reticular or network-like architecture of lymphoid and myeloid tissue. They are found also in the interstitial tissue of glandular organs, the papillary layer of the skin, and elsewhere.

Adult connective tissues are classified into three types by the nature of the cells and matrix. Fibrous tissue is connective tissue proper. Fluid tissue is a special type which includes blood and lymph. Supporting tissue includes cartilage and bone.

The nature of the connective tissue cells varies. The most numerous are fibroblasts, occurring in all kinds of connective tissue. These cells are descendants of the mesenchyme, and they appear as star-shaped bodies with oval nuclei. They can become phagocytes or scavengers, and they can also differentiate into osteocytes (bone cells). Mast cells are a second but less frequent variety. They are highly granulated. Their function is uncertain. Histiocytes are variably shaped cells with a small, bean-shaped nucleus and many cytoplasmic inclusions. They are numerous and act as scavengers, having the power to move like an ameba toward particulate matter. There are other scavenging cells similar to histiocytes whose main function is phagocytosis. They occur in the spleen, liver, lymph nodes, bone marrow, and elsewhere. Collectively, they form a reticulo-endothelial system which is indispensable in bodily defense and immunity. A rare cell in the connective tissue is the plasma cell, whose numbers increase in certain diseases. The eosinophils, lymphocytes, and neutrophils of the blood represent the wandering cells of the connective tissues.

The embryonic connective tissue has been described as mesenchyme, or a network of branching cells with long processes within an abundant fluid intercellular substance. It fills the spaces between developing organs, and it differentiates to adult connective tissues and smooth muscle. There is a second embryonic type called mucous connective tissue, which is found in the umbilical cord as Wharton's jelly.

In the adult the fibrous tissue, or connective tissue proper, takes many forms. These types are adipose, areolar, collagenous, elastic, reticular, and others.

The most widely distributed is the areolar type. It is found in the lower layers of the skin, around blood vessels and nerves, under mucous and serous membranes, and in any unoccupied region. Within the semifluid or amorphous matrix there are many kinds of cells, such as fibroblasts, histiocytes, and others. The fibers are yellow (elastic) and white (collagenous). This loose connective tissue in the region of muscles and beneath the skin stores water, sugar, and salt (sodium chloride). It connects the skin and membranes with the deeper structures, and it serves as a packing between organs.

The fibers of areolar tissue come from the fibroblasts, which represent the typical cells. Areolar tissue contains many cells in contrast to tendons or ligaments where cells are relatively scarce.

Adipose or fatty connective tissue is a second or modified type. Certain cells of areolar tissue obtain the power to absorb fat from the blood vessels and to deposit it in their cytoplasm. The liquid fat or oil

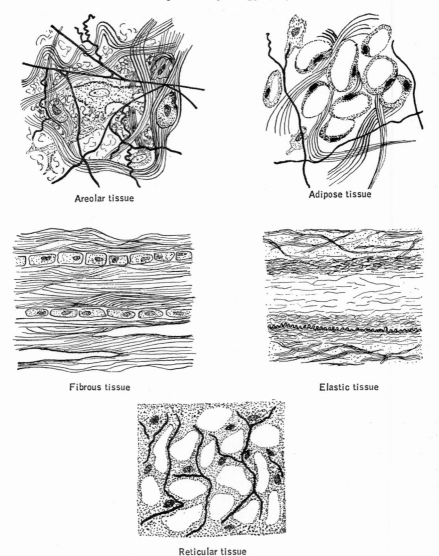

Areolar tissue

Adipose tissue

Fibrous tissue

Elastic tissue

Reticular tissue

Fig. 4—4. The major varieties of connective tissues. Note the difference in the kinds and arrangements of the fibers.

fills the cell and displaces the nucleus so that it is flattened against the cell membrane. This tissue is much more cellular than fibrous or intercellular. It occurs chiefly in the subcutaneous structures called superficial fascias, in mesenteries, in the axillary and inguinal regions, and around the heart and kidneys. It pads the joints and occurs in the marrow of the long bones. It supports and protects organs like the kidney, acts as a heat insulator, serves as a reserve source of food, and gives the body its contours.

The third type is designated as reticular connective tissue. It forms a network of cells with numerous fine fibers traveling in all directions. This tissue provides the framework of the lymph nodes, liver, bone marrow, and spleen. It lies just inside the lining of the digestive tract.

Although the covering or epithelial membranes have been described as being constructed from epithelium, they also have an underlying layer of connective tissue. In the mucous membranes the connective tissue underlying the epithelium is called the lamina propria. In the serous membranes such as the peritoneum, pleura, and pericardium, the free surface is loose mesothelium and the deeper surface is loose connective tissue. The connective tissue component not only cements the epithelium to structures below but also allows the passage of blood and nerves to the epithelium.

Another major type of membrane is called fibrous. This is made up entirely of fibrous connective tissue. It exists to connect adjacent structures or to form capsules around organs. Thus, for example, the periosteum surrounds bone, the interosseous membranes connect adjacent bones such as the radius and ulna, and the synovial membranes line joint cavities.

The connective tissues harden to cartilage or bone in specific regions. In cartilage formation the intercellular matrix becomes a solid mass within which the cartilage cells are trapped and scattered and come to lie in spaces called lacunae. Since the cells usually have no processes and the substrate is compact and devoid of blood vessels, lymphatics, and nerves, the fluid from the outer blood vessels must penetrate the interstitial substance to reach the cells. Except for joint cavities, cartilage is enclosed by a vascular sheath called the perichondrium.

The most common type of cartilage is hyaline, which occurs in the costal cartilages of the ribs, in the covering over bone surfaces within joints, and in the cartilages of the nose, larynx, and respiratory passages. In the embryo it forms most of the temporary skeleton. Hyaline cartilage is flexible, slightly elastic, and semitransparent. Its cells, which are typically spherical, divide several times within the solidifying matrix.

Elastic cartilage occurs in the epiglottis, in portions of the corniculate and cuneiform cartilages, the external ear, the external auditory canal, and the Eustachian tubes. It is more flexible, elastic, and opaque than hyaline cartilage. The cells are spherical and become encapsulated singly or in groups. The interstitial substance is not clear, but it is penetrated by a network of elastic fibers continuing into the perichondrium.

Fibrocartilage is found in the intervertebral disks, in the interarticular cartilages of many joints, and elsewhere. It is a strong and flexible variety which is transitional between cartilage and connective tissue. It contains many collagenous fiber bundles arranged in rows, as in tendons. The capsules containing the cells are located in the narrow spaces between the bundles.

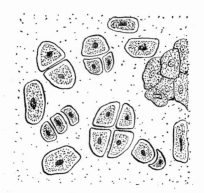

Hyaline cartilage

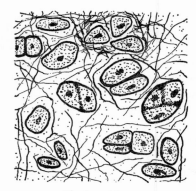

Elastic cartilage

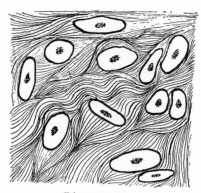

Fibrous cartilage

Fig. 4—5. Varieties of cartilage showing arrangement of cells and fibers.

Bone is the densest variety of connective tissue. It contains cells called osteocytes and a matrix which contains collagenous fibers and several minerals, including chiefly calcium and phosphorus. It has been demonstrated from X-ray diffraction and other methods that the bone salt belongs to the apatite series of minerals (McLean, 1958), whose prototype is fluorapatite, $3Ca_3(PO_4)_2 \cdot CaF_2$. In bones the compound corresponds chiefly to hydroxyapatite, $3Ca_3(PO_4)_2 \cdot Ca(OH)_2$.

Bone also contains carbonate and citrate, but these substances may be related to the surfaces of crystals of hydroxyapatite rather than being a part of the bone lattice. Other mineral elements may be regarded as chance impurities which are brought in from the body fluids during salt crystallization in the bones. There is also a view that the essential bone mineral is hydrated calcium triphosphate.

Most of the organic material of bone is collagen, which is a common fibrous protein of the connective tissues. The collagen may be secreted from osteoblasts, which are the bone-producing cells. In between the collagen and the mineral deposits is the organic ground substance. This substance constitutes about 5 per cent of the organic matter, and is protein and carbohydrate in nature.

Some bones develop by direct mineralization of membranous tissue (membrane bones), but others develop by depositing minerals in pre-existing cartilage (cartilage bones). The mineral salts constitute about two-thirds of the weight of any bone.

Every bone has two types of bony material, an external, dense substance called compact bone and an internal, more porous material called spongy or cancellous bone. The proportion of each type varies in different bones and in different regions of the same bone. The shafts of long bones are composed almost wholly of compact tissue except for their central or medullary canal.

A fibrous membrane called the periosteum covers the external surface of a bone except at its joint surfaces and sends perforating fibers into the underlying bone. The periosteum allows tendons and ligaments to gain attachment to the bone. It contains an inner layer which produces bone cells, or osteoblasts, particularly in youth. Blood vessels penetrate the periosteum as a rich network from which minute branches go into the underlying compact layer through spaces called Volkmann's canals. The vessels communicate with an inner system of Haversian canals and also independently supply the spongy bone. Bones may have an adjunctive blood supply through an artery which enters a nutrient foramen in the outer compact layer and then enters the inner medullary cavity. Arterial branches reach the internal cancellous substance in the region of the bone where the blood cells are being produced, and veins then return from this area.

In the microscopic anatomy of compact bone the structural unit is the osteon or Haversian system. This unit has a central lumen called the Haversian canal in which capillaries and venules run. Around each canal are concentric layers, or Haversian lamellae. Although the osteons generally travel longitudinally, the Haversian lamellae run spirally to the axis of the canal. In a long bone there are circumferential lamellae which run parallel to the surface of the bone on the exterior and interior. Also, there are interstitial lamellae which occupy the intervals between the Haversian lamellae.

Any single osteon contains, in addition to its central canal and fibrillar structure, many spaces, or lacunae. These lie between the Haversian lamellae and are therefore arranged in circular fashion. The lacunae contain the bone cells (osteocytes).

The bone cells which are trapped in such spaces in the compact bone can be nourished through a system of microscopic intercommunicating

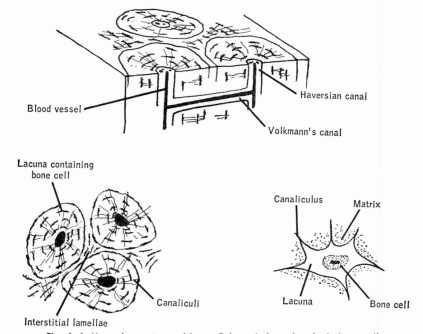

Fig. 4–6. Haversian systems of bone. Enlarged view of a single bone cell.

channels. Such a system radiates everywhere from the lacunae as canaliculi. The innermost canaliculi run into the Haversian canals, which travel almost longitudinally through the compact bone. This allows interchanges between the vessels in the Haversian canals and the bone cells in the circular lacunae around the canals. The fluid from the blood vessels of the Haversian canals reaches all parts of the Haversian system through the circulatory tract involving the lacunae and their extending canaliculi. In the spongy, or cancellous, bone the Haversian systems are deficient, and the lamellar arrangement differs.

The canaliculi of the lacunae communicate with Volkmann's canals and thus with the blood vessels of the vascular periosteum. They are also in contact with the internal lining, or endosteum, of the marrow cavity if it is present. The periosteum sends nerve fibers as well as arteries into the bone. These fibers are afferent myelinated and autonomic unmyelinated.

The calcium of the bones is dynamically related to the blood through parathyroid gland control. This gland determines the hourly and daily adjustments of the calcium level of the blood and bones, but it does not fully account for the minute-to-minute dynamics between the blood and bones. The parathyroids respond slowly to calcium-ion changes, and they probably regulate dissolution of the stable bone salt by influencing resorption through the activity of giant cells (osteoclasts). The more rapid interchange involves the more labile fraction of the bone mineral. This action may be effected by passive diffusion or else by active passage into the blood through parathyroid activity. Vitamin D is involved because it facilitates absorption of calcium from the digestive tract.

Bone marrow fills the irregular spaces of spongy bones. It also fills the central medullary cavity of long bones. It has a framework of reticular tissue containing blood vessels, and it retains blood cells in all stages of maturation. The red marrow produces red cells and also some white cells. In the adult it is found typically in spongy bones such as the sternum, ribs, vertebrae, the proximal ends of long bones, and elsewhere. The yellow marrow contains fat cells; it is located in the medullary cavity of a long bone.

Anatomical terms used frequently in describing skeletal structures belonging to the vocal mechanism are defined below.

Crest—a prominent ridge
Condyle—a rounded or knuckle-like process for articulation
Fossa—a pit or hollow
Foramen—an opening in a bone
Groove—a furrow
Head—an enlargement at one end of the bone beyond its neck
Meatus—a tube or passage
Process—a bony prominence
Sinus—a cavity inside a bone; a groove on the inside of the skull
Spine—a sharp projection
Sulcus—a furrow
Trochanter—a very large bony process
Tubercle—a small round projection
Tuberosity—a large round projection

Muscular Tissue. There are three types of muscles, and these are differentiated through structure and function. They are smooth (plain, unstriated), skeletal (striated, voluntary), and cardiac (heart). All have contractility or the power to shorten and this is expressed in a direction parallel to the long axis of their cells. The contractile element of the cells is a myofibril. The fibrils tend to aggregate as fine parallel filaments into fibers which are long, slender threads.

Smooth muscle cells are spindle-shaped, thick in the center, and tapering at each end, with cytoplasmic myofibrils and a central nucleus. Such muscles are found in the walls of visceral tubes, e.g., the digestive tube and urinary tubes. They also occur in the walls of blood vessels, in

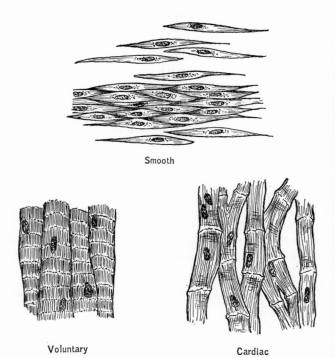

Smooth

Voluntary   Cardiac

Fig. 4—7. Comparison of fiber arrangements in the different kinds of muscle tissues.

the bronchial tubes, and elsewhere. Their general occurrence in the speech apparatus is not extensive. They regulate the diameter of the blood vessels, determine the caliber of the bronchioles, and are generally essential to the movements of the internal organs. They are innervated by the autonomic nervous system.

Cardiac muscle forms the major portion of the heart wall. The fibers branch and interlace into a syncytium, or net-like structure. Myofibrils are present and the sarcoplasm is abundant. There is a rich coronary blood supply. The nerve supply is autonomic. This kind of muscle is necessary as a pump to aid the circulation of the blood.

Striated muscle is concerned with the voluntary movements of skeletal structures. It is especially involved in the speech apparatus where it adjusts many localized speech structures to specific demands. It occurs in the vocal mechanism as muscles attached to cartilages or bones which form the skeletal framework of the larynx, respiratory system, face, and other speech structures. It is made up of bundles containing long cylindrical fibers that run parallel. Each fiber is developed from multinucleated cells. A thin membrane or sarcolemma covers each fiber. Surrounding the fibers is a rich blood supply.

The myofibril components of each fiber are embedded in the sarcoplasm, and each myofibril is striped periodically by alternate transverse dark and light bands. This arrangement makes the muscle look cross-striated. The muscle fibers are bound by areolar connective tissue into bundles, or fasciculi, and in turn the fasciculi are collected into larger bundles. Finally, a fibrous membrane called the deep fascia encloses the entire muscle. The fascia continues into the coverings of the cartilaginous and bony skeleton. The muscle in this way gains attachment to the structures it will move.

Cerebrospinal nerves supply voluntary muscles. This machinery involves (1) motor nerve fibers which run through a myoneural junction or motor end plate to collections of muscle fibers, and (2) afferent nerve fibers which run from specific receptors in the muscles and their tendons to the central nervous system.

Nervous Tissues. These have been described in Chapter 2. The cells specialize to neurons which become the microscopic units of structure and function.

ORGANS

The tissues combine to form organs. Each organ is a functional unit built up from two or more tissues which are associated to perform some special function. The tongue and larynx are organs, but their next simpler constituents are tissues. The larynx contains epithelium, connective tissue, muscles, nerves, and blood vessels. Any organ generally has a characteristic or predominant tissue and accessory supporting tissues.

SYSTEMS

Systems are arrangements of closely allied organs which unite for a common function. This category includes the nervous, muscular, integumentary, skeletal, circulatory, respiratory, endocrine, excretory, digestive, and reproductive systems.

The systems themselves work in close coordination to produce specific bodily activity. In speech, muscular and skeletal activity under nervous and endocrine control simultaneously comes into play with adjunctive respiratory, circulatory, and other system activity.

In the study called systematic anatomy, the body is divided into a set of functional systems which are studied one at a time with little or no regard to any other system. This text is concerned with the activities of specific regions, and the method of regional anatomy is used somewhat as it is employed in a local dissection upon the human cadaver. All systems or parts lying within the localized region are collectively considered at the same time and only so far as they are found within the region under discussion. The gross regions which most concern us are the head, neck, thorax, and abdomen.

THE JOINTS

The bones, cartilages, and softer connective tissues are assembled in given areas to form joints. Some generalized descriptions are supplied in order to give a basic understanding of the structures and movements of joints found in the vocal apparatus.

The synarthrosis, broadly interpreted, is the immovable or slightly movable joint found in the union of bones of the skull, in the insertion of teeth into sockets in the mandible and maxilla, in the joining of ribs with costal cartilages, and elsewhere. There is no joint cavity so that motion is limited or absent. Several subtypes are evident. In sutures, as in the skull, the bone ends are serrated and approximated by fibrous tissue. In synchondroses, as between ribs and costal cartilages, the bone ends are approximated by cartilage. In syndesmoses, as between the spinous processes and laminae of adjacent vertebrae, the connection is made by dense fibrous connective tissue which is deposited in the form of ligaments. In symphyses, as between the bodies of adjacent vertebrae, the ends of the bone are covered by cartilage and are separated by an intercartilage disk. In this instance the approximation is through a fibrous capsule.

Most of the bodily joints are diarthroses, and these have variable degrees and directions of free motion. The bones are joined by a peripheral band of fibrous tissue called the articular capsule, within which is a joint cavity. The internal layer of the capsule secretes a minute amount of synovial fluid into the joint cavity to nourish and lubricate the articulation. In some joints, like the temporomandibular, the cavity is divided by a fibrocartilage disk. The opposed ends of the bones in a diarthrosis are covered by a layer of hyaline or articular cartilage.

Diverse movements are permitted in diarthroses. The simplest is gliding in which one part moves or glides over another. In the movement called flexion there is a bending or a decrease in the angle between parts of the body, but in extension there is a stretching or an increase in the angle. Adduction implies movement toward the median line whereas abduction is the opposite. Rotation involves turning a part about a fixed axis. The arytenoid cartilages, which are important agents in the movements of the vocal folds, are capable of rotating clockwise or counterclockwise. The exact effect of such movements upon the vocal folds and the glottis is still inconclusive. In circumduction the end of a structure describes a circle while the structure itself describes the side of a cone.

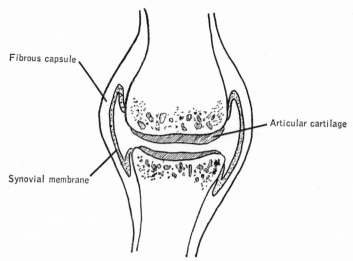

Fibrous capsule

Articular cartilage

Synovial membrane

Fig. 4–8. A typical variety of a freely movable joint.

In the shoulder joint the apex in the socket describes the circle while the hand describes the base of the cone.

The diarthroses are classified into groups by their varieties of motion. In the hinge joint, or ginglymus, motion is in one plane, usually forward or backward. The pivot joint, or trochoid, is limited to rotation. In the condyloid joint, a condyle or ovoid surface fits into an elliptical cavity, and all movements except rotation are permitted. This is illustrated in the wrist joint. In the ball and socket joint, or enarthrosis, a rounded head of one bone moves in a cup-like cavity of another, as in the hip joint, and motion occurs around an indefinite number of axes. In the saddle joint, opposing surfaces are alternately concave and convex, as in the carpometacarpal joint of the thumb, and a great freedom of motion is permitted. In the gliding joints, or arthrodia, where plane surfaces or those alternately and slightly concave and convex meet, only gliding motion is permitted. This occurs between the articular processes of vertebrae.

In the areas about joints in which friction occurs, bursae, or sacs, which contain synovial fluid appear. These sacs smooth over the gaps in the joint and facilitate the sliding of muscle and tendons over prominences of bones or ligaments.

SUMMARY

The human body follows a plan common to that of all vertebrate animals. In this scheme several partitioned body cavities are laid down. The terms used to describe the spatial relations of vertebrates are somewhat modified in man because of his erect posture.

The construction blocks of the vertebrate body are cells, tissues, organs, and systems. Cells produce tissues, the latter combine to organs, the proper combination of organs forms each system, and a set of systems represents the living body. The basic material of the body is protoplasm.

The science of cytology deals with protoplasm and the cell. Histology is the study of tissues and organs. Gross anatomy commonly emphasizes the bodily systems while classical physiology considers the functional interactions of the systems.

Chapter 5

THE RESPIRATORY SYSTEM IN SPEECH

Respiration is a process used primarily for gas-and-energy exchange between an organism and its environment, and breathing for speech is a secondary function. In spite of this fact, respiration is very importantly involved in speech. It provides the air that will be phonated, resonated, and articulated into meaningful sounds.

Breathing is involved in speech not only because of the use made of the exhaled air but also in the negative sense that abnormal breathing is usually associated with certain speech disturbances.

The exact function of the apparatus laid down for the exchange of the respiratory gases, the transportation of these gases in the blood, and their final utilization in the cells are highly complex problems. Only those problems most pertinent to the speech function will be considered in this chapter.

VISUALIZATION OF RESPIRATORY MOVEMENTS

In biological or physiological breathing (without speech) the inspiratory and expiratory phases of a breathing cycle are almost equal. This is seen in a pneumogram, which is a record of external thoracic movements. It is obtained by strapping a tube around the chest and leading off the varying air volumes within the tube through one open end to an expansible tambour. A pen seated upon the tambour writes a record on special paper. The paper is mounted on a drum that commonly has a rotary movement. The instrument, with its provisions for the mechanical or electrical movement of the drum, is a kymograph. There are also more complex instruments called multichannel recorders.

If the subject talks while his breathing is recorded, the inspiratory phase is seen to be shortened while the expiratory phase is more prolonged. Expiration is even more prolonged in trained speakers and in singers. During speech the rhythm of breathing changes from smooth, regular, and periodic to one that follows the rhythm of thinking. The breathing may occasionally have to be deeper and fuller.

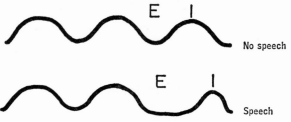

Fig. 5—1. Record of thoracic breath during speech and silence.

COORDINATION OF BREATHING WITH SPEAKING

Neuroendocrine agencies coordinate breathing with speaking. This coordination becomes automatic with conditioning.

We have seen in previous discussions that the integrated responses can break down in emotional disturbances. Respiratory processes are readily altered by fear and anxiety. The respiratory system is one of the most sensitive indicators of emotion. Changes in the rate and depth of breathing thus constitute the basis of lie-detector tests.

Fear changes diaphragmatic physiology with subsequent dyscoordination between diaphragmatic and laryngeal pressures. If the pulmonary pressure is less than the pressure needed at the glottis to approximate the vocal folds, the tone contains quavering tremors. If the pulmonary pressure is disproportionately high, however, an excessive flow of "wild air" can escape. In neurosis, vocal disturbances are characteristically accompanied by respiratory disturbances. In heart and lung diseases and in other maladies with altered respiration, symptomatic speech patterns may occur.

The readjustment of breathing to normal may aid in correcting certain speech disorders (Hahn et al., 1952). Exercises in breathing, which are part of a regimen called breath control, are employed to augment the tone volume, the pitch, and the range.

Stetson and Hudgins (1930) discussed breathing with respect to the syllable. In rest breathing, air is expelled through pressure caused by the weight and elasticity of the structures displaced by inspiratory muscles. Forced expiration is effected chiefly by the contraction of the abdominal wall musculature. In breathing for speech where more than 2.5 to 4 syllables per second are uttered, the abdominal muscles are held rigid and fixate the inferior border of the rib cage. In this way they afford resistance for the muscular pulses accomplished by the internal intercostal muscles.

The term 'chest pulse' has been used to indicate the actual production of the air pressure needed to generate sound (Johnson, Curtis, and Keaster, 1956). It refers to the breathing movements that build up the pressure needed in the activation of the vocal folds. These pulses are produced by costal muscles. The abdominal muscles may contract every few syllables while the chest pulse occurs with each syllable.

Stetson (1951) related chest pulses to normal phonation. The necessary air pressure is developed just prior to vocalization by the activity of respiratory muscles. Any failure in timing between the chest pulses and muscular activity at the glottis may produce phonatory disorders. Van Riper and Irwin (1958) refer to the synchrony between glottal closure and the chest pulse as the "vocal attack." Patients with certain disorders of phonation may be trained to change their vocal attack.

THE STRUCTURE FOR BREATHING

Respiration involves the action primarily of voluntary or skeletal muscles energized by spinal nerves and moving a skeletal framework

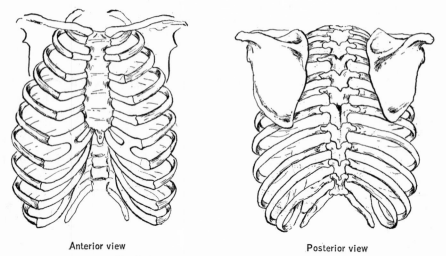

Anterior view   Posterior view

Fig. 5–2. Bony framework of the thoracic cage.

composing the thorax. The active muscles are usually thought of as being localized in the thorax and abdomen, but depending upon the character of the breathing, they may also include some muscles of the neck. Accessory respiratory movements involve smooth, or nonstriated, muscles, such as those in the walls of the bronchial system of tubes. These muscles are energized by autonomic nerves, and they keep the tubes ordinarily in a protective state of partial closure.

The Skeletal Framework. The bony thorax is composed of twelve thoracic vertebrae posteriorly, the sternum anteriorly, and the twelve pairs of ribs laterally.

The vertebral column of the adult is a flexible, multijointed pillar of twenty-six vertebrae. Each vertebra is separated from the others by a cartilaginous intervertebral disk. The joints between the vertebrae are held sturdily in place by complex ligaments. The uppermost seven vertebrae, situated in the neck, are cervical. The next twelve, to which

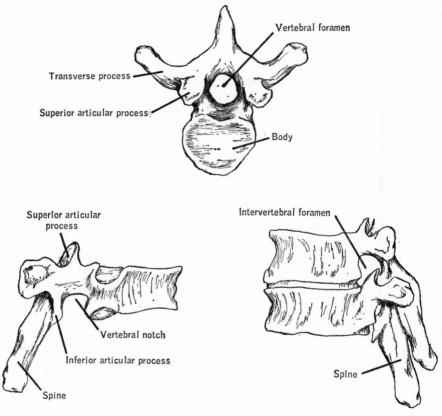

Fig. 5–3. Superior and lateral views of thoracic vertebrae. Method of joining vertebrae.

the ribs attach, are thoracic. These are followed by five lumbar vertebrae of the lower back, and then by five fused vertebrae forming the single sacrum. The lowest end of the column contains variably four rudimentary vertebrae, usually considered as one structure called the coccyx.

A typical thoracic vertebra has the following features. The body is the unpaired anterior cylindrical part. From this a pair of legs or pedicles stems dorsally. Two broad plates called laminae project backward from the pedicles. The laminae fuse in the posterior median line and thus complete an arch which encloses a space called the vertebral foramen. The arch protects the spinal cord which is inside the vertebral foramen.

Each arch supports several processes. The spinal process is the single dorsal projection. There are two superior and two inferior articular processes for connecting adjacent vertebrae. These form freely movable

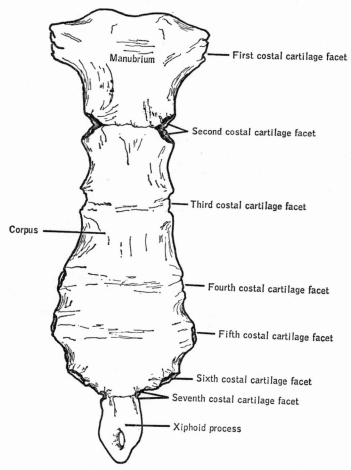

First costal cartilage facet

Manubrium

Second costal cartilage facet

Third costal cartilage facet

Corpus

Fourth costal cartilage facet

Fifth costal cartilage facet

Sixth costal cartilage facet

Seventh costal cartilage facet

Xiphoid process

Fig. 5—4. Anterior view of the sternum to show its sections and their landmarks.

joints. Less movable connections are also provided by the bodies of the vertebrae piling on top of one another with an intervening intervertebral disk. There are also paired transverse processes that jut out laterally on either side for muscle attachment.

The sternum (breastbone) is a somewhat oblong plate of bone which ends below typically in a cartilaginous process. It forms the anterior central part of the thorax. It articulates with the upper seven ribs on each side and with the clavicles above.

The manubrium is the uppermost and widest sternal segment. Its inferior border is fused to the body, or corpus sterni, by fibrocartilage. This joint forms a palpable protuberance, the sternal angle. Palpation of the prominence is used to find the position of the second costal cartilage and rib.

The corpus sterni comprises about two-thirds of the sternum. It has three transverse ridges that result from fusion of four separate bony

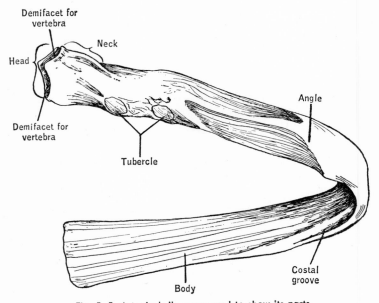

Fig. 5—5. A typical rib, overcurved to show its parts.

pieces. The cartilages of the third, fourth, and fifth ribs fit into facets on either side of the body. The last section of the body articulates with the sixth and seventh costal cartilages.

The lowest part of the sternum is the easily palpable xiphoid, or ensiform, cartilage, which eventually ossifies.

The sternum provides more space for the thoracic cavity by its anterior convexity and by its downward and forward slope.

There are twelve pairs of ribs. These constitute a series of curved elastic bones that make up most of the thoracic walls. Each rib is a bony rod that is continued anteriorly by a clear or hyaline costal cartilage. Each rib is posteriorly connected to the vertebral column, and this is effected typically by two demiarticulations. The anterior attachments are as follows. The upper seven pairs of ribs have their cartilages joined directly to the sternum and are "true" ribs. The next three pairs are indirectly connected with the sternum by long cartilages and are "false" ribs. The lowest two pairs are too short to be attached anteriorly, but they have their front ends embedded in the abdominal musculature and are "floating" (false) ribs.

The greatest space of the thorax lies between the third to the eighth ribs, and the greatest amplitude of rib movements occurs there. The ribs above and below that region are shorter and move considerably less.

The curves of a typical rib in the middle of the series are important in respiration. Such a rib has a head, neck, tubercle, and shaft. The head has two facets to articulate with two vertebrae and their intervening disk. The neck is attached by ligaments to the transverse process of the lower of the two vertebrae associated with it. A tubercle at the end of the neck articulates with the facet on the transverse process. The rib thus forms a costocentral and costotransverse joint with the vertebral column, and respiratory elevation and depression are permitted by these joints. The shaft distal to the tubercle bends laterally and posteriorly to the rib angle, thus giving more space to the posterior thoracic cavity. The angle marks the point where the rib abruptly changes its direction to run anteriorly and inferiorly. Its bend is then such that its inferior border tilts outward and its outer surface is both outward and upward. This eversion of the inferior aspect augments the transverse diameter of the thorax between successive ribs, thus increasing the lung space during respiration. In every rib the vertebral end is higher than the sternal end. Fulton (1955) states that the ribs of a baby tend to be horizontal rather than to slant down in front. This makes costal breathing to enlarge the thorax less efficient, and the diaphragm becomes the more important agent.

The movements of the thoracic framework change the dimensions of the thoracic cavity and permit the exchange of air in breathing. The lungs expand primarily because the thorax expands. In a closed space the pressure is inversely proportional to the volume, other things being equal. As the thoracic pressure decreases with its expanding volume, the lungs expand into the partially evacuated thorax, and the intrapulmonic pressure decreases. Atmospheric air is then drawn into the lung passages through a gradient of pressure. The lungs operate with the changing pressures of the thorax. This is the physical theory of respiration. Actually, the lungs do, to a certain degree, influence their own operation through a stretch-reflex feedback system connected with the control centers of breathing.

The basic movement in respiration is an upward expanding movement of the thorax. The upward motion of the ribs increases chiefly the anteroposterior and lateral thoracic diameters. The sternum moves upward and forward during inspiration, and, by working in conjunction with the ribs, increases the vertical as well as the other two thoracic dimensions. Every rib travels up at the same time during inspiration and down at the same time in expiration. The resulting thoracic expansion is not of equal amplitude in all directions.

Although the clavicle and scapula are parts of the pectoral, or shoulder, girdle, which serves to support the upper extremity, they also act as points of attachment for several muscles that can elevate the ribs.

MACHINERY OF RESPIRATION

Inspiration requires muscular effort, but expiration is to a large extent passive, although there are expiratory muscles. Even in inspiration very few muscles are required, except during a deep inspiration. There is some doubt as to whether certain muscles are inspiratory or expiratory. An inspiratory muscle may be defined as one that contracts when the diaphragm contracts whereas an expiratory muscle contracts when the diaphragm relaxes. Both inspiration and expiration constitute a respiratory cycle whose frequency varies with age, size, and sex. There are about 16 cycles per minute in the adult male, and 17 to 18 in the female.

In quiet inspiration the first two ribs are fixated by neck muscles. The third to the sixth ribs, comprising the upper costal series, are elevated to this fixed region. This activity involves the external and internal intercostal muscles, aided by the serratus posterior superior, serratus anterior, levatores costarum, and other muscles. Concomitantly, the seventh to the tenth ribs, comprising the lower costal series, rotate outward and forward, widening the subcostal angle and increasing chiefly the transverse diameter of the lower thorax. Ribs eleven and twelve are not effective in inspiration but follow the movements of the anterior abdominal wall. There are many other accessory muscles, chiefly on the back and pectoral region, which can help to raise the ribs even higher, particularly in deep inspiration.

Expiration, although involving considerable elastic recoil, includes muscles which not only force the diaphragm back up from the abdomen into the thorax but which also depress the ribs. These include the anterior abdominal wall muscles and others. The muscles usually involved in ordinary breathing (called eupnea) are described individually below.

Muscles of the Thorax. These include the diaphragm, external and internal intercostals, subcostals, transversus thoracis, levatores costarum, and serratus posterior superior and inferior. Accessory respiratory muscles in the thoracic region include the pectoralis major and minor, the serratus anterior, and the subclavius.

The diaphragm is a musculotendinous partition which completely separates the thoracic and abdominal cavities. It may be regarded as having right and left parts. Its fibers arch the structure into a dome-shaped mass, and all the fibers insert above into a common aponeurotic central tendon. The posterior or vertebral fibers have their main origin on the deep surface of the first few lumbar vertebrae. The sternal part originates on the inner aspect of the xiphoid process of the sternum. The paired costal sections originate from the inner surface of the anterior ends of the lowest six ribs and from the costal cartilages of these ribs.

Contraction draws the central tendon down and slightly forward. This enlarges the chest chiefly in the vertical plane. The lungs then expand into the partially evacuated thorax. The central tendon presses upon the abdominal viscera, pushing them downward and forward, so that the anterior abdominal wall protrudes with each inspiration. This activity, which is called abdominal or diaphragmatic breathing, characterizes the male. It is in contrast with a type called costal or rib breathing which characterizes the female. Teleologically explained, the action at a higher level is an adaptation to prevent undue pressure on a rising uterus in the gravid female.

In man the diaphragm is the chief inspiratory muscle. It is innervated through the paired phrenic nerves which come from the cervical-plexus roots C-3, C-4, and C-5. Unilateral phrenicectomy paralyzes the corresponding side of the diaphragm. In expiration the diaphragm is actively pushed back toward the thorax by contraction of the muscles of the anterior abdominal wall.

The actual excursions of the diaphragm are not extensive, the maximum movement being less than 3 inches and the ordinary movement for respiration or speech being less than 1 inch. The greatest movement of the diaphragm is not in the relatively fixed central tendon, but in the more peripheral regions.

The *external intercostal* muscles (paired) contain thin layers of oblique fibers which fill the intercostal spaces. There are eleven pairs, and each extends within its own intercostal space from the vertebral column to the lateral ends of the costal cartilages. The central region that continues medially to the sternum is filled in by the anterior intercostal membrane. The course of each segmental muscle slip is from the lower margin of one rib to the upper margin of the rib below. The direction of the fibers is downward and medialward anteriorly but downward and lateralward posteriorly.

These muscles elevate the ribs and add to the diaphragmatic effect of increasing the vertical dimension of the thorax. They also enlarge the lateral and the anteroposterior dimensions. The muscle fibers prevent an alternate sucking in and bulging out of intercostal tissues during respiration. Their innervation is through spinal intercostal nerves.

The *internal intercostals* (paired) are somewhat weaker, and they are covered by the external intercostals. They travel from the lower border of one rib to the upper border of the rib below. Although the eleven pairs begin anteriorly at the sternum or between the costal cartilages, they do not extend more posteromedially than the angles of the ribs. The deficient muscular space in back is filled in by the aponeurotic posterior intercostal membrane. The direction of the muscle fibers is at about right angles to that of the external intercostal muscle, and this cross lattice strengthens the thoracic wall. The internal muscles may also elevate the ribs, but this is inconclusive. They are supplied by spinal intercostal nerves. The diaphragm and the intercostal muscles are the chief agents of quiet inspiration.

The *levatores costarum* are twelve pairs of muscles originating from the transverse processes of the seventh cervical and first eleven thoracic vertebrae. The fibers travel laterally and inferiorly parallel to the external intercostal fibers. They insert into the ribs just below their vertebrae of origin and end between the angle and the turbercle of each rib. The four lower muscle segments insert, in addition, into ribs two segments below their origin. The muscle fibers can elevate the ribs, and they also act to rotate, extend, or laterally flex the vertebral column. The innervation is through the spinal intercostal nerves.

The *serratus posterior superior* (paired) is on the upper posterior aspect of the thorax, originating variably from the vertebral spines of C-7, T-1, and T-2. The fibers travel down and laterally to insert distal to the angles of the first three or four ribs. The muscle elevates the upper ribs, acting mainly on their posterior sections. The innervation is through the first four thoracic nerves.

The *transversus thoracis,* or *triangularis sterni* (paired), originates from the inner surface of the body and xiphoid process of the sternum. It runs obliquely lateralward and upward to insert into the posterior surfaces of the second or third to the sixth costal cartilages. It depresses the ribs in expiration. The innervation is through intercostal nerves. This is the only truly thoracic muscle which is definitely expiratory.

The *subcostals* (paired) are variable in number. They lie deep to the internal intercostals, both muscles running parallel. They are developed best in the lower thorax. They arise at points just lateral to the vertebrae on the inner surfaces of several ribs and then travel upward and lateralward to insert on the deep surfaces of ribs a few segments above their origin. They appear to depress the ribs in expiration. The innervation is through intercostal nerves.

The *serratus posterior inferior* (paired), situated between the thoracic and lumbar regions is as much a muscle of the lower back as it is of the thorax. It originates variably from the spinous processes of vertebrae T-11, T-12, L-1, and L-2. Its fibers course laterally and upward to insert into the last four ribs distal to their angles. It may depress the lower four ribs and pull them laterally in expiration. The innervation is through the last four thoracic nerves.

There is some uncertainty about the action of this muscle as there is about most other respiratory muscles. It may possibly assist the diaphragm in forced inhalation by fixation of the lower ribs.

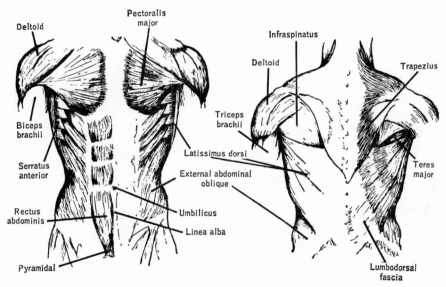

Fig. 5–6. Superficial muscles of the abdomen and back.

Accessory respiratory action is brought about in the thoracic region through elevation of the ribs by muscles that serve primarily to connect the upper extremity with the anterior and lateral thoracic walls. The four muscles described below can all help to elevate the ribs during inspiration.

The *pectoralis major* (paired) is a fan-shaped muscle superficially located on the anterior thoracic wall. It originates from the medial half of the clavicle and from the second to the seventh costal cartilage. Its fibers course lateralward, forming the anterior axillary fold that ends below the greater tubercle of the humerus. Although its action is primarily upon the arm, it can elevate the ribs if the shoulder girdle is fixed. It is innervated by the medial and lateral anterior thoracic nerves from the brachial plexus.

The *pectoralis minor* (paired) is a thin, triangular muscle found deep to the pectoralis major. It originates between the second or third through the fifth ribs near the costal cartilages. The fibers go laterally and upward to insert upon the coracoid process of the scapula. If the shoulder girdle is fixed, the muscle assists the pectoralis major in elevating the ribs. It is innervated by the medial anterior thoracic nerve.

The *subclavius* (paired) is a narrow, cylindrical muscle stretching between the clavicle and the first rib. It originates from the anterior surface of the first rib and its cartilage and goes laterally and upward to the inferior surface of the clavicle. If the clavicle is fixed, the muscle may

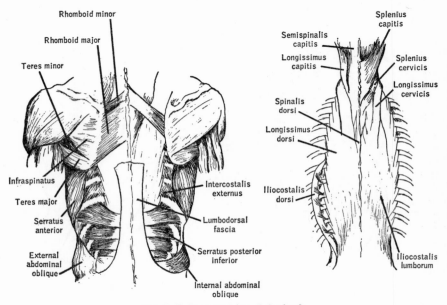

Fig. 5–7. Deep muscles of the back.

draw the first rib upward. It is supplied by C-5 and C-6 running out from the lateral trunk of the brachial plexus.

The *serratus anterior* (paired) is a thin, quadrangular muscle on the posterolateral surface of the thorax. It originates along the ventral aspect of the vertebral border of the scapula. It runs downward and forward to insert by several individual slips into the outer surfaces of the upper eight or nine ribs. Although generally considered to have an action upon the scapula and arm, it elevates the ribs when the shoulder girdle is fixed. Its innervation is through the long thoracic nerve from the brachial plexus.

Muscles of the Neck. At times certain muscles in the neck region elevate the sternum or the uppermost ribs. This action aids the vertical expansion of the thorax and provides a fixation point toward which the superior ribs may be drawn by the activity of the upper costal series of muscles.

The *sternocleidomastoid* (paired) is a strong, cylindrical muscle going upward and laterally along the side of the neck. It has a sternal origin from the manubrium and another origin from the clavicle. These unite to one belly that inserts upon the mastoid process and the superior nuchal line of the occipital bone. With the head fixed, the muscle elevates the sternum and indirectly elevates the ribs. The innervation is from the spinal part of the spinal accessory nerve (XI) plus branches from C-2 and C-3.

The sternomastoid and perhaps the other neck muscles are active in clavicular breathing, or raising the sternum and clavicle. This is a practice discouraged in breathing for speech. It seems to produce an unsteadiness in tone because of the fluctuations in the rise and fall of the clavicles. It may also produce insufficient air intake resulting in a loss of strength in the vocal tones.

The *scalenus anterior* (paired) is part of a triangular group of scalene muscles in the anterolateral region of the neck. The most anterior muscle is on the side of the neck deep to the sternocleidomastoid. Its origin is from the transverse processes of the third through the sixth cervical vertebrae. The fibers descend nearly vertically and insert along the upper border of the first rib. If the cervical spine is fixed, the action is to elevate the first rib.

The *scalenus medius* (paired) is just posterior to the anterior scalene, and it is the longest muscle of this group. It originates from the transverse processes of the lower six cervical vertebrae. It travels down the side of the vertebral column and inserts along the superior border of the first rib. It elevates this rib.

The *scalenus posterior* (paired) is the deepest and the smallest of the group. It originates from the transverse processes of the lowest two or three cervical vertebrae and inserts into the outer surface of the second rib. Upon fixation of the cervical spine, it elevates the first two ribs.

As a group, the innervation of the scalenes is from lower cervical nerves.

Muscles of the Back. The serratus posterior superior and inferior muscles, forming the third depth layer of back muscles, have already been described.

The *latissimus dorsi* (paired) is a superficial or first-layer back muscle whose primary function is to move the arm and shoulder. It has several origins, from (1) the spinous processes of the lowest six or seven thoracic vertebrae; (2) the lumbar fascia; (3) the external surfaces of the lowest three or four ribs; and (4) the iliac crest. Its fibers all converge in going laterally and upward to form the palpable posterior axillary fold that inserts by a long tendon into the intertubercular groove on the humerus. When the arm is fixed, the muscle helps elevate the lowest three or four ribs during inspiration. Innervation is through the thoraco-dorsal nerve from the brachial plexus.

The *quadratus lumborum* (paired) is a flat muscular sheet deeply placed in the dorsal abdominal wall between the last rib and the iliac crest (upper surface of the hip bone). It originates along the iliac crest and iliolumbar ligament and travels upward and somewhat medially to insert along the last rib and the upper four lumbar vertebrae. It may depress the last rib, anchor it against the pull of the diaphragm, and fix the last two ribs in forced expiration. It is a muscle of expiration. Its nerve supply is from 12-T and L-1.

The *sacrospinalis* (paired) is a strong, cord-like muscle running along the whole length of the back from the occiput to the sacrum in the vertebral groove on either side of the spinous processes of all the vertebrae. It forms the fourth or deepest layer of the back muscles. The muscle is thickest in the lower thoracic and in the lumbar regions, where it becomes enclosed within the fibrous lumbodorsal fascia.

The muscle has a common origin below from the spines of all the lumbar vertebrae, the sacrum, the posterior sacroiliac ligament, the iliac crest, and the lumbodorsal fascia. In passing upward it splits to three parallel columns, the medial spinalis, the middle longissimus, and the lateral iliocostalis. Each of these is in turn divided from below upward generally into three sections. To illustrate, the iliocostalis lumborum inserts into the angles of the lower six or seven ribs, the iliocostalis dorsi inserts into the angles of the upper six ribs, and the iliocostalis cervicis inserts into the transverse processes of the lower three or four cervical vertebrae. Where the iliocostalis lumborum fibers travel up and depress their ribs of insertion during expiration, the cervicis section may be thought of as traveling down from lower cervical vertebrae to upper ribs and thus elevating these ribs during inspiration. The iliocostalis dorsi travels upward from the lower six ribs to the angles of the upper six ribs, and it may typically depress these structures. The respiratory actions of the separate vertical divisions of a single muscle column are thus variable with the segmental location of the division.

The longissimus and spinalis muscles are also variably concerned with action upon the ribs, and therefore with respiration. The main activity of this entire group of muscles is postural and adapted to maintaining man's gravitational position as an upright animal. These muscles are also responsible for flexion and extension and for rotational movements of the trunk. The nerve supply is from posterior rami of the spinal nerves at different levels of the spinal cord.

Muscles of the Abdomen. This group includes four muscles on the anterior abdominal wall which are expiratory in action and which work to thrust the descended diaphragm back into the thoracic cavity. Unless the ribs are fixed by other muscles, these draw the ribs downward and thereby help to lower and to decrease the volume of the thorax. Among their other great functions they form a wall that encloses and supports in position the abdominal viscera. They assist in defecation, voiding of urine, vomiting, delivery of the fetus, and other activities involving increased intra-abdominal pressure. When the vertebral column is not made rigid, they act in corresponding pairs to flex the body, or singly to bend it lateralward, or with one another (as the external oblique of one side with the opposite internal oblique) for rotation.

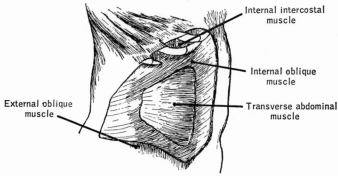

Fig. 5–8. Abdominal wall muscles in depth, observed by cutting sections out of the overlying muscles.

The *external oblique* (paired) is the most superficial member. It is a flat, broad structure covering the surface of the lower thoracic and abdominal walls. It originates from the outer surfaces and inferior borders of the lower eight ribs. Its fibers course downward and forward to a three-fold insertion. Most of the fibers join the most superficial layer of the tendinous abdominal aponeurosis, which covers the whole front of the abdomen. Through this aponeurosis the muscle inserts into the linea alba, which is a system of interlacing fibers in the mid-line of the abdomen. Inferior to these centrally directed fibers others go downward and end not in a tendon but in an inguinal ligament, which is a cord palpable in the groin between the anterior superior iliac spine above and the pubic tubercle below. The lowest and most posterior fibers travel almost vertically downward and end along the external aspect of the iliac crest. The nerve supply is from the eighth to the twelfth intercostals and from the iliohypogastric and ilioinguinal nerves.

The *internal oblique* (paired) is deep to the external oblique in the anterolateral abdominal wall. It arises from the lumbodorsal fascia, the anterior half of the iliac crest, and from the inguinal ligament. Many of its fibers go vertically up and end in the cartilages of the lower three or four ribs. The main mass of fibers passes from the iliac crest forward around the abdomen and eventually inserts into the linea alba by first entering the abdominal aponeurosis. The most inferior fibers, which arise from the inguinal ligament, run downward and forward to the pubis. The nerve supply is from the eighth to the twelfth intercostals and from the iliohypogastric and ilioinguinal nerves.

The *transversus abdominis* (paired) is the deepest of the anterior abdominal muscles. It originates from (1) the inner surfaces of the

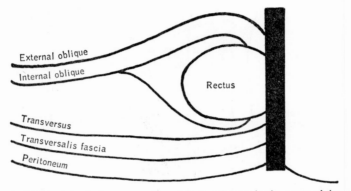

Fig. 5—9. The abdominal aponeurosis and its constituents in the upper abdomen.

lower six ribs; (2) the lumbodorsal fascia; (3) the inner edge of the iliac crest; and (4) the inguinal ligament. Its fibers run horizontally forward and around the abdomen. Some insert into the deepest layer of the abdominal aponeurosis and from there extend to the linea alba. A few of the lowest fibers go to the pubis and the inguinal ligament. The muscle is innervated by the seventh to the twelfth intercostal and also by the iliohypogastric and ilioinguinal nerves.

The *rectus abdominis* (paired) is a long, flat muscle longitudinally placed in the anterior abdominal wall. It parallels the mid-line on either side, just lateral to the linea alba. Its origin is the outer surface of the xiphoid process and also the fifth, sixth, and seventh costal cartilages. It courses vertically downward to insert into the body of the pubic bone and into the symphysis pubis. The muscle is crossed by three fibrous bands, or tendinous inscriptions, which represent the septa between the original embryonic muscle building blocks called myotomes. The innervation is from the seventh to the twelfth intercostal nerve.

The contracting rectus fibers push inward upon the abdominal viscera and in turn force the diaphragm upward. They may also assist in depressing the ribs by pulling the sternum downward.

In connection with the anterior abdominal musculature, a fibrous sheath encloses the rectus muscle and covers a large portion of the anterior wall. The sheath is formed by the aponeuroses of the external oblique, internal oblique, and transversus muscles. In the upper two-thirds of its course the anterior and posterior rectus sheaths are of equal thickness. In the lower third the anterior sheath consists of all three aponeuroses and is considerably thicker than the posterior sheath. The

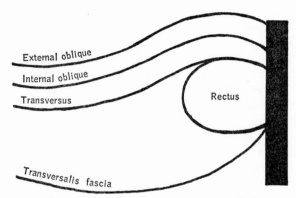

Fig. 5—10. The abdominal aponeurosis and its constituents in the lower abdomen.

latter sheath in this area consists solely of transversalis fascia. This is a layer of fascia that is deep to the transversus muscle and just external to the peritoneum. It lines the whole interior of the abdomen.

MACHINERY USED IN BREATHING FOR SPEECH

The muscles used in quiet inspiration are mostly thoracic. The muscles used in quiet expiration are primarily abdominal. Actually, quiet expiration is predominantly passive. The muscles are active, however, in forced expiration.

In speech the situation changes. Since expiration must be controlled, the expiratory muscles of the abdomen become tensed to regulate the expenditure of air. The thoracic and abdominal muscles are unequally active. The contraction of the abdominal muscles just prior to phonation sets the form of the thoracic and abdominal walls.

Van Riper and Irwin (1958) compared the relative durations of inspiration and expiration in speech. Whereas in quiet breathing the duration of inhalation divided by the duration of the whole breathing cycle is 0.40 to 0.45, this ratio decreases to 0.16 during speech. They also stated that the amount of air used in speech exceeds that used in quiet respiration.

The upper and lower chest muscles may be activated almost independently in breathing, and historically, arguments arose over which type was preferable for speech. Many French workers of the early nineteenth century emphasized upper-chest breathing. In 1855 Mandle, a French physician, attacked this view, and his counterproposal for abdominal breathing was carried to an extreme by English investigators. There are also advocates of a medial breathing between the chest and abdominal types. There are claims that air volumes are important, which has given strength to the proponents of exercises for deep breathing.

Descriptive terms, such as clavicular, thoracic, and abdominal breathing are in common usage (Akin, 1958). In clavicular breathing, discussed previously, there is an elevation of the shoulders which raises the abdominal musculature and interferes with the descent of the diaphragm. Not enough air for speech or singing is taken in. Thoracic breathing emphasizes inhalation, or the initial phase of the respiratory cycle, and by itself does not exist. Abdominal breathing emphasizes exhalation through the local activity of muscles activating the abdominal region; this is also unlikely to occur in isolation.

There is the current view that speakers have just as effective a voice with acceptable quality no matter how they breathe. It is not necessary to change a person's way of breathing so long as it is normal. The exception to this may be in singing but not in speech.

There is also said to be no significant relation between lung volume and acceptable tone. This view implies that ordinary speech does not require deep breathing. The pressure and volume of air must of course be adequate and not subliminal. Voices do not fail because of insufficient air intake but because not enough is taken in at the proper time or the air is not used correctly.

If increased loudness of sound is desired, it may be necessary to increase the demands upon lung volume and pressure. In this instance the pressure is to be increased from below the larynx rather than from the throat muscles. Concomitantly, the activity is to be directed to the diaphragmatic region while the pharyngeal area is kept relaxed.

Berry and Eisenson (1956) claim that changes in sound intensity are less dependent upon the pressure and volume of the exhaled air than they are upon a machinery which involves a balance among contracting respiratory muscles. To effect speech, the lower ribs become fixed in an elevated position in exhalation while the attached abdominal muscles compress the abdomen. Tension resulting from the maintained thoracic activity increases the diaphragmatic tension, which in turn opposes the abdominal activity. The breath stream is delicately controlled by this unstable equilibration of forces.

RESPIRATORY VOLUMES AND PRESSURES

The volumes and pressures in the respiratory apparatus are perpetually altered in rhythmic fashion by the integrated action chiefly of the voluntary muscles. Let us briefly examine some basic facts about these functional parameters of breathing.

Respiratory Volumes. The changes in air volume under different conditions are analyzed with a spirometer, which is a tank for collecting and measuring expired air. With each quiet respiration about 500 cc of air enter and leave the pulmonary passages. This is the tidal air. This air enters a reservoir of about 3,000 cc, the stationary air within the lungs. By forcing an inspiration, 1,500 cc can be inspired in excess of the tide, and this excess is complemental air (inspiratory capacity). By forcing an expiration, 1,500 cc can be exhaled in excess of the tide, and the excess is supplemental air (expiratory reserve). The stationary air is made up of 1,500 cc of supplemental and 1,500 cc of residual air that cannot be forced out by any expiration.

The total lung capacity is 5,000 cc, or the sum of the tidal, complemental, and stationary air. For practical purposes another factor called the vital capacity is much more often considered. This capacity represents the amount of air that can be expelled by an individual after as deep an inspiration as possible. If the numerical values above are employed, the vital capacity might average 3,500 cc, or the sum of the tidal, complemental, and supplemental air. Vital capacity measurements are usually reduced to standards based on an individual's surface area (obtained from tables computed from height and weight). As an approximation, the standard is 2,600 cc per square meter for adult males and 2,000 cc per square meter for adult females. A reduction exceeding 15 per cent of the norm for a given group may be suggestive of pathology.

The vital capacity in man is significantly lowered in certain cardiac and pulmonary conditions, and it is therefore used in the diagnosis and prognosis of cardiac decompensation and pulmonary tuberculosis. Pulmonary diseases may lower the vital capacity for a number of years. In a healthy person the vital capacity is used as an approximate measure of lung capacity and therefore of respiratory physical fitness.

The vital capacity has been variably emphasized in the physiology of speech on the theory that ample lung volumes are essential to normal tone quality. This has already been discussed and qualified. Even when one speaks loudly, more breath is not necessarily used, and the adjustments may involve changes in resonance. In fact, respiratory defects in disease are very often compensated with regard to speech. A person with a collapsed lung and low vital capacity does not need to have any inadequacy of voice.

In a study of defective and normal speech groups among children, Carrell (1936) claimed to observe a difference in vital capacity. He concluded that the speech-defective children were physically inferior, and they also made poor use of their structural possibilities.

Respiratory Pressures. The pulmonary or intrapulmonic pressure is the pressure of air within the lungs and respiratory passages. It is measured most simply by inserting a tube connected to a mercury manometer into a single nostril. The pressure at rest is atmospheric, since the respiratory passages communicate freely with the air. A negative pressure of 2 to 3 mm (below 760) develops during inspiration, and a positive pressure of 2 to 3 mm develops during expiration. If there is obstruction to the air passages, the variations in pressure are much greater. Expiratory pressures as high as 10 to 40 mm are attained in coughing, in which the pressure is built up by inhaling deeply, closing the glottis, and producing a forced expiration against the closed glottis. In speech, variable expiratory pressures are built up against the closed or partly closed glottis, and these events help determine the qualities of the voice. Usually the blast pressures employed in speech are not very great. Some of the highest expiratory pressures are produced in certain pathology, as in bronchial asthma, where it could take 100 mm of pressure to force the lung air up through the functionally closed passages.

The second kind of respiratory pressure is the intrapleural, or intrathoracic, which is the pressure in the pleural cavities and in the mediastinum. The pleural cavities are potential spaces within the double walled sac that surrounds and encloses each lung. The mediastinum is the central region of the thorax. It lies between the two lungs and their pleural investments.

The intrathoracic pressure is always negative. This is because the thorax, which is a closed chamber, expands at birth and permanently reduces its internal pressure. Moreover, the lungs stretch and, being elastic, tend to produce a continuous pull away from the chest wall. These factors explain a permanent negative pressure, which is about 5 mm at the end of expiration. With each inspiration the thorax expands more than the lungs do, and the intrathoracic negativity increases to about 10 mm below atmospheric pressure.

This changing negativity prevents collapse of the lungs, and it is also responsible for the rhythmic expansion and compression of the lungs. For the most part the lungs are controlled by the thoracic movements. We have previously called this the physical theory of respiration.

THE LUNGS

These are the essential organs of respiration, situated on either side of the mediastinum in the thorax. They lie fairly free, being attached by the root and the pulmonary ligament. They are roughly conical masses of porous, spongy, highly elastic material, covered by serous pleural membranes. The apex of each lung projects into the root of the neck, and the base rests upon the diaphragm.

Each lung has a costal, mediastinal, and diaphragmatic surface. The costal surface is convex, and it comes into contact with the inner surfaces of the ribs and their intercostal muscles. The mediastinal surface is medial and concave. It contains the root, or hilus, through which pass the bronchus, bronchial and pulmonary blood vessels, lymphatics, and the autonomic regulatory nerves. The mediastinal surface of the left lung has a decided cardiac notch to receive the heart. The diaphragmatic surface lies at the base of each lung, and it is concave to fit over the diaphragm.

The right lung is divided by two fissures into superior, middle, and inferior lobes. The left lung is divided by a single fissure into superior and inferior lobes.

The trachea splits its lower end to two main stem bronchi, and each travels laterally and downward to enter the corresponding lung. The walls of the bronchi are semirigid because they contain cartilaginous rings bound together by membranes. Within the lungs the rings become replaced by irregular cartilage plates. As the stem bronchi divide to many collaterals ending in bronchioles, the cartilages progressively disappear. When the bronchiole diameter is about 1 mm, no cartilage is present.

The bronchioles are tubes without an outer coating or serosa. They present an exposed smooth muscular layer for the action of the vagal bronchoconstrictor fibers and the thoracolumbar or sympathetic bronchodilator fibers. The terminal bronchioles eventually lead to air spaces, or atria, and each of these terminates in several air sacs, or alveoli.

The alveoli are the final subdivisions, and they are the units of structure and function. The alveolar wall is a one-layered selectively permeable epithelium which is intimately surrounded by a blood capillary. The capillaries have a one-cell-layered endothelium. The interchange of gases takes place in both directions between the alveolar epithelium and the capillary endothelium. The direction and extent of the exchange are determined physically by the gradient of pressure for any given gas between the air and the blood.

The bronchi and lungs are nourished by the bronchial arteries. The bronchial veins bring the blood back. The pulmonary arteries bring impure blood from the right ventricle of the heart to the pulmonary capillaries in a separate circuit, and the purified blood is returned by the pulmonary veins to the left atrium of the heart. It is then pumped into the systemic or general vascular system by the left ventricle.

The only muscle fibers within the lungs are in the walls of the bronchi and bronchioli. The muscles alter the diameters of these tubes so that the regulation of the air volume in the pulmonary passages is effected proximal to the alveoli.

THE REGULATION OF RESPIRATION

The control of the voluntary muscles of respiration, which alter the thoracic volume to produce interchange of gases and more pertinently to provide the air blast necessary for speech, is from the motor and associated areas of the cerebrum. This muscular apparatus is put into the realm of the reflex, or the unconscious. It is automatically controlled by a pair of respiratory centers, or bilateral group of cells, situated in a groove called the calamus scriptorius. The apparatus lies in the ventral wall of the medulla. Each cell group is cross-connected and controls both sides of the body. The centers are chiefly inspiratory centers and are in control of active inspiration. If there are expiratory centers, they are dependent upon the inspiratory centers. There are also subsidiary nuclei of control at lower levels. The centers control many muscles. All those for inspiration contract together, and all those for exhalation contract alternately.

The respiratory centers of the hindbrain are always under the potential control of the higher brain centers, and respiration can thus be modified at will. In speech we can spend the air blast in accordance with the need. We can vary the location in the body where the respiratory activity is most emphasized. We can change the parameters of sound, such as loudness, pitch, quality, and duration, although respiration may not be primary in this activity.

The voluntary changes impressed upon the biological or medullary breathing are temporary. The chemical status of the blood, as we shall indicate presently, is a prime factor in preserving a steady state, particularly in regard to a continuity of respiratory rhythm.

The respiratory centers display tone or automatic rhythm even when isolated. The nature of their responses, however, depends upon continuous bombardment, chiefly by chemical and nervous stimuli. The centers operate the thoracic machinery adaptively through efferent nerve impulses. The regulation of breathing is reflex in nature.

The motor nerves belonging to the efferent limbs of the reflex machinery have already been listed for each one of the respiratory muscles so far described. The cranial nerves are hardly involved, and the spinal nerves belong to the cervical, thoracic, and lumbar segments of the spinal cord.

There are eight pairs of cervical nerves, and the anterior rami of the first four plus the hypoglossal form the cervical plexus. The last four cervical plus the first two thoracic nerves form the brachial plexus. Many of the respiratory nerves come from these plexuses. Examples include (1) the phrenic from C-3, C-4, and C-5 to the diaphragm; (2) the anterior thoracic from C-5, C-6, C-7, C-8, and T-1 to the pectoralis major and minor; (3) the long thoracic from C-5, C-6, C-7, and C-8 to the serratus anterior; and (4) the thoracodorsal nerve from C-6, C-7, and C-8 to the latissimus dorsi muscle.

There is no plexus formation for the thoracic nerves from T-2 through T-12. The anterior rami of the upper six pairs produce the intercostal nerves to the thoracic musculature, and those of the lower six produce the thoracoabdominal nerves to the abdominal as well as to the thoracic musculature. The true back muscles involved in respiration and situated in the deeper regions of the back are innervated by the posterior rather than the anterior rami of the cervical, thoracic, and lumbar nerves.

Accessory motor nerves forming part of the functional efferent limb from the respiratory centers to the muscles of breathing include cranial nerves, such as the vagus nerve to the larynx and the facial nerve to the muscles of the nose.

The reflex arc involving the respiratory centers also implies the existence of afferent limbs. Afferent nervous impulses come to the centers not only from the respiratory structures but from any part of the body. Certain afferent nerves excite the centers, and they are designated as pressor fibers; but other fibers, which are called depressors, inhibit the centers. The centers are, for example, excited by cold but inhibited in swallowing. In the latter activity the bolus of food reaching the throat sets up inhibitory impulses in the glossopharyngeal nerve fibers leaving that region for the respiratory centers, and the thoracic cage is temporarily held in suspended animation.

The respiratory centers are influenced by stimuli arising directly in the lungs. The alveoli contain stretch receptors. Upon inflation of the alveoli, afferent proprioceptive impulses travel up through the vagus nerve to inhibit the centers and cut short the inspiration. The collapse of the lung may be passive. At a given degree of deformation a second set of vagal impulses is discharged from other alveolar stretch receptors. These impulses stimulate the centers to initiate the next inspiration. This is a self-regulating mechanism, whereby the lung feedback controls the lung movements, and it does so somewhat independently of the intrathoracic pressures. These are Hering-Breuer reflexes.

The respiratory centers are also influenced by nerve impulses arising in specialized receptors within the walls of blood vessels. Impulses from pressure receptors in the arch of the aorta and in the carotid sinus at the beginning of the internal carotid artery travel up to the centers through the sinus nerve and other nerves. These impulses generally act to inhibit the centers. Thus, a rise in blood pressure depresses respiration. In a similar manner, impulses from chemoreceptors, which are located in the carotid and aortic bodies, stimulate the centers. Acids thus adaptively increase respiration.

Respiratory fibers go to the centers from accessory respiratory structures, and such impulses usually protect these accessory structures against the entrance of foreign bodies. The trigeminal nerve supplies the nasal mucosa, the glossopharyngeal supplies the pharynx, and the vagus supplies the larynx.

The centers are influenced by alterations in blood chemistry. In fact, they are so sensitive to minute changes in the pressure and concentration of carbon dioxide that this gas has been called the respiratory hormone. If the gas is washed out, breathing is suspended (apnea). The action occurs either locally in the blood perfusing the centers or indirectly by way of the peripheral chemoreceptors. A decrease in oxygen is also stimulating, but it takes a considerable oxygen deficiency to produce a change in ventilation. This is more a pathological (anoxic) control than a normal one. Oxygen acts indirectly by exciting the chemoreceptors. The centers are also responsive to changes in the hydrogen-ion concentration (acidity) of the blood. The importance of general acidity has been admitted, although the importance of carbon dioxide as a prime factor has been attacked (Winterstein, 1956).

APPLIED ANATOMY AND PHYSIOLOGY OF BREATHING AND SPEECH

The basic rhythm of breathing, as recorded in a pneumogram, and also the normal alterations of breathing for speech have already been discussed. Although respiration is ordinarily turned over to centers below consciousness in the hindbrain, voluntary control again takes over, even though subconsciously, in respiration during speech. The column of air must be controlled (breath control) so that inhalation is quick, with a larger amount of air inhaled, and exhalation is prolonged. Ventilation becomes more active than in the purely respiratory rhythm. The regularity is changed because of sentence patterns.

The exhaled air should not escape prior to vocalization, and the breath is parceled out as required. To determine to what extent your own breath is being conserved, inhale deeply without strain, then count as far as you can at a rate of just over two counts per second and observe how far you can get without forcing the last few counts. If you use the alphabet, see if you can get through twice with only one forced inhalation. This improves with practice (Anderson, 1942). The most efficient sounds, in the sense that they require the least breath expenditure, are vowels. The voiceless fricatives, such as f and s, use the most breath output, and one must learn to sound these with minimal exhalation.

Faulty breath control characterizes many speech deviations. In the condition of breathiness there is too little tension in the region of the vocal folds and insufficient resistance to exhalation; the wasted breath therefore contributes to an unpleasant, mousy tone. The loss of energy in wasted breath could necessitate a hyperventilation which may be ameliorated through a learned reduction of respiratory movements. The breathy or husky voice may result either from disorders of respiration or disorders of phonation. We shall discuss this again in connection with phonation and resonance.

The harsh voice, to be discussed later, may also show both respiratory and phonatory deviations. There is not only an excessive general bodily as well as laryngeal tension, but also in many cases abnormal respiratory movements, including marked abdominal contractions.

In the hoarse voice, which has both husky and harsh qualities, an individual may voluntarily force his breathing in addition to overtensing his larynx.

There are many other deviations. The residual breather takes too little breath for speech, and his voice is hard to hear. People who are subbreathers, or hypothyroid, or in poor health may release the air in insufficient bubbles to a larynx that gets too tense. They sound as if they were ill, and the condition is described as unsustained phonation. Cerebral palsy may affect breathing so that the tone may not be sustained. The afflicted patients may have to be taught to avoid the "spastic" effect by learning to sustain a tone without tension. The stutterer may try to speak during inhalation or else speak so that the thoracic and abdominal muscles are working antagonistically. This is held to be the result, and not the cause, of stuttering.

The respiratory system becomes utilized in a unique manner in ventriloquism (Kodman, 1955). The operator inhales powerfully and keeps his diaphragm in a relatively fixed and depressed position. The thorax and abdomen are forcibly distended, and the thorax is reexpanded between extended sounds to obtain renewal of air. Speech is accomplished by a very slow expulsion of air following one maximum thoracic inspiration. A steady contraction of thoracic and abdominal muscles puts a greater force on the vocal folds. Pneumograms reveal the decreased amplitude in the thoracic and abdominal movements while speaking.

SUMMARY

Respiration is significantly involved in speech, both in health and disease.

The structural apparatus for breathing is not strictly localized within the thorax but includes the abdominal musculature as well as muscles located elsewhere. Much of what is used depends upon the conditions of activity.

The pressures and volumes of the pulmonary passages and of the intrathoracic spaces are continuously changing. These physical changes are linked with the flow of air in and out of the lungs along gradients of pressure.

The control of breathing is both local and reflex. Respiratory centers respond adaptively to chemical and physical changes. Such changes occur anywhere in the body, but they are most apt to stimulate specialized chemo- and pressoreceptors.

Chapter 6

THE STRUCTURE FOR PHONATION

The larynx is the phonating mechanism. Through movements of its cartilages, which are activated by voluntary muscles and controlled by cerebrospinal nerves, it produces sounds. These sounds will be translated to intelligible speech by articulatory and resonating structures lying above it.

The larynx is roughly tubular in form, and it is located in the neck directly anterior to the esophagus. It is in continuity with the pharynx above and the trachea below. The paired lobes of the thyroid gland lie on either side of it. The transverse isthmus that connects the two lobes crosses in front of the larynx at the lower section of that organ. The larynx should be considered to be a specialized part of the respiratory system.

THE LARYNGEAL FRAMEWORK

The supporting structures of the larynx consist of cartilages and membranes.

The unpaired hyoid bone is just above the larynx. Although it is primarily a support for the tongue, it may still be considered a part of the laryngeal framework. The larynx is suspended from the hyoid, and many of the laryngeal muscles have a hyoid attachment.

The hyoid bone is unique in having no direct attachments to any other bone. It is held in position by muscles and ligaments. These supports go into it from the bones of the skull above and from the laryngeal cartilages below.

The hyoid is slender and U-shaped. It lies in a horizontal place with the limbs of the U pointing posteriorly. The outer surface of the bone can be felt through the skin at the junction of the front of the neck and the floor of the mouth.

The anterior section of the hyoid bone is called the body. The posteriorly directed limbs of the U are called major horns or greater cornua. The posterior tip of each limb has a tubercle to which the lateral thyrohyoid ligament connects. This ligament provides stability to a joint in which the major horns of the hyoid articulate with the superior horns of the thyroid cartilage.

At the junction between the body and each major horn, a small conical spike juts upward. These spikes are the paired minor horns, or lesser cornua. They allow hyoid suspension to the temporal bones of the skull by means of a connecting thread on each side called the stylohyoid ligament.

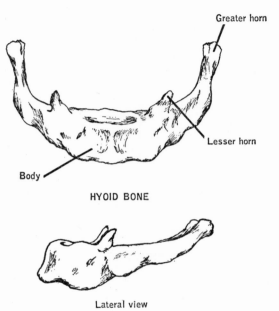

Greater horn

Lesser horn

Body

HYOID BONE

Lateral view

Fig. 6–1. Anterior and lateral views of the hyoid bone.

The larynx proper has nine cartilages. The most prominent is the unpaired thyroid cartilage. The thyroid cartilage is made up of right and left quadrilateral plates, or laminae. These are easily palpated in the anterior and lateral walls of the neck. The laminae fuse to a thyroid angle in the median ventral line. The superior aspect of the fused plates is the especially prominent Adam's apple. The upper border of each lamina drops sharply in the central anterior region above the prominence to produce a V-shaped superior thyroid notch.

The laminae diverge in back so that they enclose a wide space. The posterior border of each lamina is prolonged above and below into superior and inferior horns respectively. Each superior horn attaches to the corresponding major horn of the hyoid bone. Each inferior horn connects with the arch of the cricoid cartilage. A cricothyroid joint is formed on each side.

The superior border of the thyroid cartilage provides attachment for the thyrohyoid ligament. On either side of the inferior border near the junction of its anterior two-thirds with its posterior one-third, there is a downward projecting tubercle. This projection marks the lower end of a ridge called the oblique line. This line travels diagonally down the external surface of each lamina, starting from a superior tubercle which lies near the root of the superior horn. The thyrohyoid, sternothyroid, and inferior pharyngeal constrictor muscles use the oblique line for attachment to the cartilage.

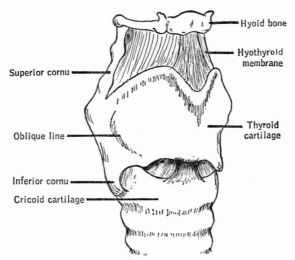

Fig. 6–2. Laryngeal cartilages seen in an oblique anterior view.

The internal surface of each thyroid lamina is smooth and somewhat concave. Several structures are attached internally at the angle formed by the union of the two laminae. These structures include the thyroepiglottic, ventricular, and vocal ligaments, the stem of the epiglottis, and also the thyroarytenoid, thyroepiglottic, and vocalis muscles.

When the larynx rises, the thyroid cartilage slips up under cover of the hyoid with a synovial bursa between them. Any enlargement of the bursa, as a cystic dilatation in the region of the thyroglossal duct, may cause pain or difficult swallowing.

The unpaired cricoid cartilage lies between the thyroid cartilage above and the tracheal cartilages below. It has the shape of a signet ring. The front and sides of the ring form the cricoid arch. The posterior section of the ring is a flattened hexagonal plate, or signet, which extends upward to fill the region not occupied by the divergent thyroid laminae. The signet is about 25 mm in height, and the arch is about 8 mm in height (Morris, 1953).

The signet, or lamina, has a median vertical ridge on its posterior external surface. The longitudinal muscle fibers of the esophagus attach to the lower part of this ridge. A shallow depression on each side of the ridge allows attachment of the posterior cricoarytenoid muscle.

The arch of the cricoid provides for attachment of muscles to its external surface. The cricothyroid muscles attach in front and at the sides. A portion of the inferior pharyngeal constrictor muscle attaches more posteriorly. The inferior cornu of the thyroid cartilage connects with the cricoid on each side at the junction of the cricoid arch with the signet.

The lower border of the cricoid is fairly horizontal and allows attachment of the cricotracheal ligament. The upper border provides attachment for the median cricothyroid ligament and the more lateral paired conus elasticus ligaments. The upper border has a posterior central notch, on each side of which is a smooth surface that faces upward and outward. This arrangement provides for the paired cricoarytenoid joints. The joints are on the downward-sloping portion of the cricoid, lateral to the horizontal section. The arytenoid cartilages must not be thought of as resting upon the horizontal section of the superior border of the cricoid.

The paired arytenoid cartilages are located in the posterior section of the larynx. They are approximately three-sided pyramids. Since each has a triangular base as well as three triangular sides, each could be considered tetrahedral in shape (Cates and Basmajian, 1955).

The surfaces of the triangular sides of each arytenoid are medial, posterior, and anterolateral. The medial surface is almost vertical, and it faces the medial surface of the opposite arytenoid. The posterior surface is concave and smooth, and it is covered by the oblique and posterior arytenoid muscles. The anterolateral surface is the largest. It presents two pits, a triangular fovea above, which contains mucous glands, and an oblong fovea below for the vocalis muscle. An arcuate crest horizontally separates the two pits. The anterolateral surface also has in its upper part an eminence called the colliculus.

Each arytenoid has an apex and base. The apex is pointed, and it curves medially and posteriorly. The base is concave. It articulates with the cricoid as described above. A posterolateral projection called the muscular process is at the lateral angle of the base. The lateral and posterior cricoarytenoid muscles insert at the lateral angle. A vocal process, which gives attachment to the vocal ligament, forms the prominent anterior angle of the base.

The corniculate cartilages (of Santorini) are small paired conical elastic-tissue nodules, each capping the arytenoid apex. Possibly they protect the arytenoids.

The paired rod-like cuneiform cartilages (of Wrisberg) are yellow elastic cartilages located in the posterior parts of the aryepiglottic folds, which are membranes stretching between the epiglottis above and the arytenoids below. The cartilages are not always present, and they are said to be degenerate structures that may have served historically to support the aryepiglottic folds. When the arytenoids are large, as in the

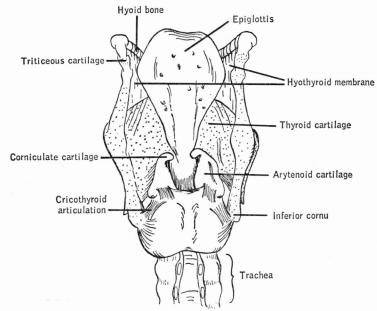

Fig. 6–3. Posterior view of larynx to show the cartilages and their connecting ligaments.

deer, the aryepiglottic folds contain cartilage supports almost through-out their length.

The highest laryngeal cartilage is the unpaired epiglottis. This is elastic cartilage resembling a leaf. It lies in the front of the larynx just behind the root of the tongue. The epiglottis forms the oblique anterior wall of that section of the larynx which is the entrance, or vestibule.

There are two surfaces, anterior or lingual and posterior or laryngeal. The anterior surface curves forward. A mucous membrane covers its upper aspect and is extended onto the sides and root of the tongue as the median and paired glossoepiglottic folds.

The posterior or laryngeal surface of the epiglottis is concavoconvex in passing downward. The lower posterior aspect has a prominent epiglottic tubercle, or cushion, which lies over the upper part of the thyroepiglottic ligament. The cushion is visible in a laryngoscopic examination. It seems to descend toward the vocal folds in high-pitched and falsetto tones. Mucous glands lie in recessed pits in the surface of the cartilage.

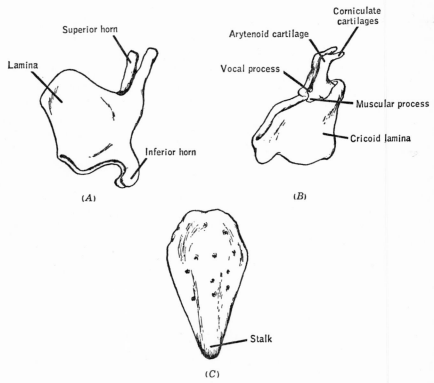

Fig. 6–4. Individual disarticulated laryngeal cartilages. A. Lateral view of thyroid. B. The cricoid and arytenoids in lateral view. C. Anterior view of the epiglottis.

The stem of the epiglottis is long and narrow. It is attached anteriorly to (1) the thyroepiglottic ligament, which meets the angle of the thyroid cartilage just below the superior thyroid notch, and (2) the hyoepiglottic ligament, which connects the epiglottis with the superior border of the body of the hyoid bone.

The epiglottis is related to the partition of air and food during swallowing. The food, or bolus, in passing into the pharynx is reflected upon the upper surface of the epiglottis, and it is then sent down the posterior part of the pharynx into the esophagus. If inhalation is at the same time reflexly inhibited and the pharynx actively elevated, then the glottis will be narrowed, and no food will be taken into the windpipe.

There is some controversy about how the epiglottis can keep material out of the glottis. In the early literature it was claimed to act as a movable lid which protected the larynx. More recently it was considered to be a fairly rigid, semiupright structure which served to deflect the bolus of food to the posterior channel of the esophagus. Its positional movements have been analyzed by fluoroscopy, through a surgical pharyngostome, in cinefluorography, by spotting its dorsal surface with ink and observing the imprints that reflect its oppositions during swallowing, and by other methods.

There is radiological evidence from a subject who had a silver clip placed on the tip of his epiglottis that this structure does turn down during swallowing (Jenkins, 1954). The situation was not entirely definite inasmuch as the movements were very rapid. There is confirmatory evidence of movement in another subject whose pharynx could be observed from the exterior. Also, by the use of high-speed cineradiography (Saunders et al., 1951), the epiglottis has been seen to act as a trap door which bends backward and seals the larynx during swallowing. At the same time, the aryepiglottic folds shorten, apparently to assist in pulling the epiglottis down and back. These newer observations are contrary to conventional views.

In its speech function the epiglottis may add to resonance by producing changes in the size of the laryngeal cavity. It is also said to be involved in the production of intense high-pitched tones.

The epiglottis is not a vital organ, since it may be removed without serious consequences. The removal of a large part of it does not prevent swallowing. It may serve chiefly for respiration and make no real contribution to swallowing. Bosma (1957) discusses these problems.

Perhaps the epiglottis is the phylogenetic rudiment of a once larger organ. Negus (1949) claims that the epiglottis evolved primarily in association with the nasopharynx and soft palate for the purposes of olfaction. The structure is almost universally absent in amphibians, reptiles, and birds, and these animals have in general a poorly developed sense of smell. All mammals possessing a keen sense of smell also have a well-developed epiglottis which lies in contact with the soft palate. There is also the view that this organ is concerned phylogenetically with taste.

The epiglottis may become important in pathology. It may, for example, develop cysts at any age. In the newborn these cysts can produce laryngeal stridor or even death from laryngeal obstruction (Asherson, 1957). In adults the cysts may vary from a painless and harmless type to those associated with infection or obstruction. They can interfere with deglutition and phonation.

There are some inconstant or supernumerary cartilages in the human larynx. Small paired sesamoid cartilages occur at the lateral edges of the arytenoids. Small paired triticeous cartilages are found in the postero-lateral margins of the thyrohyoid membrane. A tiny single interarytenoid cartilage is enveloped by the cricopharyngeal ligament and underlies the mucous membrane of the pharynx.

THE LARYNGEAL JOINTS

The laryngeal cartilages are united by joints. The arytenoids and cricoid form a pair of cricoarytenoid joints. Grant (1944) says that the under surface of each arytenoid and the lateral sloping parts of the superior border of the cricoid lamina have oval articular facets. The long axes of the ovals are at right angles to each other, which allows the arytenoid to glide medially and laterally, forward and backward, and to rotate.

Grant's statements are essentially followed by Woodburne (1957). The latter claims that each cricoarytenoid joint has two oval facets, convex on the upper border of the cricoid and concave on the base of the arytenoid. The long axis of the arytenoid facet is anteroposterior while that of the cricoid facet is transverse. This arrangement determines the types of movement. The arytenoids can glide medially and laterally, and also forward and backward. The backward motion tilts the vocal process of the arytenoid upward. The forward motion brings it downward. This action is a result of the curvature and slope of the cricoid facet. There is also a rotary motion which brings the vocal processes together or pulls them apart to variable degrees.

Morris (1953) states that the cricoarytenoid joint is a typical arthrodial or gliding joint and that motion at the articulation is very free. A posterior cricoarytenoid ligament is important in keeping the arytenoid upon the sloping articular surface of the cricoid and in limiting its movements.

Gray (1954) states that two movements of the cricoarytenoid joint are allowed. The arytenoid can rotate on a vertical axis and move the vocal process medially or laterally, which narrows or widens the glottis. In the second movement the arytenoids glide toward or away from each other. The direction and slope of the approximating cricoid surface causes the lateral motion to have also a forward and downward direction. Both rotation and gliding are so associated that medial gliding and medial rotation occur together, and the same holds for lateral gliding and lateral rotation.

A cricothyroid joint is formed on each side between the round lateral facet on the cricoid and a facet on the medial aspect of the inferior horn of the thyroid cartilage. This is a typical arthrodial joint. There is a joint capsule, synovial membrane, and accessory ligaments posteriorly. The cartilages may glide anteroposteriorly against one another. Gray (1954) says that in gliding there is a limited shift of the cricoid on the thyroid in different directions. The cricoid may also rotate upon the inferior thyroid horn around an axis passing transversely through both joints.

THE LARYNGEAL MEMBRANES

Several membranes and ligaments connect the cartilages of the larynx. By uniting the individual cartilages and by limiting the extent and direction of their movements, the membranes contribute to orderly laryngeal activity. These membranes divide the larynx into three vertical compartments. Some of the membranes enter into the construction of the ventricular and the vocal folds.

The unpaired thyrohyoid membrane suspends the larynx from the hyoid bone. The membrane is attached above to the superior margin and greater horns of the hyoid bone. It passes downward behind the hyoid and ends upon the superior border and superior horns of the thyroid cartilage. The median section of this membrane is thick and is called the median thyrohyoid ligament. The posterolateral sections of the membrane connect the greater horns of the hyoid bone with the superior horns of the thyroid cartilage. This section is the lateral thyrohyoid ligament.

We have already noted that the epiglottis is connected to the hyoid bone by the hyoepiglottic ligament and to the thyroid cartilage by the thyroepiglottic ligament. At the lower end of the larynx, the cricoid is connected to the uppermost tracheal ring by the cricotracheal ligament.

The cricothyroid membrane is another important structure. It becomes involved in the construction of the vocal folds. This membrane has a central and paired lateral sections. The thick central section, or middle cricothyroid ligament, travels as a vertical anterior band between the cricoid arch and the lower border of the central part of the thyroid cartilage.

The paired lateral sections are known as the conus elasticus. Synonyms are the elastic cone and the cricovocal membrane. The middle cricothyroid ligament is actually the vertically directed central part of the conus elasticus (Morris, 1953).

The lateral sections have free cephalic margins. As these lateral folds extend horizontally on each side of the median line from front to back, their somewhat thickened margins become the vocal ligaments. These ligaments are significant structures since they lie within and form the medial part of each vocal fold. They have a thick layer of elastic tissue, and they are the chief support of the vocal folds.

Each vocal ligament is attached ventrally to a perichondral process at the posterior surface of the thyroid angle. At its dorsal end each vocal ligament has a broad insertion to the upper and medial surfaces of the vocal process of the corresponding arytenoid cartilage.

The paired quadrangular membranes are important structures. They appear as irregular vertical folds. Each structure arises anteriorly from the lateral border of the epiglottis and the posterior surface of the thyroid angle. The membrane on either side extends posteriorly in a downward slope to the corniculate cartilage and the medial margin of each arytenoid.

The lateral parts of the quadrangular membrane are widely separated superiorly. As the membrane on each side descends somewhat vertically, it also turns medially. The paired membranes thus tend to converge inferiorly. The terminal inferior borders are free and thickened, and these free edges are called the ventricular (vestibular) ligaments. The ligaments are horizontal and well developed ventrally. They are attached close to the thyroid angle ventrally. At their dorsal ends they are attached to the medial border of the triangular fovea of the arytenoid cartilages.

The paired ventricular ligaments constitute the framework of the ventricular or false vocal folds. The ligaments also help support the aryepiglottic folds which bound the laryngeal entrance.

The term vestibular membrane is occasionally used to describe the structure which forms the ventricular ligaments. The vestibular membrane is the quadrangular membrane. Woodburne (1957) says that the vestibular membrane is a weak submucosal sheet of connective tissue. It is covered posteriorly by the aryepiglottic and thyroepiglottic muscles.

The paired aryepiglottic folds form the superior aperture of the larynx. These folds begin at the sides of the epiglottis. They slope downward as they are extended backward. The folds envelop the supporting cartilages of Wrisberg posteriorly, and they terminate at the cartilages of Santorini and the arytenoids. When the posterior cricoarytenoid muscles act to open the laryngeal aperture, the aryepiglottic folds are simultaneously pulled backward.

The aryepiglottic folds help form lateral channels on each side. Fluid can travel down from the tongue base and be channeled into the troughs between these folds and the lateral wall of the pharynx. The sphincter muscles within the aryepiglottic folds close the laryngeal aperture during swallowing to prevent inundation of the windpipe by solid and liquid food.

Cleary (1954) gives a detailed description of the aryepiglottic folds with particular reference to the otolaryngologist. The muscles of these folds were called the constrictor vestibuli muscles by Luschka in 1871. At that time the folds were thought to contribute to phonatory movements. It now appears that their main function is related to the epiglottis in swallowing. Pressman (1954) suggests that they constrict the larynx in swallowing.

Cleary asserts that the aryepiglottic folds are of paramount importance in the active closure of the larynx. If there is swelling of these folds, choking may occur even if very small amounts of water are ingested. This is because the edema prevents adequate muscular closure of the folds, and the water gets into the windpipe. There is inadequate tensing of the edges of the aryepiglottis. Although susceptible to swelling, the aryepiglottic folds are rarely the cause of laryngeal obstruction. The ventricular folds are more often at fault.

INTERNAL DIVISIONS OF THE LARYNX

The cavity of the larynx (cavum laryngis) is continuous below with the cavity of the trachea. Superiorly, the cavity is an anterior diverticulum of the lowest part of the pharynx. The laryngeal interior is somewhat funnel-shaped, and it has three divisions from above downward.

The superior division, or vestibule, includes the space between the entrance to the larynx above (aditus laryngis) and the ventricular folds below. The entrance is shaped like a triangle, wide in front, narrow behind, and sloping down from front to back. The vestibular cavity is wide above, but it becomes narrowed from side to side as it approaches the glottis.

The middle division, or ventricle (sinus), extends from the ventricular folds above to the vocal folds below. This provides a space for free vibration of the vocal folds, and it functions perhaps as a resonator. The space was known to Galen in 300 A.D., and it was described by Morgagni in 1741—thus the name, ventricle of Morgagni. This area is well described by Moore (1922), Freedman (1938), and Gray (1954).

Anteriorly, the sinus, or ventricle, on each side is prolonged upward. This produces a pair of cul-de-sacs, each of which is a laryngeal sacculus, or appendix of the ventricle. Each sacculus projects between the ventricular fold and the thyroid cartilage. The sac goes as high as the upper border of the thyroid cartilage.

The sacculus represents an atavistic (throwback) structure which is better developed in monkeys and other anthropoids than in man. This is a weak area from which a laryngocele may develop. A herniation may occur through the thyrohyoid membrane, and a cyst may pass into the superficial structures. The mucous membrane of the sacculus contains many glands. Their secretion is expressed by muscles upon the vocal folds for lubrication. More will be said about this function later.

Freedman (1938) states that because the ventricle and sacculus are blind and stagnant recesses which are rich in lymphoid tissue, they, and not the vocal folds, may be the primary site of development of many

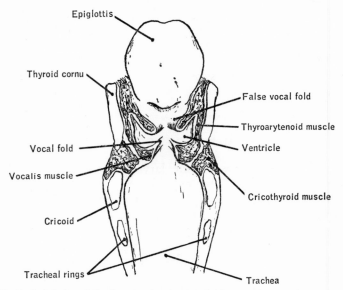

Epiglottis

Thyroid cornu

False vocal fold

Thyroarytenoid muscle

Vocal fold

Ventricle

Vocalis muscle

Cricothyroid muscle

Cricoid

Tracheal rings

Trachea

Fig. 6—5. Interior of the larynx, showing its divisions and internal structures.

pathological conditions of the larynx, such as cancer, tuberculosis, and benign cysts, which encroach upon the vocal folds.

The inferior division of the larynx includes the space between the vocal folds above and trachea below.

Everything in the larynx above the vocal folds is referred to as hyperglottic and everything below as hypoglottic.

VENTRICULAR AND VOCAL FOLDS

The true and the false folds are normally visible in technics to visualize the interior of the larynx.

The paired ventricular or false vocal folds (plicae ventriculares) are thick rounded folds of mucous membrane developed around the ventricular ligaments. They are soft and somewhat flaccid. Each contains the lower portion of the quadrangular membrane, including the ventricular ligaments. Each also contains a few muscle fibers and numerous mucous glands.

The ventricular folds reach the angle of the thyroid laminae anteriorly, where they are most prominent. They do not reach the dorsal laryngeal wall posteriorly. They are attached posteriorly to the arytenoids, and like the true folds, they can move with the arytenoids. In forced closure of the glottis they may contract with the true folds (Van Riper and Irwin, 1958).

The opening between the edges of the false folds is the false glottis (glottis spuria, rima vestibuli). The size and shape of the aperture is variable with circumstances. The separation is wider than that of the true glottis; this is particularly true in trained singers.

The ventricular folds can be brought together and serve as a valve to build up air pressure within the deeper lung passages when excess intrapulmonary pressure is needed (Boies, 1954).

Sound production is related to the ventricular folds, although rarely under ordinary circumstances. Pressman (1942) pointed out that these folds can be approximated and separated and this can occur with or independently of the activity of the true folds. The tone is unpleasant because of interference with the upward passage of the sound waves. Vibrations can be reflected downward. Closure of the ventricular folds may be fleeting and unpredictable.

If the true folds are excised, the false ones can substitute, a condition called dysphonia plicae ventricularis. The voice is husky, and the pitch is low (Pressman, 1942).

The false folds can alter the resonance function of the vestibule by the effect of their closure upon the shape of the vestibule. Berry and Eisenson (1956) cite evidence that during very high frequencies the false folds influence the vibration of the true folds, since they just impinge upon the true folds. As a result they give enough pressure to the upper surface of the latter to restrict the width of the vibrating sector; this could increase the vibrational frequency.

An important function of the false folds is to lubricate the true folds (Gray and Wise, 1946). By the use of cinematography during speech, drops of mucus have been traced in passage from the false folds to the true folds. This action is likely to facilitate the rapid alterations in shape and tension which the true folds undergo.

The paired vocal or true folds (plicae vocales) lie parallel and inferior to the ventricular folds, and they extend from the posterior surface of the thyroid angle to the vocal processes of the arytenoids. They diverge from a common anterior fixation point, and each band then becomes attached like a shelf of tissue to the lateral wall of the larynx. Each vocal fold contains the vocal ligament, the vocalis muscle, and a covering of mucous membrane.

The vocal folds are occasionally called cords or bands, and at times the free fibrous borders of the folds are called the bands. Cords is a term which suggests vibrational strings. The term bands has gained favor. The term folds is descriptive, since the structures are actually prominent folds which project from the inner walls of the larynx.

When viewed from above, the true folds are seen as paired strips of muscle with inner or medial borders of connective tissue. When seen from below, they are arched structures. The arching is produced by the

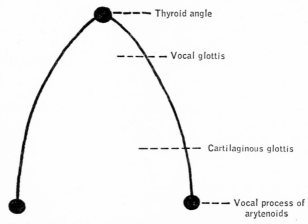

Thyroid angle

Vocal glottis

Cartilaginous glottis

Vocal process of arytenoids

Fig. 6–6. Shape of the glottis, showing vocal and cartilaginous sections. (Diagrammatic.)

relatively great thickness of the muscles at the lateral borders in contrast with the thin medial borders.

The varying descriptions of the vibrating edges of the folds as being rounded or else sharp and thin are related to the kind of activity in which the folds are being engaged. Also, there are individual differences, as in every other bodily structure.

Each true fold is nonvascular and therefore displays a pale mucous membrane. The free edge of the fold appears white except at the anterior terminal where there is a yellow spot produced by the presence of cartilage or elastic tissue.

The mucous membrane is firmly adherent about the vocal folds and the laryngeal aspect of the epiglottis. Its looseness elsewhere in the larynx facilitates swelling with subsequent dysfunction in breathing and speaking.

The mucosa covering the apposed surfaces of the folds is stratified squamous while it is ciliated columnar in the other parts of the folds. According to Gray (1954), the squamous epithelium is characteristic of the upper posterior surface of the epiglottis and the upper part of the aryepiglottic folds. It also covers the anterior or pharyngeal surface of the epiglottis. Ciliated columnar epithelium covers the remainder of the laryngeal surface. This respiratory kind of epithelium extends down into the trachea and bronchi. The cilia beat toward the pharynx.

Histological structure should in general be regarded as having some correlation with function. Thus a squamous covering is advantageous over the free border of each fold, because it resists the severe trauma produced by the repeated contact of the opposite fold (Pressman, 1942). The remainder of the fold is not subject to this trauma. A columnar ciliated covering is most advantageous near the inpocketing of the ventricle inasmuch as cilia are needed to drive away foreign matter and the mucus globules which normally collect in that region.

There are some differences of opinion among histologists about the nature of the epithelium of the larynx. Hopp (1955) reviews the literature. In his opinion the embryonic epithelium of the vocal folds becomes cuboidal and then stratified, and this includes the region extending into the ventricle. The other areas of the larynx, except where the vocal folds extend into the interarytenoid region, develop ciliated epithelium of a columnar and pseudostratified type. Hopp claims that islands of squamous epithelium occur rarely in the adult larynx, and they may in general be considered to be a result of pathological changes.

The lining of the larynx is variably supplied with glands. A rich supply of mucous glands is found in the lower epiglottis, the aryepiglottic folds, ventricular folds, ventricles, and in the areas below the glottis. Such glands are missing on the upper epiglottis and on the parts of the vocal folds that meet. Morris (1953) speaks of the tendency of the glands to form clusters. An anterior group belongs to the epiglottis. A middle group is in the ventricular folds, in the triangular fovea of the arytenoid cartilages, and about the cuneiform cartilages. A posterior set is located about the transverse arytenoid muscle.

The various glands keep the vocal folds well lubricated, especially in the active regions. A few drops of mucus are characteristically present on the inner margin of each fold. Mucus flows to the folds particularly from the paired saccules, which are membranous reservoirs. They have been described earlier in this chapter. The submucous coat of the saccule contains sixty to seventy glands which open onto the mucous membrane.

The saccular glands are emptied by the action of intrinsic laryngeal muscles. This action includes the compression exerted by muscle fibers originating in the apex of the arytenoids and running into the aryepiglottic fold of mucous membrane (Gray, 1945). Freedman (1938) stated that the mucus is periodically squirted as a thin stream from the ventricles upon the true folds.

THE GLOTTIS AND ITS CHANGING CONTOUR

The glottis (rima glottidis) is the variable opening between the vocal folds. It is the narrowest part of the laryngeal cavity.

The anterior section of the glottis, which is bounded by the folds, is membranous and is termed the vocal glottis. This section comprises about three-fifths of the total length. The posterior section, which is bounded by the medial surfaces of the arytenoid cartilages and posteriorly by the transverse arytenoid muscle, is termed the cartilaginous glottis.

In the quiet state the average length of the membranous glottis is 15.5 mm in the male and 11.5 mm in the female. The length of the cartilaginous glottis is 7.5 mm in the male and 5.5 mm in the female (Morris, 1953). These portions can be elongated by stretching the vocal folds.

The widest part of the glottis is 6 to 8 mm in the male, and this can increase to about 12 mm, according to conditions.

The variations in the shape of the glottis are involved in the production of the complex waveform of sound. The width and general shape of the glottis are changed primarily by movements of the arytenoid cartilages through muscle action. There are many degrees of the open and even of the closed position.

Any section of the glottal edge can be adducted or abducted without necessarily relating to any other part (Pressman and Kelemen, 1955). This is because the paired thyroarytenoid and vocalis muscles of the vocal folds seem to be capable of differential or segmental contraction. This activity can occur independently of the arytenoid movements.

When the arytenoids glide toward each other, the glottic opening, or chink, is narrowed. The same result is anatomically possible by rotation of the arytenoids such that their anterior vocal processes are brought closer together. The tendency to close the glottic margins is called adduction whereas the opposite motion constitutes abduction.

When the arytenoids are tilted backward, the vocal folds may be stretched between their origin and insertion. This action can increase the tension. Relaxation can be produced by forward tilting. The degree of tension is influenced by rotary movements exerted at the cricothyroid joint and also by changes in the mode of contraction of the intrinsic muscles located in the vocal folds. The relationships between movements and tension are not all clear-cut. This will be discussed later.

When the larynx is at rest and quiet breathing prevails, the glottis is open but narrow and has the shape of a long triangle. The vocal folds move slightly toward and away from each other. The aperture is wider during inhalation, and it is narrower during exhalation. In forced respiration the glottic chink can practically attain the capacity of the trachea, the widest part of the opening being at the extremities of the vocal processes of the arytenoids; Morris (1953) says it becomes lozenge-shaped.

FACTORS INFLUENCING PHONATION

The pitch of the voice is influenced by such factors as the length, tension, elasticity, and mass of the folds, the subglottal breath pressure, and the shape of the glottis.

Length is significant. The male vocal folds are about one-third longer than those of the female. This difference in length partly accounts for the lower pitch of the male voice. This statement about the influence of length should not suggest that the pitch lowers as the folds are actively elongated. There is the need to differentiate between structurally longer folds and actively lengthened folds.

There is an effect of mass. The chief mass of the true folds is the paired vocalis muscles. We shall see that these may be an inner part of the larger thyroarytenoid muscles. The more massive the folds, the lower will be their vibrational frequency and the resulting pitch. Persons with thin and light vocal folds are not likely to have low voices. The male has heavier folds than does the female.

The effect of increasing the tension is to increase the frequency and the resulting pitch. By altering string tension on a violin without changing the mass or length, the instrument may be tuned. In the body it is possible to alter the tension of the vocal folds at relatively constant length by variations in the shape of the folds brought about by muscle action. The thickness of the parts is changed. The edges of the folds can vary from round and thick to sharp-pointed and thin. If the attachments of the vocalis and thyroarytenoid muscles are fixed by other laryngeal muscles, then their contractions increase the fold tension. Fixation anteriorly is accomplished by the infrahyoid muscles and posteriorly by the posterior cricoarytenoid muscles. The external laryngeal muscles may increase their contractile power and pull outward upon the fold attachments. Since the motion is highly limited, the folds are tensed rather than elongated.

Another factor influencing pitch is air pressure. By increasing forced expiration, the air pressure can produce not only an increase in loudness but also a small rise in pitch.

A vibrational frequency (F) may be halved by doubling the length

(L), or multiplying the mass (M) by 4, or dividing the tension (T) by 4 in accordance with the equation $F = 1/2L \sqrt{T/M}$

GENERAL PHONATORY ACTIVITY

Changes in blast force, glottal shape, and laryngeal contours are all seen to be important during phonation. The general activity of the entire larynx and also of the true folds will now be briefly described.

The larynx changes its position in space during phonation. In low tones it rises slightly. In very high tones and in the falsetto it rises considerably. During inspiration the larynx tends to lower. There may be adjunctive movements dorsally and also often to the left, but all the movements are of small amplitude (Pressman, 1942).

The activity of the folds has been studied in several ways. One technic has been motion pictures. These have evolved from high speeds to ultrahigh speeds. Another aid has been the stroboscope, which produces an optical illusion such that fast-moving objects are seen as though they were motionless or moving slowly. The old type of stroboscope, used first in 1932 to describe details of laryngeal vibratory movements in living human subjects, has now evolved to a device called an electronic synchronstroboscope (Timcke et al., 1958). The larynx has also been observed in action in other ways. One technic has employed cineradiography, still radiography, and tomography (Ardran et al., 1953).

To produce varied tones in normal activity (average conditions of voice production), the vocal folds are first approximated all along their length just prior to phonating. The folds are put under different degrees of tension and elongation. They open to variable degrees with the pulmonary air blast, depending upon the tone to be produced. The entire fold may be displaced from the mid-line. The everted edges of the folds then return to the initial position. This action is repeated rapidly. The folds meet along their edges.

The folds do not move as stiff bands. The opening may develop from front to back or from back to front (Isaac Brackett, in a personal communication) in an undulating or wave-like progression.

The vibration of the folds is chiefly horizontal, with a maximum displacement of about 4 mm which is in contrast with a vertical displacement of 0.2 to 0.5 mm.

The original classification of the vocal fold activity was as a cycle having two phases. The activity is also now classified as a three-phase process. There is a period of approximation, an opening phase (abduction), and a closing phase (adduction). Each phase may be approximately equal in normal voice production.

Synchronstroboscopic measurements (Timcke, 1958) have been made of the *open quotient*. This is a ratio of the fraction of the cycle during which the glottis is open compared with the duration of the entire cycle. In normal voice production the open quotient changes very little with respect to the frequency of vibration, with a tendency to increase slightly with a rise in pitch. The quotient decreases with increasing intensity and increases with decreasing intensity.

The vocal folds vibrate in a characteristically altered manner with specific conditions. In activity at a low frequency they seem relaxed, and their horizontal displacement is the greater. The edges of the folds are rounded. The entire fold vibrates, and the main mass of the muscles of the fold participates in the activity.

Starting from the closed part of the cycle at low frequency, the folds begin to open from below, and the opening progresses upward with an outward unfolding of the vocal bands. The lower part is also first to close. During closure, a wave-like ripple passes over the upper surface from the glottis toward the pharyngeal wall, while the fold edges approximate.

In the 1937 high-speed motion pictures at the Bell Telephone Laboratories, with subjects using sounds ranging from 120 to 350 cps, the vocal folds were thought to be tightly closed for nearly half the two-phase cycle. Timcke et al. (1958) cite evidence that the opening phase of the glottic wave is shorter than the closing phase.

Let us now examine the conditions in which the frequency of the sounds increases above normal. The folds seem to lengthen and stiffen. They change shape from round and thick to wedge-shaped. The margins of the folds sharpen and are the only parts that vibrate. The glottis is a narrow slit under these conditions.

In the original analysis of the Bell Telephone Laboratories film it was said that the time in which the folds remain tightly closed at high pitch is smaller than at low pitch. However, the opposite conclusion has also been reached (see Timcke et al., 1958).

When very high tones such as those of the falsetto are produced, the folds are firmly adducted longitudinally except in a part of the anterior section. In this less tensed area, vibrations occur at high speed (Greene, 1957). Apparently only a limited section of the folds vibrates, and the smaller the length of this freely vibrating section, the higher is the pitch. The fold margins are elongated and thinned out.

Pressman (1942) expressed the falsetto in the language of physics as a damping process. If a violin string vibrates throughout its length, a given tone results. If it is fingered so that a part of its length is isolated from the bow, the isolated part does not vibrate, or it is said to be damped. The shorter vibrating section emits a higher tone. By firm apposition of the vocal folds the anterior segments can be variably fore-shortened to produce higher tones.

Van Riper and Irwin (1958) cite evidence that it is not true that only a part of the folds vibrates in the falsetto. The entire edges of the folds are said to be displaced. Except for the free edges, the folds remain fixed, since the thyroarytenoid muscle is markedly relaxed.

The vocal folds vibrate variably not only with changes in pitch but also at different intensities and tonal qualities. The early Bell Telephone film indicated that the vocal folds adducted feebly or did not close entirely at low intensities of sound production. At high intensities without changing the pitch, the folds are alternately closed tightly and abducted appreciably. The amplitude of the laryngeal vibrations increases markedly with greater intensity, and the open quotient is inversely proportional to the intensity (Timcke et al., 1958).

The manner of vibration of the folds seems to vary also with environmental factors, as in training. Closure time is greater for the trained speaker, and the amplitude of vibration is less. A trained voice produces a given sound intensity with less volume of air, and it covers a wider range of pitch and intensity than does the untrained voice.

The movements of the true folds in whispering are of clinical interest, as pointed up by Pressman (1942) in discussing whether the voice can be rested by whispering instead of speaking. Pressman states that the laryngeal movements differ in speaking and whispering, but traumatization from fold movements, as well as from the subglottal air blasts, is possible in both activities. Morrison (1955) says that the vocal folds come together anteriorly in whispering, and that trauma to damaged or inflamed folds is possible.

In Pressman's description of the anatomy of whispering, the interarytenoid muscles are inactive so that posterior adductive gliding motions do not occur, thus leaving a wide posterior gap for air leakage. The resonating cavities are active. There is irregular vibration of the folds, and friction noises make up the tone. Significant vibratory movements occur anteriorly, particularly if the whisper is intense, even when little or no activity occurs at the posterior gap region. Greene (1957) agrees that in a strong whisper the folds are firmly adducted along the anterior two-thirds. In the posterior third they are abducted, and this produces a triangular opening.

Isaac Brackett (in a personal communication) states that considerable confusion can arise in the analysis of whispering unless the terms movement and vibration are differentiated. Although, in a physical sense, muscular movements might be thought of as involving vibratory phenomena, the two concepts should ordinarily be considered independent processes in laryngeal terminology. The vocal folds can move without necessarily vibrating. Thus it is the censensus of opinion that the vocal folds do not vibrate in true whispering. This statement is said to hold even if the whisper is lively (Bocock and Haines, 1954).

Although the over-all movements of the folds have been clarified by stroboscopic, cinematographic, and other studies, the knowledge of the intrinsic laryngeal muscles which are active in fixing and stretching the folds and in producing movements of the folds has been obtained by the technic of electromyography. Faaborg-Andersen (1957) discusses electromyography and reviews the literature.

An interesting question attacked in this manner is whether the intrinsic muscles move during silent speech. In 1924, Watson, a behaviorist, described thinking as subvocal talking, but Wertheimer in 1954 denied that silent speech is necessary to the thinking process. Faaborg-Andersen has found increased action potentials in the vocal muscles of subjects thinking without audible phonation.

The muscles will be described in the next chapter mainly from the standpoint of classical anatomy. The actual relationships of muscle contraction to vocal fold activity are still experimental (Michel, 1954).

THEORIES OF SOUND PRODUCTION

Sound is produced by laryngeal processes initiated when the exhaled air passes up through the glottis. Just prior to speaking the vocal folds

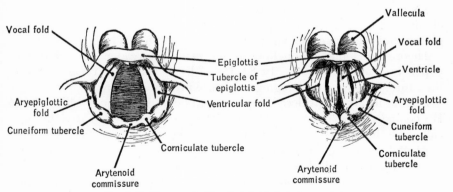

Fig. 6–7. Changes in the glottal chink during speech.

are adducted while the thoracic and abdominal muscles compress the pulmonary tissue actively but slightly. In the classical view all these events increase the respiratory pressure to a threshold necessary to force open the glottis and produce sounds. The sounds coming from the larynx are not the same as the sounds which finally emanate from the mouth.

It is not yet definite what the mechanism is which causes vibration of the vocal folds. One view, known as the vibrating string theory, holds that a blast of air passing between the true folds sets them into vibration. The folds are regarded as cords or as strings which are the individual fibers of the vocalis muscle. These may be sounded in whole, which produces the fundamental tone, or in part, which produces the overtones. Pitch can be changed by altering the tension in the folds. This is analogous to raising the pitch in a violin by increasing the tautness of its strings. There can be a damping effect of foreshortening the vocal folds. The segments left free to vibrate produce a higher-pitched sound. In the violin the length of the strings is shortened with the fingers.

One objection to the string theory is that in a direct blast, certain tones would submit the folds to excessively high tensions.

There is a theory which proposes that subglottic explosions of air are blown as discrete puffs upward through a variable laryngeal opening that alternately opens and closes. The rapid escape of puffs of air causes the sound. In this view the folds behave like the reed of a musical instrument. A reed acts like an outlet constrictor which opens and releases puffs of air. Pitch is changed by varying the size of the opening, varying its shape and rigidity, and altering the force of the exhaled air. Pressman (1942) says this theory is faulty in that pitch in a reed instrument changes with the action of the resonating cavities whereas in the body the alterations in pitch are highly dependent upon the length, tension, and shape of the vocal folds.

There is the theory that air passing through the glottis causes vibration of air in the supraglottic cavities, or those areas which are above the glottis, and this makes the vocal folds vibrate responsively.

Theories of sound production are not new. The reader is referred to a paper by van den Berg (1958) for a brief historical review of the literature. Some of the changing views are presented below.

Ferrein in 1741 considered the larynx to be an instrument with strings. He compared the ligaments of the glottis to the strings of a violin and called the ligaments vocal cords. The muscles were the powers designed to stretch or relax the cords. Guilmette in 1877 protested against this theory, " . . . for it has a tendency to bring on physical disease by concentrating the mind on the throat, instead of fixing it on the diaphragm as the grand propelling agent."

Another objection to the Ferrein view is that the scale of changes produced by the tension of strings is not the same as that produced by the tension of the vocal folds. Also, it does not seem possible for strings as short as those of the vocal ligaments to produce the resonant low tones of the deep bass voice.

Guilmette stated the following:

The voice, the breath rendered vocal, is expelled from its reservoirs, the lungs, by the diaphragm and auxiliary muscles. It then traverses the entire isthmus of the throat . . . and is accumulated in the concavity of the epiglottis. . . . This pulmonic stream, which . . . from its very starting-point in the lungs has been made vocal by the mucous membranes under the influence of those nerves from which they derive their mobility and sensibility . . . is next radiated by the epiglottis to the posterior wall of the pharynx: proceeds to the soft veil of the palate; and finally . . . issues through the lips, if the latter be open, or if they be closed, the column is driven into the nasal cavities, till it finds its exit, after reverberating, more or less, over every sinus of the face and skull . . . and the throat receives no more injury, in its strictly physiological or healthy use, than the pipe of a bellows from a steady column of air.

Note in this view that the respiratory mucous membranes are the phonators that emit the sound. The larynx by lengthening and shortening the so-called vocal tunnel modifies the sound in respect to pitch only and makes it high or low. The mind was conceived by Guilmette as the engineer that directs, controls, and governs this complicated mechanism at will.

It is far from our purpose to enshrine Guilmette who had some ideas about vocal physiology which are highly contradictory to modern knowledge. The emphasis upon the diaphragm, for example, is questionable. The quotations are used, however, to put into historical perspective one kind of thinking that existed.

Long before such views as those presented, Aristotle and then Galen had compared the larynx to a flute; the trachea was thought of as the body of the instrument. Dodart in 1700 modified this view by stating that the voice is produced upon the principle of the trumpet; the glottis is the place corresponding to the lips of the player, and the body of the instrument extends from the glottis to the mouth.

An objection to the flute-pipe theory is that the pitch in this kind of instrument is governed by the length of the tube. It would, however, require an open tube of about 6 feet to produce the low G of a bass voice, so that the comparison breaks down.

A whole succession of names is associated with speculations on sound production after Ferrein. Magendie compared the larynx to reed instruments. The vocal ligaments cut up the air column, as reeds do, into a rapid and regular succession of puffs. We may possess a flexible organic reed.

Savard in 1825 likened the larynx to a kind of whistle. He attempted to account for the presence of the ventricles of the larynx and the superior ligaments not mentioned in previous theories; the ligaments of the glottis and the ventricles that open between them play an essential role in the primitive formation of sound. Air passing through the glottis strikes the superior ligaments. These ligaments bind the upper opening and have the same function as the stopper that apportions the wind in an organ pipe. Then the air within the larynx vibrates, giving out a sound that increases in intensity because the sonorous waves that form it are prolonged into the pharynx, mouth, and nasal cavities.

Helmholtz in 1863 demonstrated that puffs of air escaping through the glottis are the primary source of the sound. A glottis generator exists in the larynx.

Husson (1950) advanced a neuromuscular theory in which the vibrational frequency of the folds at a given pitch results directly from the nerves energizing the muscles involved. The highest frequency is limited by the refractory period of the nerves, which Husson takes to be 2 msec. The folds are said to vibrate maximally at 500 cps. For frequencies between 500 and 1,000, single muscle fibers receive impulses at alternate movements of the folds. At still higher frequencies, single muscle fibers may be similarly activated at every third or higher movement of the folds. Faaborg-Andersen (1957) points up that it is the refractory period of the muscles (3 to 4 msec) and not that of the nerve which determines the maximal tone frequency at which the muscle fibers are energized with each movement of the folds. It has also been demonstrated in dogs that the fold vibrational frequency follows the stimulating frequency only up to 7 cps, and that the muscles tetanize (convulse) at 25 cps.

The view proposed by Husson in 1950 has been called the clonic theory. In this view the thyroarytenoids rhythmically contract and relax because of repetitive nervous discharges into them. The active agent is the glottic margin, which allows tracheal air to be released in a series of puffs. The rhythmic impulses of the thyroarytenoid muscle are produced by nerve action with the same rhythm as that of the recurrent laryngeal nerve and with a frequency corresponding to the emitted sound. The origin of the vibrations must be sought for in the rhythmic activity of the brain cells governing the recurrent nerve fibers. The larynx in this view is not an important muscular organ with an independent peripheral physiology.

The clonic theory may be contrasted with the classical myoelastic or tonic theory (Portmann, 1957; Negus, 1957). In the tonic theory sounds are associated with the rhythmical opening and closing of the glottis. The vocal folds are opened by the variable intratracheal pressures. The subsequent loss of pressure allows the folds to close again because of their elasticity. The active agent is the tracheal pressure which produces a series of puffs through a tonically closed glottis.

Pressman (1942) says that phonation is an aerodynamic process in which the thyroarytenoid muscles only adjust the folds to a given tension and shape while the exhaled air from the lungs does the rest. Changes in the shape of the glottic chink plus changes in the elasticity of its margins produce variations in pitch.

Portmann (1957) cited objections to the tonic theory. It was originally based upon fragmentary data obtained by Ferrein in 1731 and by Lermayez in 1886 upon human cadavers. Some data were collected by Mueller in 1839 in experiments with an artificial larynx. Portmann pointed out that the vocal folds vibrate without being closely approximated, and they fail to vibrate when tensely adducted in spite of a strong subglottal pressure. A probe placed on the active fold does not stop the vibrations, although it should if the subglottic pressure produced the disturbance.

Freund (1958) discusses Husson's theory. The concept is said to influence current views about the relations between voice and breathing. The exhaled air does not cause the vocal folds to vibrate. Adduction and vibration are independent phenomena, the former being respiratory and the latter phonatory.

Speaking and singing are differentiated. In singing, the motion for inhalation and exhalation is said to be determined by the subglottal pressure and by the duration and maintenance of this pressure. In speaking, the subglottal pressure is weak and often repetitive.

In singing, the energy needed is much greater, and the concomitant sensations can be localized. Freund (1958) says that speech is controlled chiefly in the diencephalon, while singing requires cortical control. The cortex is essential for regulation of the pitch, the tone intervals, and the emotional expression. Laughing and crying similarly involve different physiological mechanisms.

The voice of the singer is influenced by several factors. One is an air-impedance effect, or resonance phenomenon, in which reflection into the larynx from the pharyngeal, nasal, and oral chambers hinders vocal-fold vibration. To restore the stability of the exhaled air stream, the glottic sphincter contracts. Proprioceptive impulses that give information about the positions and tensions of the active muscles are transmitted through the trigeminal, glossopharyngeal, and vagus nerves. According to Husson, such impulses are significant in vocal training. The effects of vocal impedance should be correlated with respiratory movements.

Many arguments have been presented against Husson's neurochronaxic theory (van den Berg, 1958). The role of the vocalis muscle is said to be overestimated. Also, because the left recurrent nerve is longer than the right, there should be phase differences between the vibrations of the right and left vocal folds. There are several other objections.

Many acoustical analyses have treated the larynx as a high-impedance generator (Bogart and Peterson, 1957). The tone emitted from the larynx has a complex frequency composition. The fundamental frequency corresponds with the rate of glottal opening and closing, and it is determined by the bursts of periodically expelled air. The oscillations within the vocal tract do not essentially bear an integral relationship to the vocal fold frequencies. The term formant frequencies is used for the resonant frequencies. The upper formant frequencies are considerably dependent upon the details of cavity shape, but the shape is less important for the lower formant frequencies.

Perkins (1957) says that phonation occurs when the dynamics between subglottal air pressure and the resistance of the glottal margins are such that a slight subglottal pressure is favored. The tension and thickness of the vocal folds are important in this dynamic balance, since they hold the subglottal pressure at a given value. The tension and thickness are determined by the extent to which the folds are stretched. It takes more pressure to displace thick rather than thin vocal folds. In turn the folds yield to the greater force with a greater displacement.

The vocal fold displacement in Perkin's view should not be equated with vocal intensity, since displacement only partially accounts for the dynamics affecting volume. It is not true per se that abducting the folds raises the sound volume by increasing the amount of the breath stream. In phonation the air is compressed above the folds when they are abducted, and the degree of supraglottic compression is important.

The two most important events in phonation, according to Perkins, are the force with which the folds are abducted and the degree to which the glottal edges billow. They are observed to billow when they are thickened in emitting low tones, and this may hold true when they are thickened for high, heavy tones. In high, thin tones the glottal edges are thin, and the release of explosive compression waves is sharp and firm, the effect being less than optimal, as heard in the falsetto.

COMPARATIVE ANATOMY OF THE LARYNX

From a biological standpoint, the larynx is not primarily an organ of voice. Most aquatic animals close the glottis except during brief periods of respiration, and this closure is adequate for excluding water. The larynx appears to be a device to close the tracheal passageway and prevent the entrance of foreign bodies. In man there may be an additional protective closure at the level of the sphincteric aryepiglottic folds. The human glottis is importantly concerned with breathing in that it has an obstructive influence upon the air current, and it regulates the pressure and volume of air in the lungs and pulmonary tree. The voice is a by-product of these laryngeal activities, and it has developed along with the human brain and man's needs as a social organism.

According to Boies (1954), the human larynx can do the following: (1) It prevents ingress and lodgment of foreign bodies by valving pulmonary air such that the pressure necessary for coughing is built up. (2) It is involved in moderating the exchange of respiratory gases. (3) It can alter the air pressure in the pulmonary system. The changing pressures in the lung and tracheobronchial system in turn act like a pump on the circulating blood. (4) Lifting and straining are facilitated by laryngeal closure and fixation of thoracic air. (5) The larynx works with the epiglottis in swallowing, by elevation and by guiding the food into lateral channels. (6) It is expectorative and tussive, expelling secretions. (7) It helps to express the emotions. (8) It is the organ of phonation.

Negus (1949) has made a detailed study of the comparative biology of the laryngeal structures. In a 1957 paper he makes a plea for emphasizing the study of comparative anatomy and physiology because of their aid in interpreting the functions of the larynx. The primitive functions become explainable as well as the modifications laid down to meet functional demands. Negus's early study (1929) is monumental.

Negus speaks of a larynx in the bichir (*Polypterus*). This is a fish that has an air bladder shut off from the alimentary canal by a muscular, sphincter-like valve. Negus contends that in certain "air-breathing" fishes, water and noxious substances must be prevented from getting into the structures which are acting like lungs. An opening into the floor of the pharynx modifies to become a valve. This valve develops sphincteric muscle fibers which contract when the fish is in water but which relax when air is breathed out of water.

In Negus's view the next stage in evolution is the development of fibers to dilate the opening, or glottis, and the origin of these fibers is the pharyngeal floor. Lateral cartilages develop for muscle attachment and facilitate the pull upon the edges of the glottis. This is seen in the axolotl (*Amblystoma*). These larynges are very small. They are situated in the pharyngeal floor where they do not obstruct the digestive passage and where they can serve the needs of a simple respiratory device. In salamanders each lateral cartilage has a cephalic segment corresponding to the arytenoid of higher animals and pulled apart by muscles. Although the caudal segments are separated in the amphibians, they fuse in the higher vertebrates to produce a cartilage ring around the breathing tube.

Among the amphibians a urodele called *Necturus* is a good type form to show the rudiments of a larynx. There are two lateral cartilages on either side of a glottal opening to the lungs.

In the higher or anuran amphibians, such as the frog, the development is more complex. The lungs produce the pressure for sound. There is a pair of arytenoid cartilages, and also a cricoid cartilage modified from the upper tracheal rings. The arytenoids are operated by dilator and adductor muscles. A pair of vocal folds develop as two folds parallel with the glottis on the inner wall of the laryngotracheal chamber. In the

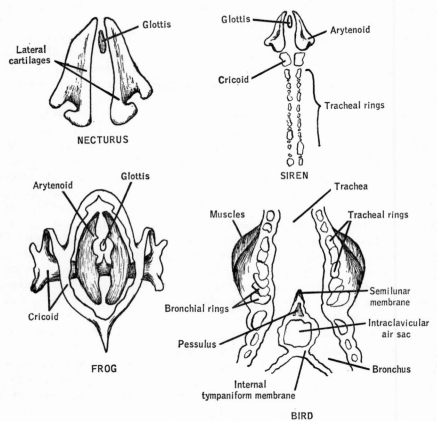

Fig. 6—8. Outline of the larynx in some lower vertebrates.

anurans, the males, especially, develop accessory resonating chambers, or vocal sacs, in the throat.

Among the reptiles and birds the larynx is more deficient than in amphibians, but the trachea is better developed. In the alligator (*Crocodilia*) another ring-like cartilage, or fused cricothyroid, appears. This will become the thyroid cartilage of higher animals. This cartilage separates to a thyroid and a cricoid cartilage by a joint forming between them. The articulation facilitates opening and closing of the laryngeal cavity.

The birds develop a secondary larynx called the syrinx. This forms below the larynx at the junction of the trachea and bronchi as an adaptation to centralize weight for flying. The reduced primary avian larynx has no vocal folds, and sound is produced by vibration of membranes in the syrinx. At the opening of each bronchus in the median wall there is a thin internal tympaniform membrane that vibrates with the exhaled air. Singing birds have an additional unpaired semilunar membrane stretching from front to back near the union of the trachea and bronchi. This membrane is supported by a bony ridge called the pessulus. The bird can change the shape of its tracheobronchial chamber, and it can activate the modified tracheobronchial rings which build up the syrinx. It combines such a structure with intercartilages, membranes, and muscles to form an efficient phonating device.

Although in man the arrangement of the vocal folds presents difficulties to inspiratory speech, the folds of some singing birds react with equal ease to the inspiratory or expiratory stream of air. A canary or lark may warble for minutes without obvious inspiration, and its voice is produced both during inspiration and expiration. Bocock and Haines (1954) say that vibrations of the human vocal folds during inhalation occur in the intake sound of stertorous breathing or in such involuntary efforts as the first sound of a sneeze.

The major cartilages of the human larynx correspond with those in aquatic vertebrates which support the fourth and fifth branchial (visceral) arches and serve a respiratory function. The muscles of these arches produce the muscles of the human larynx.

A great diversity of air sacs occurs in connection with the larynx of many animals. Most sacs develop muscles which expel the trapped air. The air is pushed into the lungs for greater respiratory utilization. The buccal air sacs of frogs, the laryngeal sacs of apes, and the abdominal sacs of birds function in this manner in the rebreathing of air. This may be advantageous for conserving energy or even air where a fresh supply is difficult to obtain.

The air sacs are seen to occur not only as diverticula of the larynx but also in connection with other parts of the respiratory system. The lateral buccal air sacs of the tree frog are supralaryngeal. The tracheal sacs of chameleons, the syringeal sacs of certain ducks, and the pulmonary air sacs in birds are infralaryngeal.

In mammals, where the ventricle first appears as a chamber, air sacs are produced that may serve for the rebreathing of air (Freedman, 1938). Thus when muscle activity is employed as in climbing, the thoracic structure becomes fixed to allow maximal pectoral muscle play, and the air sacs can be temporarily used in place of the lungs for re-breathing air. The sacs are large among anthropoid apes but small in man. We have already considered the saccules of the laryngeal ventricle in man.

It has been thought that air sacs provide a mechanism for voice production, but the evidence does not bear this out. An adult male gorilla with large sacs is usually silent, while the young gorilla with small or no sacs may be noisy. Some of the noisiest gibbons have no sacs. The presence of these sacs, however, is thought in many instances to influence or improve the quality of the voice.

The reader is referred to Walter and Sayles (1949) for a classical description of the comparative anatomy of the larynx. Eggston and Wolff (1947) devote a chapter of their text to the comparative anatomy and embryology of the larynx.

DEVELOPMENTAL ANATOMY

Hollinger (1954) has reviewed the congenital anomalies of the larynx and has stated that they can be understood only through developmental anatomy. He classified the anomalies into five groups: (1) laryngeal stridor; (2) webs; (3) atresia; (4) subglottic stenosis; and (5) cysts and laryngoceles.

The larynx differentiates in the embryo of about 3 mm as a laryngo-tracheal groove in the anterior mid-line of the pharyngeal floor of the fore-gut. This stage corresponds to the third week, but most of the subsequent development occurs between the fourth and tenth weeks. Malformations occur readily during this period. The hind part of the groove becomes the esophagus while the front part proliferates to a larynx and to the respiratory system below the larynx.

The primordium is entoderm. At 4 mm the entoderm has produced lung buds which are beginning to bifurcate. The respiratory organs at that stage are represented by a laryngeal slit, a tracheal tube, and two primary bronchi. The bronchi will branch repeatedly and produce all the peripheral divisions of the respiratory tree.

The upper and lower sections of the larynx develop somewhat differently. The upper part comes from the pharyngeal floor. The lower part develops around the tracheal stem.

The epiglottis appears at 5 mm. It is a rounded prominence that arises as a mid-ventral mass condensing from the material of the third and fourth arches. This mass becomes a valve-like structure placed transversely in front and above the entrance to the larynx. Cartilage develops within it.

The original slit that opens into the trachea from the pharynx is the glottis. Material from the fourth and fifth arches swell upon each side of the glottis. These protuberances are the beginnings of the arytenoid cartilages. They appear in the fifth or sixth week (Patten, 1953), and they are well defined by the early third month.

The arytenoid swellings proliferate tongueward and meet the epiglottis primordium against which they arch upward and forward. In the seventh week this activity adds a transverse groove to the original sagittal slit and makes the laryngeal opening T-shaped. Because of epithelial blocking, the laryngeal entrance is at first blind, but at ten weeks the opening is more evident. Lateral recesses called laryngeal ventricles appear, and each becomes bounded by lateral shelves, of which the vocal folds are the caudal pair.

The thyroid cartilage condenses from lateral masses within the fourth arches sometime during the first month, and it chondrifies considerably by the seventh week. Cartilages from the mesenchyme of the fourth and fifth arches are added to the epithelial larynx also in the seventh week.

The cricoid cartilage appears paired in the sixth arch at the sixth week. By the end of the second month both halves have fused and chondrified.

Laryngeal muscles develop from the fourth and fifth arches. The vagus nerve to the muscles and other elements of the primitive arches remain constant, and the nerve continues to supply the laryngeal muscles and the other derivatives of the arches. The outer musculature surrounding the fore-gut produces the paired cricothyroid muscles.

Morris (1953) raises the question whether the arytenoid, epiglottic, and other lesser cartilages of the larynx are derivatives of the branchial arches, but he admits that the evidence is strong.

By the close of the second month the internal laryngeal structures, including the vocal and ventricular folds, have been laid down. Patten (1953) says that the later details are added slowly and the larynx takes on a definitive configuration only in the last trimester of gestation.

Positional changes in the larynx occur early in development. The larynx of the 14-mm embryo, which is five or six weeks of age, is opposite the basiocciput. By the fourth month it has descended so that the inferior boundary of the cricoid is opposite the superior boundary of the fourth cervical vertebra. This boundary shifts by the fifth month to the inferior boundary of the fourth cervical vertebra. At term, the reference line is at the level of the body of the sixth vertebra, and the descent has not ended since in the adult the lower border of the sixth vertebra has been reached. The highest laryngeal structure, the epiglottis, eventually comes to lie opposite the inferior border of the third cervical vertebra.

The laryngeal descent is ascribed to a recession of the jaws along with alterations in the pituitary and vertebro-occipital angles. This explanation is questionable (Morris, 1953).

AGE CHANGES IN THE LARYNX

The larynx at birth is relatively larger than in the adult, although it is smaller in actuality; the vocal folds are both actually and relatively shorter in length. The larynx grows to about the third year and then shows no marked development until puberty. Prior to about the twelfth year there are no major laryngeal sex differences.

At puberty, especially in the male, the walls become strengthened, the cavity larger, the vocal folds thicker, and the laryngeal prominence, or "Adam's apple," becomes conspicuous. The progressive laryngeal development continues in many instances up to twenty-five years of age.

In the adult male the angle between the paired thyroid laminae, or alae, is approximately a right angle, but in the adult female the alae are more divergent and form an angle of approximately 120 degrees.

The length of the vocal folds increases gradually in both sexes to puberty; then there is an abrupt increase in the male. The figures below illustrate the change with time. The values of 23 mm in the adult male compared with 17 mm in the adult female are common in the literature.

Age	Length, mm
Three days	3
Two weeks	4
Two months	5
Nine months	5.2
One year	5.5
Five years	7.5
Six and one-half years	8
Fifteen years	9.5
Adult male	17 −23
Adult female	12.5–17

There is a sex difference in the dimensions of the larynx as a whole (Morris, 1953). The vertical diameter, from the upper border of the epiglottis to the lower border of the cricoid, is 70 mm in the adult male and 48 mm in the adult female. The transverse measurement is 40 mm in the male and 35 mm in the female. The greatest anteroposterior diameter is 40 mm in the male and 35 mm in the female.

The thyroid, cricoid, and most of the arytenoids are derived from branchial cartilages and are composed of hyaline cartilage (Grant, 1944). A variable calcification and ossification occurs with age, beginning at about twenty-five years in the thyroid cartilage and later in the others. Consequently the cartilages are entirely bone at about sixty-five years of age. As calcification proceeds and the cartilages and muscles become less elastic, there is a decrease in the range of the voice, particularly for the high frequencies, along with a decrease in resonance and steadiness. Gradual ossification is more important than any other factor in accounting for senescent changes in the quality of the voice.

Except for the hyaline cartilages, the other laryngeal cartilages do not come from branchial arches. They are of the yellow elastic variety. They do not calcify or ossify. The vocal processes and the apices of the arytenoids are in the yellow elastic group.

Structural modifications in the larynx change the voice at many stages of life. The frequency range of the newborn is a few semitones, and it increases chiefly by adding higher tones until a maximum frequency is reached at about the eleventh year. Structural changes at puberty are rapid, and the pitch lowers by an octave in boys and generally by two notes in girls. The voice in eunuchs remains infantile in puberty. Yet, in comparison with the female, the voice power of the male castrate remains relatively strong. The causes of this are obscure. Perhaps they are related to lung capacity and a genetic or inherent difference in the general body form and structure.

The range of pitch in normal speech may be about half an octave, and the whole range of male plus female voices may cover four octaves. According to Van Riper and Irwin (1958), the widest limit in adults is about three octaves, and one and one-half octaves are used in speech.

The voice range in music can be divided into registers. The head register includes high tones with few overtones, and the vibrations are subjectively referred to the head. The chest register is referred to the chest, and it includes low tones with many overtones. The human being has a capacity to pass easily from high to low tones, but the emission in animals is restricted to a certain range.

There are several educational films about the larynx in current circulation. These films have resulted from the ability to evaluate the movements of the vocal folds through high-speed photography (Moore, 1938; Farnsworth, 1940; Fletcher, 1953).

Farnsworth at the Bell Telephone Laboratories produced a high-speed motion picture of widespread interest showing how the larynx operates under diverse conditions. Paul Moore at Northwestern produced films dealing with normal laryngeal activity, movements associated with phonetics, and laryngeal pathology. The concepts concerning arytenoid motion in his 1938 films are altered in the *Normal Larynx,* produced in 1956 by Moore and Von Leden. These investigators are among a growing number of speech scientists working with visual aids.

SUMMARY

The human larynx has evolved from the simple structure first found as a constant organ in amphibians. Phonation developed as a by-product of more basic purposes such as the protection of the lung against inundation. The analysis of the historical development provides a sound basis for understanding the structure and operation of the human larynx.

The mobile laryngeal cartilages are moved by voluntary muscles, and the actions at the joints are precise. The motions of the arytenoid cartilages are especially important, since they greatly determine the movements of the vocal folds which are attached to them. The mode of vibration of the vocal folds is influenced by localized contractions of the vocalis muscle within each fold.

Many factors influence phonation and vocal quality. Thus the pitch is affected by the length, tension, elasticity, and mass of the folds, as well as by the subglottal breath pressure and the shape of the glottis.

Although the structure of the vocal folds is fairly well known, their specific activities in different phonatory conditions are still controversial. New devices, like the synchronstroboscope and ultra-high-speed motion pictures, permit observation of the larynx *in vivo* and facilitate quantitative measurements. The vocal folds are found to vibrate differently under dissimilar conditions of voice production. Changes in pitch and intensity importantly influence the manner of fold activity.

There are several theories of how sound is produced. Many questions arise concerning the mechanisms which cause the vocal folds to vibrate and how alterations in the form and activity of the folds are related to the qualities of sound.

The laryngeal structures change with age, and the voice is altered characteristically. The most abrupt and marked changes occur at puberty in both sexes.

Chapter 7

LARYNGEAL CONTROL AND BLOOD SUPPLY; THE TRACHEA

The larynx is mechanically operated by skeletal muscles innervated by cerebrospinal nerves. There is also adjunctive glandular and vascular machinery, which is regulated by the autonomic nervous system.

Although the voluntary mechanism has been well described by anatomists, its exact functioning in speech is still to a considerable extent inconclusively known. This is illustrated, for example, in the changing ideas of the muscle relationships in the movements of the vocal folds. To what extent does rotation or any other movement of the arytenoid cartilages explain the opening and closing of the glottal margins? These are some problems of the present chapter. The trachea has only arbitrarily been placed in this section.

THE LARYNGEAL MUSCLES

The laryngeal muscles are divided into two groups. The extrinsic muscles support the larynx and change its spatial relationships. They have at least one attachment to some structure outside the larynx. The intrinsic muscles control phonation and have both their origins and insertions within the larynx.

Extrinsic Muscles. (1) *Elevators of the Hyoid and Larynx.* The elevators are called the suprahyoid muscles. The entire larynx including the hyoid bone may be raised, or the larynx proper may be raised toward a fixed hyoid.

If the larynx is elevated while the hyoid bone is fixed, the thyrohyoid would be the chief muscle concerned. The hyoid could be fixed in position chiefly by the hyoglossus, geniohyoid, mylohyoid, and the middle pharyngeal constrictor muscles. Others are also involved.

The elevation of the larynx tends to decrease the length and caliber of the laryngopharynx. This affects resonance. Basically, laryngeal elevation is more related to swallowing than to phonation. The chief elevator muscles are described individually below.

147

The *digastric* muscle (paired) has two bellies. The posterior one originates on the mastoid process of the skull and passes downward and forward to an intermediate tendon which gains an attachment to the body of the hyoid bone. It draws the hyoid upward and backward, and it also tilts the bone. This belly is innervated by the facial nerve.

The anterior belly descends from the inner surface of the mandible, near the symphysis, to the intermediate tendon and body of the hyoid

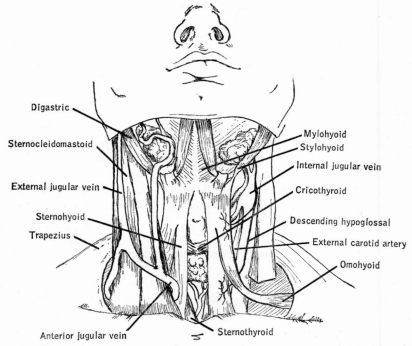

Fig. 7–1. Extrinsic muscles and the superficial relations of the larynx viewed from the anterior aspect of the neck.

bone. With the mandible fixed, it brings the hyoid upward and forward. It is innervated by the mylohyoid nerve, which is a derivative of the inferior alveolar branch of the mandibular division of the trigeminal nerve.

The *stylohyoid* (paired) is a slender muscle located along the upper border of and roughly parallel to the posterior belly of the digastric muscle. It originates from the styloid process of the temporal skull bone and runs downward and forward to the greater cornu of the hyoid bone, which it elevates and retracts. It may also tilt the bone. It is innervated by the facial nerve.

The *mylohyoid* (unpaired) forms the muscular floor of the mouth. It originates from the inner aspect of the mandible along the mylohyoid line, which runs forward from the last molar tooth to the point of the jaw (mental symphysis). It goes medialward and downward and fuses with the fibers on the other side in a median line (raphe) that extends from a point near the symphysis back to the hyoid bone. The most posterior fibers attach directly to the body of the hyoid. With a fixed mandible, the muscle elevates and draws forward the hyoid, and it also raises the tongue, whose root is attached to the hyoid. This action is typical of the initial phase of swallowing. Acting reversely from the hyoid, it can depress the lower jaw, as in chewing or speech. The muscle is innervated by the mylohyoid nerve.

The *geniohyoid* (paired) is a cylindrical muscle situated on the upper (buccal) surface of the mylohyoid. The paired fibers lie in mutual contact on either side of the mid-line. The muscle originates at the symphysis of the mandible and runs backward and downward to insert upon the body of the hyoid. With a fixed mandible, it elevates the hyoid and tongue and also protrudes these structures. Acting from below, it assists in depressing the mandible. The muscle is innervated by the hypoglossal nerve plus nerve fibers from C-1.

There are three other muscles, described below, which might also be classified with the suprahyoid musculature. These muscles are discussed elsewhere in the text.

The *genioglossus* muscle originates on the superior ventral spine on the inner surface of the mandibular symphysis. Its lower fibers insert upon the hyoid bone. Its middle and upper fibers have a broad insertion upon the under side of the tongue from root to apex.

The *hyoglossus* muscle arises from the body and greater cornua of the hyoid bone and travels almost straight upward to insert upon the posterolateral areas of the tongue.

The *middle pharyngeal constrictor* muscle could be classified as a weak elevator, although its chief action on the hyoid bone is to pull it backward. To accomplish its actions upon the hyoid, it may be considered to travel from the posterior median septum of the pharynx to the greater cornua of the hyoid and to the stylohyoid ligament.

(2) *Depressors of the Hyoid and Larynx.* These are called the infrahyoid muscles, and they actively depress the larynx. The sternothyroid muscle is perhaps the most significant in such activity.

The *sternohyoid* (paired) is a flat muscle located on the deep anterior surface of the neck. Just above their origin the paired sternohyoids may lie in mutual contact. Each arises on the manubrium sterni, on the clavicle, and also along the sternoclavicular ligament and runs upward to attach to the inferior border of the hyoid body. The muscle depresses the hyoid bone. It is innervated by the ansa hyglossi containing fibers from C-1, C-2, and C-3.

The *omohyoid* (paired) is a long, narrow muscle with two bellies. The inferior belly originates from the scapula and goes almost horizontally forward to terminate at an intermediate tendon that is held fixed chiefly by cervical fascia. The superior belly passes vertically and medially upward from the tendon and inserts along the lower border of the hyoid lateral to the sternohyoid insertion. Acting from the scapula, it depresses and retracts the hyoid. The muscle is innervated by the ansa hypoglossi containing fibers from C-1, C-2, and C-3.

The *sternothyroid* (paired) is a long ribbon-like muscle deep to the omohyoid and sternohyoid on the anterior surface of the neck. It

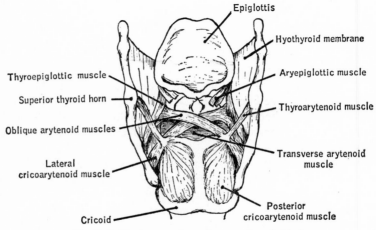

Fig. 7–2. The laryngeal muscles seen from behind.

originates on the sternum and goes upward to insert upon the corresponding thyroid lamina. A few fibers continue superiorly to end in the thyrohyoid and the inferior pharyngeal constrictor muscles. The sternothyroid depresses the thyroid cartilage. It is innervated by the ansa hypoglossi containing fibers from C-1, C-2, and C-3.

The *thyrohyoid* muscle (paired) arises on each side from the thyroid lamina and goes vertically upward to insert on the major cornu and body of the hyoid bone. It depresses the hyoid or, with a fixed hyoid, elevates the thyroid cartilage. It may tilt the hyoid backward. The muscle is innervated by the descendens hypoglossi and the first two cervical nerves.

Intrinsic Muscles. The intrinsic muscles may be grouped according to their general effects upon the glottis.

The abductor opens the glottis. Only one muscle is involved, the *posterior cricoarytenoid* (paired). This muscle arises as a flat, triangular structure on the posterior surface of the cricoid and goes upward and lateralward to the muscular process of each arytenoid. It rotates each arytenoid outward so that the muscular process is drawn posteriorly and the vocal process laterally, thus widening the intervening glottic space. The more lateral fibers draw the arytenoids laterally. The muscle may also tilt the vocal processes backward. This muscle is especially active during inspiration.

The adductors narrow the glottis. Four muscles are involved.

The *transverse arytenoid* muscle (unpaired) is a thick, rectangular mass covering the entire deep posterior surface of both arytenoids. It

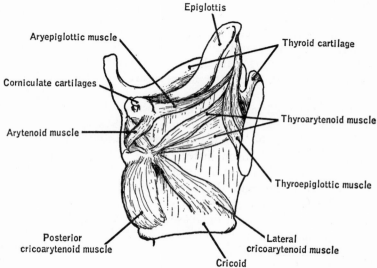

Fig. 7–3. The muscles along the sides of the larynx.

may be considered to originate along the muscular process and lateral border of one arytenoid and to cross over to reach the lateral edge of the other arytenoid. It draws the arytenoids medially by a gliding action which adducts the vocal folds. The activity of this muscle is said to precede phonation.

The *oblique arytenoid* muscle (paired) is placed externally upon the transverse arytenoid, and its two limbs form the letter X. Each member arises on the lower posterior surface of one arytenoid and goes upward and across the mid-line to insert at the summit of the other arytenoid. The muscle adducts the vocal folds, and it acts as a weak sphincter for the superior opening of the larynx.

Some of the muscle fibers, in rising to their insertion, continue upward and forward, as the *aryepiglottic* muscle of the aryepiglottic fold. These fibers insert upon the lateral edge of the epiglottis and upon the quadrangular membrane.

The *lateral cricoarytenoid* (paired) is a small, rectangular muscle in the lateral wall of the larynx, lying deep to the thyroid cartilage. Its own deep surface is seated upon the conus elasticus. It originates from the arch of the cricoid and goes upward and backward to insert upon the front part of the muscular process of the corresponding arytenoid. It rotates each muscular process forward and inward and thus brings the vocal processes toward each other. This is adduction, and it seems to be essential in phonatory activity.

The *thyroarytenoid* muscle (paired) lies parallel to each vocal fold. It arises on the posterior surface of the thyroid cartilage, and its lateral fibers insert on the lateral edge and muscular process of each arytenoid.

The vocalis muscle is considered by some investigators to be the medial part of the thyroarytenoid (Houssay, 1955) or its lower and deeper fibers (Gray, 1954). In this sense there is an external and an internal thyroarytenoid. The latter fibers insert upon the vocal processes of the arytenoids.

In the thyroarytenoid mass there is a question about fibers which may run perpendicular to the main stream of fibers (Strong, 1935) and could control the length of the segment that is vibrating. Evidence for the existence of these fibers is inconclusive.

The thyroarytenoid has several functions, but not all are conclusively demonstrated. It could pull the thyroid cartilage upward and backward, but this is unlikely since it would occur only if the arytenoids were fixed. This action would decrease the tension on the folds. It may help in the formation of a sphincter ring around the superior aspect of the larynx. It has been said to be an adductor in that it helps to rotate and draw forward the muscular processes of the arytenoids. Van Riper and Irwin (1958) state that it can alter the loudness of tones. If it relaxed slightly while the cricothyroid and lateral cricoarytenoid pulled constantly, the pitch would fall and the loudness would rise. The relaxed thyroarytenoids would permit the folds to be blown further apart with the same amount of air pressure.

Greene (1957) says that the thyroarytenoid shortens but does not relax the vocal folds. She notes that the lengthening of the folds does not mean an increase in tension and, similarly, the shortening of the folds does not mean a decrease in tension. In explanation, the vocal fold has fibers running in all directions. Squares of this network can be converted into diamonds by lengthening the folds, and the tension need not increase. Greene calls the thyroarytenoid the internal tensor of the larynx. She denies that the cricothyroid (below) affects tension simply by its lengthening effect. This point of view may have to be taken into account in evaluating the conventional anatomical ideas about laryngeal motor activity.

The tension upon the vocal folds is determined by several muscles. Of these, the effect of the thyroarytenoids has already been suggested.

The *cricothyroid* (paired) is a broad muscle superficially placed upon the larynx. The anterior section originates along the lower border and outer surface of the cricoid arch and runs almost vertically up to the thyroid laminae. The posterior section, which has the same origin, goes upward and backward to the inferior cornu of the thyroid.

The vertical anterior section can tilt the front part of the thyroid cartilage down, if the cricoid is fixed. In reverse, the cricoid can be elevated toward the thyroid. This is a rocking action at the cricothyroid joint. Both activities seem to tense the vocal folds.

The posterior section pulls the thyroid cartilage forward. The distance between the angle of the thyroid and the arytenoids is increased. The vocal folds are tensed. Van Riper and Irwin (1958) state that the major effect is to tighten rather than stretch the folds. Gray (1954) states that the folds are elongated.

The cricothyroid may act secondarily as an external adductor of the arytenoids.

The *vocalis* muscle (paired) forms the main mass of the vocal folds, and it importantly influences their mode of vibration. It is enclosed within each fold, bounded medially by the conus elasticus and laterally by the thyroarytenoid muscles. It originates chiefly from the posterior aspects of the thyroid angle and to a small extent from the upper section of the conus elasticus. It goes horizontally back to each vocal process and to the lateral surface of the corresponding arytenoid.

Its characteristic action is to increase tension. By partial or differential contraction it may change the vibrational mode of the folds and determine the register. It can possibly shorten the folds and reduce the tension by bringing the arytenoids toward the thyroid angle. The ability of its fibers to contract in separate bundles brings about modifications of the inner margin of the folds and the contour of the glottis. The term aryvocalis muscle refers to shorter fascicles running from and into the vocal ligament. This muscle is said to bring about the tiny adjustments of the vocal ligament occurring in phonation.

Several muscles exert their main effect upon the aryepiglottic folds, the ventricular folds, or the epiglottis. The *ventricularis* muscle (paired) goes from the lateral border of the arytenoid to the side of the epiglottis. The *aryepiglottic* muscles are in this category, and they have already been described. The *thyroepiglottic* (paired) is a thin and variable muscle directly above the thyroarytenoid muscle, arising on the inner surface of the thyroid close to its angle and going upward and backward to the aryepiglottic fold and margin of the epiglottis. This muscle may depress the epiglottis, widen the upper laryngeal port, or perhaps, be part of the sphincter ring in that area.

Fink and Basek (1956) studied laryngeal movements through electromyography, roentgenograms, and motion pictures. Their findings are presented as follows. In quiet respiration some activity was found in all the muscles of the larynx, in both inspiration and expiration. The activity of all the muscles increased with strong respiratory efforts, but the pattern of action changed with the phase of respiration. Thus sternothyroid activity was prominent during inspiration, and the thyrohyoid was relatively quiet. During expiration there was greater activity in both muscles, especially in the thyrohyoid, while the cricothyroid and vocalis activity heightened.

In forced respiration muscle tone increased in both phases of breathing, but in the inspiratory phase the increase affected the sternothyroid more than the thyrohyoid. At this time the larynx was descending. With deep inspiration the thyrohyoid activity increased, and at this time the larynx was ascending.

Motion pictures showed that opening and closing of the glottis are accompanied by sliding movements of the arytenoids to and from the mid-line, with no evidence that rotation of cartilages occurs. This is an important observation if it can be conclusively demonstrated.

It appears that the rhythmic rise and fall of the larynx with respiration produces folding and unfolding of the laryngeal soft tissues. This action resembles that of a bellows whose folds are the vestibular and vocal folds, and it places a mediolateral sliding motion on the arytenoids. It is said that the extrinsic muscles have a major part in regulating the lateral displacement of the arytenoid cartilages and the glottis. The intrinsic cricoarytenoid muscles are in continuous tonic activity. This activity may be needed to support the vocal processes through stabilizing the base of the arytenoid cartilages. The forward pull of the vocalis is opposed by the posterior cricoarytenoid, creating a torque which is counterbalanced by the lateral cricoarytenoid.

From the preceding observations that respiration always involves laryngeal activity, the question may be asked whether the larynx can ever be rested. In the therapy of voice abuse, silence or soft whispering is usually effective, but the time needed for a cure is influenced by the continuous biological activity of the larynx.

NEURAL CONTROL OF THE LARYNX

The extrinsic muscles are innervated by cranial nerves V, VII, and XII and also by the upper cervical spinal nerves.

The intrinsic muscles are innervated by the Xth cranial or vagus nerve. This has two branches to the larynx, the superior and the inferior laryngeal nerves. Conventionally, the motor fibers of the superior laryngeal branch are said to go only to the cricothyroid muscle. All other intrinsic muscles are said to be regulated by the inferior laryngeal or recurrent branch. A table summarizing these facts as stated is included.

In a more recent view (Vogel, 1952) the superior laryngeal nerve, through its internal branch, also supplies the interarytenoid (transverse arytenoid) muscle.

Nerves to the Laryngeal Muscles.

Muscle	*Nerve innervation*
Extrinsic	
1. Suprahyoid	
Digastric (anterior belly)	V. Mylohyoid branch
Digastric (posterior belly)	VII. Digastric branch
Stylohyoid	VII. Stylohyoid branch
Mylohyoid	V. Mylohyoid branch
Geniohyoid	XII. Geniohyoid branch plus C-1
2. Infrahyoid	
Sternohyoid	XII. Branch of ansa hypoglossi plus C-1, C-2, C-3
Omohyoid	XII. Branch of ansa hypoglossi plus C-1, C-2, C-3
Sternothyroid	XII. Branch of ansa hypoglossi plus C-1, C-2, C-3
Thyrohyoid	XII. C-1 and C-2 communicating with descendens hypoglossi
Intrinsic	
Posterior cricoarytenoid	
Oblique arytenoid	
Transverse arytenoid	
Lateral cricoarytenoid	X. Inferior (recurrent) laryngeal branch of the
Thyroarytenoid	vagus
Vocalis	
Thyroepiglottic	
Cricothyroid	X. Superior laryngeal branch of the vagus

Faaborg-Andersen (1957) says that the cricothyroid muscle is innervated by the external branch of the superior laryngeal nerve, but he holds that the interarytenoid muscle is energized by the internal branch of the superior laryngeal nerve and also by the recurrent nerve. Campbell and Murtagh (1956) note that the cricothyroid muscle may be supplied by both the superior and inferior laryngeal nerves.

The Vagus Nerve. Because of the extreme importance of the vagus nerve in laryngeal physiology, a somewhat detailed discussion is presented here concerning the distribution of its laryngeal branches and its central nuclei.

The vagal nuclei are in the hindbrain. They mediate impulses that

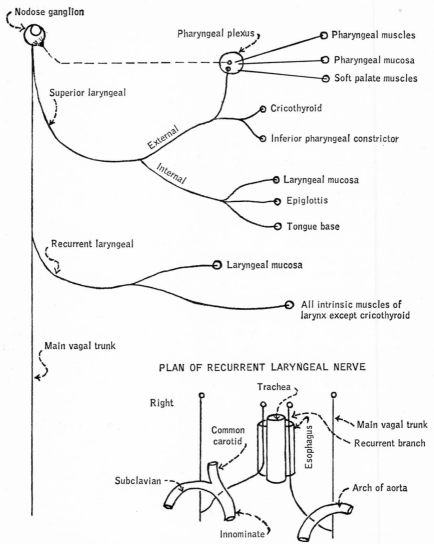

Fig. 7–4. Upper branches of the vagus nerve that energize laryngeal and associated structures.

are motor, sensory, or mixed. Sensory fibers originate from cells in the jugular ganglion and ganglion nodosum. Somatic motor fibers arise from the nucleus ambiguus and from the ganglion nodosum. Parasympathetic efferent fibers originate from the dorsal nucleus.

The cells of the jugular ganglion mediate general sensation from the cutaneous parts of the external ear. The ganglion also has connections with nerves other than the vagus.

The dorsal nucleus sends fibers to the parasympathetic vagal plexuses that supply thoracic and abdominal viscera.

The cells of the ganglion nodosum receive fibers from the pharynx, larynx, trachea, esophagus, and from soft organs in the thorax and abdomen. These fibers are the larger and more important of the sensory components.

The ganglion nodosum has a pharyngeal branch which joins with pharyngeal branches of the glossopharyngeal and with the superior cervical ganglion of the sympathetic. This union produces the pharyngeal plexus. To this plexus the vagus contributes motor fibers for the muscles of the pharynx and the soft palate, excluding the stylopharyngeus and tensor veli palatini.

At the lower end of the ganglion nodosum the superior laryngeal branch of the vagus separates from the main trunk. It travels downward and forward to the greater horn of the hyoid where it splits to two branches, external and internal.

The external branch descends vertically to the cricothyroid muscle. This branch contains both motor and sensory fibers. The internal branch is primarily sensory. It enters the larynx by penetrating the thyrohyoid membrane, and it then divides to three terminal trunks. One of these trunks innervates the mucous membrane of the aryepiglottic fold, the second supplies the mucous membrane of the lateral laryngeal walls, and the third goes to the pharyngeal mucous membrane behind the cricoid and arytenoid cartilages.

The sensory fibers are responsible for the sensation of irritation and pain in laryngeal disease. In the cough reflex, which adaptively protects the lungs, these sensory impulses represent the afferent limb of a reflex arc whose efferent limb is represented by motor impulses to thoracic and laryngeal muscles. Since the superior laryngeal branch transmits impulses for general sensation from the upper laryngeal areas, it may become clinically involved at some stage in laryngeal carcinoma, tuberculosis, and other conditions. Because of the superficial location of the nerve, it can be anesthetized topically; thus alcohol injections have been used in laryngeal tuberculosis. Such anesthesia, however, prevents the patient from sensing collected secretions in the local area, and he may choke from his own fluids unless continual aspiration is performed.

The main trunk of the vagus at the ganglion nodosum descends tnrough the neck and thorax, and it gives off the recurrent (inferior) laryngeal nerve. On the right side the recurrent nerve loops around the subclavian artery, but on the left it arises in the thorax and loops under the aortic arch. On both sides the recurrent nerve ascends in a groove between the trachea and the esophagus, and, lateral to the cricoid cartilage, each nerve bifurcates to terminal anterior and posterior divisions.

There is considerable controversy about the muscles innervated by each branch. The anterior division has been claimed to energize adductor muscles, while the posterior division supplies abductor muscles (Cracovaner, 1954). This does not seem to be borne out anatomically (Williams, 1954). The anterior branch may innervate the lateral cricoarytenoid, thyroarytenoid, vocalis, thyroepiglottic, and oblique arytenoid muscles, while the posterior branch may innervate the posterior cricoarytenoid and the transverse arytenoid muscles.

The recurrent nerve is chiefly motor, but it contains sensory fibers to the mucosa of (1) the glottis, (2) the larynx below the vocal folds, (3) the trachea, and (4) the esophagus. Even these statements have been questioned. Hollinshead (1954) denies any significant sensory components in the recurrent nerve. Gillilan (1954) restates the hypothesis that the recurrent laryngeal nerve originates in the spinal accessory part of the nucleus ambiguus and that the superior laryngeal branch is the one of true vagal origin. In this view the vagus innervates the upper pharyngeal muscles, while the accessory nerve innervates the lower muscles of the pharynx and the esophagus. The bulbar portion of the spinal accessory, which is represented in the recurrent laryngeal, is said to supply all intrinsic laryngeal muscles except the cricothyroid. It is stated that there is no recurrent laryngeal nerve when the right subclavian artery originates from the descending aorta.

The last nucleus to be considered is the nucleus ambiguus. According to Krieg (1942), the lowest fibers from the nucleus ambiguus unite with the upper part of the spinal accessory and travel with it into the jugular foramen where they join the vagus. This bundle is termed the vagal accessory to distinguish it from the spinal accessory. It is actually a part of the vagus, although it is usually stated to be a part of the spinal accessory. Krieg states that the nucleus ambiguus is the motor nucleus for deglutition and phonation, and that a lesion therein would affect phonation.

Gray (1954) defines the nucleus ambiguus as the somatic motor nucleus of the glossopharyngeal, vagal, and the cranial part of the spinal accessory nerve. It represents an extension of the dorsolateral cells of the anterior column of the spinal cord up into the medulla where it forms a slender column in the reticular formation. Krieg (1942) says that the corresponding cells in gill-breathing vertebrates supply muscles which move the third (glossopharyngeal) branchial arch and also the more caudal (vagal) arches. He calls these cells the branchial motor column, and he notes that all the muscles innervated are derivatives of the gill muscles of primitive vertebrates. Although there was originally one nerve for each arch, the nerves of all arches below the third appear to have joined into one. The muscles of the lower arches become the muscles of the larynx, and the nerve supply is from the vagus.

The nucleus ambiguus of the vagus receives fibers from the contiguous sensory nuclei, from the spinal nucleus of the trigeminal nerve, and from the nucleus of the tractus solitarius. These fibers correlate the laryngeal machinery and help complete swallowing reflexes. The nucleus ambiguus is also reached by corticobulbar fibers from the right and left precentral convolutions, and this connection helps complete voluntary control of the pharynx and larynx.

Furstenberg and Magielski (1955) describe a motor pattern of movements in the nucleus ambiguus. This nucleus supplies motor fibers to the voluntary muscles of the pharynx, larynx, and esophagus. In the cat the cricothyroid muscle is energized from the rostral area of the nucleus, and the following muscles are energized more caudally in the order listed: dorsal cricoarytenoid, thyroarytenoid, lateral cricoarytenoid, and arytenoid. The order is essentially similar in monkeys, and it is probable that the pattern holds in man. While the cricothyroid is the most cranial of the cells, the adductor muscles are the most caudal.

In such a pattern, central lesions can produce disturbed functions in some laryngeal muscles without involving all of them. This explains the observations of Pressman (1953) in a patient who had a central lesion and concomitant closure of the ventricular folds due to bilateral recurrent nerve paralysis, with no corresponding disturbance of the vocal folds.

LARYNGEAL BLOOD SUPPLY

The various components of the larynx are supplied with blood vessels chiefly from branches that originate in the superior and inferior thyroid arteries.

The superior laryngeal branch of the superior thyroid artery follows the internal laryngeal branch of the superior laryngeal nerve. It goes beneath the thyrohyoid muscle, penetrates the thyrohyoid membrane, and gives blood to the laryngeal muscles, mucous membranes, and glands. The superior thyroid artery also gives off a cricothyroid artery that passes across the cricothyroid membrane.

The inferior laryngeal branch of the inferior thyroid artery (from the thyrocervical trunk of the subclavian artery) reaches the posterior aspect of the larynx by traveling with the inferior laryngeal nerve upward upon the trachea and beneath the inferior pharyngeal constrictor muscle. It gives blood to the muscles and mucous membranes of this region, and it anastomoses with the superior laryngeal artery.

The inferior thyroid vessel also produces an ascending cervical artery whose muscular branches supply the infrahyoid group of muscles.

The description so far has been for the vascular supply chiefly to the

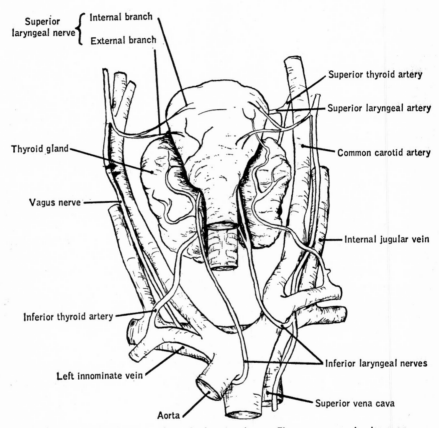

Fig. 7–5. Main blood vessels to the laryngeal area. The vagus nerve is also seen.

interior of the larynx. The exterior parts are supplied mainly by the infrahyoid and cricothyroid branches of the superior thyroid artery.

In regard to the venous return of laryngeal blood, the superior and inferior laryngeal veins are involved. The superior laryngeal veins empty into the superior thyroid veins. The latter drain into the internal jugular veins. The inferior laryngeal veins empty into the inferior thyroid veins, and the latter drain into the innominate vein.

The lymphatic drainage of the laryngeal mucosa has been investigated in detail, but much less is known about the lymph vessels of the laryngeal cartilages and musculature. The brief description herein is for the mucosa.

The lining has an upper and lower lymphatic system which are divided by the vocal folds. The vessels may be few in number or missing in parts of the true vocal folds, as along their free borders. The superior or supraglottic vessels follow the superior laryngeal artery. They leave the larynx through the thyrohyoid membrane and empty into several regions, including the subdigastric node and other nodes around or along the internal jugular vein. These vessels combine with those from the hypopharynx before leaving the larynx through the thyrohyoid membrane.

The inferior or infraglottic vessels follow two or more paths. One set, which drains the infraglottic area, leaves through the cricothyroid membrane. It may enter nodes interior to the membrane or in front of the upper trachea. Other lymphatics travel to deep cervical nodes and also to those accompanying the inferior thyroid artery.

THE TRACHEA

The trachea is below and continuous with the larynx. It is an elastic tube, about 4 inches long and 1 inch in diameter, extending from approximately the sixth cervical vertebra to the fourth or fifth thoracic vertebra where it divides to the right and left bronchial tubes. Its length in the male is about one-half inch longer than in the female.

Its outer walls contain sixteen to twenty alternate rings of cartilage and fibrous tissue. The cartilages are deficient posteriorly, and this space contains muscles which can change the bore of the tube.

The organ lies in the mid-line, and it is more superficial in the laryngeal end than it is more inferiorly. The anterior neck muscles overlap its lateral edges, but they leave an exposed mid-line strip of fascia. Additional anterior tissue which contains a rich venous network is found above the jugular notch. The isthmus of the thyroid gland crosses the organ anteriorly between the third and fourth cartilage rings. Only seven or eight rings are palpable above the jugular notch.

The internal lining is a pseudostratified, columnar, ciliated, mucous membrane. There is a submucous layer containing numerous mucous and serous glands.

The blood supply is from the inferior thyroid arteries and veins. The nerves are sympathetic and also from the vagus and its recurrent division.

The trachea in lungfish and amphibians is very short and wide, but it is much longer in most reptiles and in birds. In mammals the trachea is wide in the fast-running animals. In the human infant it is small, but in the adult it is wide and can actually transmit more air than the larynx can allow to pass.

The trachea is protected from the entrance of foreign bodies by several devices. The epiglottis partly covers it. Moreover, inhalation is reflexly

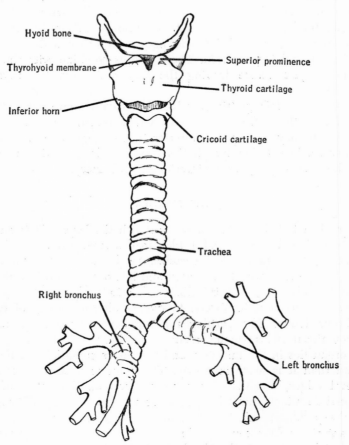

Fig. 7—6. The windpipe seen from in front.

inhibited during swallowing. The larynx may be closed above the trachea by approximating the true and false vocal folds. The cricopharyngeal sphincter at the esophageal entrance, which is normally closed, is opened reflexly when the bolus stimulates the pharynx; the bolus then passes into the esophagus rather than into the trachea.

Judson and Weaver (1942) lean to the view that the trachea is a resonator for pitches of about 128 and 256 cps, although they admit the proof is lacking. The argument is strengthened by the fact that the cartilage framework of the trachea plus the factor of length give the trachea the necessary qualities of a resonator. The effectiveness of the trachea and perhaps even of the bronchi as resonators extends through a narrow range, since they have a fairly constant shape and size which make it impossible to voluntarily adjust them adaptively. In this sense they would resonate to pitches corresponding to their natural period, or inherent power of free oscillation with regard to frequency.

According to Holmes (1940) the resonance of the trachea influences the vibratory rate of the vocal folds. At given pitches phonation is better if it is tuned to the tracheal resonator.

Not all investigators would agree that the trachea has a resonance function. Akin (1958) asserts that it is a breath-supply tube and not a resonator.

Tracheotomy, or making an opening in the trachea, is of interest in that it is often done in external laryngeal operations, as in laryngectomy, to maintain an adequate air passage or to give an anesthetic. It is achieved by a high or low operation. The former is done above the isthmus of the thyroid gland that covers the third and fourth tracheal rings. Because of the injury to the cricoid cartilage, the high operation is not in favor. In the low operation the skin over the third and fourth tracheal cartilages is anesthetized, and the anterior cervical tissues are stretched by lowering the head of the recumbent patient. The cartilages are exposed by a mid-line incision. Then the second, third, and fourth cartilages, including the mucosa, are cut through in the mid-line. A cannula is inserted, and the wound is closed around it. The cannula is eventually removed when the airway becomes free and is without obstructions. When a window is made in the trachea to insert a temporary or permanent cannula, the term tracheostomy is used. Negus (1957) cites the indications for tracheostomy.

SUMMARY

The extrinsic muscles support the larynx and change its spatial relationships. The suprahyoid group can elevate the hyoid and the larynx proper. The infrahyoid group can actively depress the larynx.

The intrinsic muscles have a more intimate control over the delicate phonatory movements. They may be classified by their general effects upon the glottis as abductors, adductors, tensors, or relaxors. A single muscle may exert a combination of effects, depending upon its manner of contraction. The roles played by each muscle in phonation are still to be conclusively demonstrated.

The intrinsic muscles are innervated by the vagus nerve, but the exact distribution of the nerve fibers is uncertain. The extrinsic muscles are innervated by cranial nerves V, VII, and XII and also by upper-cervical spinal nerves.

The laryngeal blood supply is chiefly from branches of the superior and inferior thyroid arteries. Corresponding veins provide the drainage.

The tracheal tube below the larynx is not only a respiratory passage but it may also act as a protective valve and as a resonator of the exhaled air.

Chapter 8

APPLIED ANATOMY AND PHYSIOLOGY
OF THE LARYNX

There are diverse kinds of phonatory disorders, the causes being chiefly anatomical, physiological, or psychological. In many instances the disorder is not purely of one type but represents a mixture of categories. The abnormalities of phonation are divided by some writers into two categories, organic and functional.

Many periodicals devote considerable attention to these problems. The student should become increasingly aware of the direction of ideas in the expanding literature. Among the readily available sources of information, the following journals may be consulted. The list is far from complete.

Annals of Otology, Rhinology and Laryngology
Acta oto-laryngologica
Archives of Otolaryngology
Folia Phoniatrica
Journal of Laryngology and Otology
Journal of Neurophysiology
Journal of Speech and Hearing Disorders
Journal of Speech and Hearing Research
Laryngoscope
Quarterly Journal of Speech
Speech Monographs
Transactions, American Academy of Ophthalmology and Oto-laryngology
Transactions, American Laryngological Association
Transactions, American Laryngological, Rhinological and Otological Society

Many of the pathological entities encountered are not problems within the ordinary scope and training of the speech pathologist but come into the province of pure pathology, clinical medicine, and surgery. It is easy to appreciate that phonatory disturbances are readily brought about when one realizes that at the pitch of middle C the vocal folds can make 256 contacts per second with each other.

The section that follows selectively outlines topics which may bring out some applied aspects of the study of the normal structure and function. The literature on these matters is voluminous, and it would be presumptuous for any theoretician to attempt a detailed account of the material in a basic text. The reader is referred to Berry and Eisenson (1956) and to Van Riper and Irwin (1958) for excellent reviews of this field. Milisen (1957) points up the importance of the problem in his estimate that about 1 per cent of the people of this country have phonatory defects and that such defects comprise about 5 to 15 per cent of the defective speech population. He differentiates speech deviations in general from speech defects. The former include any demarcations from an assumed normal speech pattern, whereas the latter signify extreme deviations or those which significantly interfere with communication.

Although an enormous literature about the larynx has been developed in this country, the foreign production is increasing. The research worker is faced with the need to acquire a knowledge of the languages used most frequently. As an illustration, the reader is referred to the German text of Ranke and Lullies (1953) for many aspects of laryngeal anatomy and physiology. A short text written in France by Garde (1954) is also of interest.

METHODS OF EXAMINATION

There are many methods to examine the larynx. Its status may also be evaluated more indirectly by appraising the vocal tone, which is a product of laryngeal activity. Laryngeal examination is described in several sections of the comprehensive treatise edited by Travis (1957). A bibliography of detailed methods is given.

Among the methods, laryngoscopy, or the use of a tube called the laryngoscope, permits visualization of the interior of the larynx. The fauces, or entrance to the throat, is first anesthetized with graded concentrations of cocaine.

The illuminated cavity of the larynx has been photographed by positioning a mirror in the throat so that it reflects a light beam down into the larynx and also reflects the image of the laryngeal structures back to a camera. When phonation occurs, such images are blurred out because of their high frequency of vibration. By such instruments as the stroboscope, the folds are made to look as though they were moving slowly or even standing still. Vibrations of the folds in slow motion can be visualized by the electrolaryngostroboscope.

Timcke and his coworkers (1958) describe how two new methods now permit accurate measurements of the laryngeal wave *in vivo*. One of these methods utilizes ultrahigh speed photography, and the other involves electronic synchronstroboscopy.

The rapidly advancing field of instrumentation is providing quantitative data not previously obtainable. Many of the conventional views about voice production will certainly be made obsolete.

An indirect clinical method of examination of the larynx, preferable with children but highly useful in adults, employs the head mirror along with the laryngeal mirror. This method can be used as a laboratory exercise in an introductory course in the anatomy and physiology of speech. The students work in pairs. The operator faces a good light source that shines into a head mirror held over his left eye. The mirror is adjusted to reflect the light into the subject's throat, both members being seated and facing each other. The operator uses a dry, warm, previously sterilized laryngeal (guttural) mirror, and with his right hand he inserts the mirror into the subject's mouth directly above the lower incisors, with the back of the mirror just contacting the velum. The subject's tongue may be kept lowered and out of the field by pressure of a tongue depressor held in the operator's left hand. The gag reflex caused by the contact of the mirror with the borders of the fauces has to be controlled. Visualization of the glottis is facilitated by making the subject issue the long A sound. If the individual takes a slow and deep inspiration, then sounds E (as in key), the behavior of the vocal folds may be watched.

POSITIONAL MALADJUSTMENTS OF THE VOCAL FOLDS OR OF THE LARYNX

Tone purity depends upon the evenness and regularity of the vibrations on the edges of the folds (Anderson, 1942). Anything interfering with the free vibrations of the folds or allowing unused breath to escape between them will add noise elements to the tones.

Any growth on the folds can prevent them from being normally closed. This fault results in the escape of unvocalized air. The condition is called breathiness, or pneumophonia. The voice is said to have an aspirate quality, and the effect is as though a whisper were added to the normal tone. The extra rush of air which is not modulated by the vocal folds superimposes friction noises upon the tones produced by vocal-fold vibrations. Breathiness may also be brought on functionally as a result of faulty breathing, poor vocal habits, or even general weakness. An inability to approximate the folds is also at times ascribable to weakness or paralysis of the folds.

Where the folds are drawn too tightly together during phonation rather than being lax, a shrill, harsh, creaking noise, which is called stridency, or stridor, enters the tone. An obstruction of some type is present. Some causes include general tension, spastic paralysis, or often a throat strain or "pinched throat." There is excessive constriction of muscles all through the vocal tract, and the tension is great in the external laryngeal muscles. The vibrations of the vocal folds are hindered, and supraglottal friction noises are introduced.

Anderson (1942) proposed one simple but rough test for excessive throat strain and improper voice usage by having the subject keep his finger in the notch of the thyroid cartilage while in a loud, sharp tone pronouncing, "Ready! Aim! Fire!" If the thyroid cartilage rises appreciably or if it disappears up under the hyoid bone, malfunction is said to be evidenced.

Sometimes interference with free vibration produces a status called throatiness. This is a guttural quality in which the voice seems to fall back into the throat and become harsh and raspy.

In the condition called glottal shock, the vocal folds are tensed and overly adducted. They are exploded apart in cough-like fashion under expiratory pressure, producing a click in which the tone is initially harsh and unpleasant.

A positional maladjustment involving an abnormal elevation of the entire larynx has been previously noted in the condition called ventricular phonation in which the false folds phonate. This disorder may originate from an acute laryngitis in which speech is forced during temporary dysfunction of the true folds. The false folds may also assume this function if the true folds are separated, as by a tumor. The disorder may also be congenital. Sometimes this substituted vocal activity of the false folds is desirable, as in surgical deficiencies of the vocal folds.

Positional maladjustments may also involve the joints of the larynx. Arthrology does not seem to enter the speech literature often mainly because of the infrequency of joint pathology in the laryngeal structures. The most flexible joint in the larynx is the cricoarytenoid articulation (Gisselsson, 1950), and rare cases of dislocation preferentially involve this area. The cricothyroid joint is another one that is dislocated with extreme rarity, because the joint is usually constructed like a firmly bound symphysis.

HOARSENESS

Hoarseness is a rough, harsh quality of the voice, and the pitch is relatively low. It is not a disease, but it is one of the most important symptoms of throat disorders. Its chronic form often indicates serious pathology. Although it does not exist unless the vocal folds are involved, other areas, such as the pharynx, may contribute to its duration and general pathology. Hoarseness is one of the most common of all throat disorders, and everyone should be aware of some basic facts concerning it.

A definition of hoarseness should be broad and include alterations in tonal quality that range all the way from a slight drop of pitch to practically complete aphonia (loss of voice). Hoarseness is not synonymous with laryngitis, and it is not essentially pathological. The tonal variations are usually produced by changes in the shape, tension, or motility of the vocal folds. The causes may be congenital, infectious, mechanical, psychological, hormonal, traumatic, functional, or neoplastic. The ability of the vocal folds to approximate each other is decreased. Air leaking through a deformed glottis or through a widened space between the folds can produce rasping tones.

Acute simple laryngitis is the most common cause of hoarseness, and here the vocal folds temporarily swell and thicken. This is a self-limited condition, aided by resting the voice and by local treatment. There is also an acute laryngitis accompanying upper-respiratory infections associated with streptococci and other virulent organisms.

The vocal folds can also thicken and swell in acute allergic and vasomotor disturbances. The allergy must be treated. Psychotherapy has been useful in functional or psychic dysphonia, and even galvanic shock therapy over the larynx has occasionally produced excellent results.

Papillomas, which are benign epithelial laryngeal tumors, may cause hoarseness. They grow rapidly and recur often, and they are responsible for a high mortality rate especially in very young children. These growths tend to disappear at puberty. Papillomas can also arise in adults.

Hoarseness in a child may also reflect vocal abuse, psychological changes, or precocious puberty. In the infant, congenital causes should be suspected, including laryngeal cysts, flaccid cartilages, edema from tracheal aspiration, and paralysis from disturbances of the recurrent laryngeal nerve or of the central nervous system. The control of the recurrent nerve over the laryngeal muscles is so great that any disturbance of these nerve fibers can change the mobility of the vocal folds and produce hoarseness. In surgical removal of the thyroid gland, hoarseness may result from concomitant damage not only to the recurrent nerve but also to the external branch of the superior laryngeal branch of the vagus nerve.

Several kinds of endocrine derangements may set up background conditions for hoarseness. In the thyroid deficiency called myxedema the voice can become hoarse and low-pitched. Women with the adrenogenital syndrome may develop a deep and harsh voice; they also tend to develop a temporary huskiness during treatment with large doses of the male sex hormone, testosterone.

Much hoarseness results from abuse or strain of the vocal folds. In the advanced stage of vocal strain, fibrous nodes can develop between the anterior third and middle of the folds. These are called vocal nodules, screamer's nodes, singer's nodes, and chorditis nodosa. The nodes arise by thickening of the stratified squamous epithelium. The growths develop where the folds are most active in the production of the higher tones. They are usually bilateral. Large nodes are surgically removed.

The chronic laryngitis of voice abuse may be characterized by ulceration and perichondritis of the vocal processes of the arytenoids, with a granuloma appearing on the phonating edge of the arytenoid; an ulcer may form on the opposite fold at the region of contact with the granuloma. Voice rest in these instances may be the true cardinal feature of treatment. Vocal reeducation may also be necessary.

Neoplasms associated with hoarseness are usually benign, but if the hoarseness is persistent, malignancy is a possibility. Prompt diagnosis is imperative, since early cancer of the larynx is potentially curable. It is generally agreed that hoarseness persisting more than a few weeks warrants investigation.

ANOMALIES OF DEVELOPMENT

Congenital lack of symmetry in the right and left sides of the vocal tract is not unexpected since bilaterality is not accompanied by perfect duplication of paired structures. However, it is only when one set of organs is deviated because of an excessive unilateral muscle pull that pathology is expressed, and even here a compensation is obtainable.

Embryological malformations of the larynx are very rare, and the more frequent ones are those of the epiglottis. Apart from distortions of its shape, there are the bifid epiglottis and the failure of the epiglottis to appear.

In the bifid organ there is variable splitting in the mid-line, which ranges from a slight indentation of the free border to a complete split. Montreuil (1949) explains the bifid anomaly on the assumption that there is a bilateral origin of the epiglottis from a large swelling on the laryngotracheal duct called the furcula of His. An absence or incomplete fusion of the paired primordia could occur. The furcula helps form the tongue anteriorly and the epiglottis posteriorly.

Triboletti (1958) presents a case in which incomplete separation of the laryngotracheal groove from the primitive gut produced a common laryngotracheoesophageal tract. Ordinarily, this groove appears on the ventral surface of the gut in the 3-mm fetus. Lateral projections invaginate and separate the ventral breathing tube from the dorsal digestive tube. The process should be completed by 4 mm.

PARALYSIS OF THE VOCAL FOLDS

Laryngeal palsy, or paralysis, may follow lesions of the upper or lower motor neurons. Since the muscles of phonation and articulation seem to be controlled by fibers from the upper motor corticospinal tracts of both cerebral hemispheres, paralysis of the vocal folds from upper motor lesions ensues only upon bilateral destruction of the upper motor systems. Motor speech is markedly affected. The imperfect articulation is called dysarthria.

Lesions may occur in the vagus nerve, which is the lower motor neuron. Depending upon the level of the lesion, the superior or inferior laryngeal branch of the vagus nerve or both branches may be involved.

If the superior laryngeal nerve is involved, anesthesia of the upper larynx and epiglottis may accompany paralysis of the cricothyroid muscle. The vocal fold becomes slack and, although phonation may not be seriously impaired, the voice fatigues readily. Paralysis of this nerve alone is rare.

If the inferior laryngeal nerve is at fault, one or more of the other laryngeal muscles may become paralyzed. This condition involves defects in tensing or relaxing, adduction or abduction, or there may be a loss of sphincteric action resulting from paralysis of muscles of the aryepiglottic folds along with the adductor muscles. The principal defect is usually in the loss of adductor or abductor motion. Recurrent laryngeal lesions may not significantly influence sensation from the larynx. Brain (1955) states that the left recurrent nerve is more exposed to damage because of a longer course.

From a standpoint of the muscle groups affected, there are three main groups of paralysis, the adductor, abductor, and tensor. The most common type occurs when the paralyzed cord is fixed in the mid-line and does not abduct upon inspiration.

Paralysis may be unilateral or bilateral, partial or complete. Speech disturbance is not an essential sequel to partial paralysis. If one fold is paralyzed, hoarseness is typical. If both are paralyzed, speech is lost.

Unilateral paralysis may be caused by damage to or pressure upon the recurrent laryngeal nerve on the same side. It can occur, for example, in mediastinal tumor, or aneurysm, in goiter, and in cervical lymph-node enlargement. The causes of bilateral paralysis may be the same as the above, but more often they involve postdiphtheric neuritis or disease processes affecting the hindbrain nuclei of the vagus nerve, e.g., progressive bulbar paralysis, anterior poliomyelitis.

Individuals with hysteria may simulate an organic picture of aphonia in which there is an apparent paralysis of the folds closely resembling a true paralysis.

The term paralysis usually implies disturbance in the nerve supply. In this sense it would not be the proper designation for lack of movement caused by disorders originating in the laryngeal muscles and joints.

Van Riper and Irwin (1958) cite literature on Semon's law, which deals with progressive organic lesions of the motor laryngeal systems and holds that the nerve fibers energizing the abductors of the vocal folds become involved considerably earlier than do those controlling the adductors. A paralysis limited to the adductors is said to be most always bilateral, and it is caused by functional changes in the centers. Van Riper cites evidence to show that the hypothesis is not always helpful in explaining the observed changes.

LARYNGEAL OBSTRUCTION

In the previous description of the larynx, it has been noted that its mucous membrane is only loosely bound down except at the laryngeal surface of the epiglottis and the vocal ligaments. It is this arrangement which facilitates obstruction and asphyxiation following the accumulation of fluid in the loose areolar submucous tissue.

The lumen of the larynx may be obstructed from many causes including the traumatic crushing of cartilages, the pressure of growths, and the presence of foreign bodies. In the preimmunization days of diphtheria it was common to find a membrane which formed in the throat and spread to the larynx. This occasionally necessitated tracheotomy, which involves the establishment of an airway.

LARYNGECTOMY

Growths may occur in the vocal folds or in the laryngeal walls. In some cases the partial or complete removal of only one vocal fold is indicated. Following hemilaryngectomy, a training regimen that involves the exhalation of air in a proper manner may eliminate the necessity of compensation with an exaggerated use of predominantly pharyngeal muscles, and after several weeks or more the patients may regain the ability to speak with a normal voice (Froeschels and Jellinek, 1941).

A partial laryngectomy, done when the growth is limited to the outer edge of the fold, is also called a laryngofissure, thyrotomy, or thyrochondrotomy. The surgical approach to the inside of the larynx is through the anterior angle of the thyroid cartilage.

Complete removal of the larynx may be indicated if there is fixation of one fold, extensive involvement in slow growing tumors, subglottic extension of fast growing tumors, or even involvement of an extrinsic part of the larynx. When growth has spread beyond the laryngeal boundaries, the removal of the lymph glands in the neck is also carried out. Where the pharynx becomes involved, a partial pharyngectomy is carried out in the affected region. The total operation is a pharyngolaryngectomy. The more limited term pharyngotomy implies opening the pharynx to excise a growth.

In complete removal, the larynx may be excised from below the cricoid cartilage up to the hyoid bone, although some surgeons leave the cricoid attached to the trachea. The stump of the trachea is brought out anteriorly and sutured to the cervical skin so that breathing must take place through this new opening and no longer through the nose or the mouth. The opening of the pharynx into the larynx is closed, and the pharynx communicates at that region only with the esophagus. The inferior constrictor muscles of the pharynx, which have been removed from their laryngeal attachments, are overlapped and fused.

The immediate postoperative care is demanding. Free respiration requires the continuous removal of secretions. To feed the patient, an indwelling tube is passed into the esophagus beyond the pharyngeal opening, and water is given through it periodically before feeding. Restricted quantities of food sufficiently liquid to flow by gravity are given at intervals. The tube is removed when it is found that saliva can easily be swallowed. The external laryngectomy wound generally heals in several weeks; the deeper tissues take more time. The reader is referred to Boies (1954) and Greene (1957) for details.

Speech Without Vocal Folds. The greatest handicap after laryngectomy is the absence of speech. Reeducation is necessary to rehabilitate the patient so that he may become a socially acceptable and employable member of society. The production of a pseudo voice has become an integral part of the management of these cases, and the orientation and training for this is now instituted prior to surgery. The patient learns that the larynx is not absolutely essential to speech and that words can be formed in his supraglottic structures including the lips, tongue, cheek, and palate.

Several methods exist by which artificial speech is produced, and the best methods involve teaching the patient to use the remnants of his own speech apparatus. The known artificial mechanical devices are reserved for those who can not master their own biological structures.

In the method involving a *buccal whisper* the air that is always accumulated in the mouth and pharynx is used instead of that ordinarily expelled from the lung passages. Quick articulatory movements are made. The method does not satisfactorily produce speech sounds. In many cases only the immediate family or friends of the patient are able to understand his speech.

It is the concensus that the method known as esophageal speech, if it can be learned, is preferable to other present methods. Many patients master the technic within one or two months with not many instructional lessons. The patient must not revert to the buccal whisper; in esophageal speech the esophagus must be kept open, but in the former process speech is produced by the high pressure of air built up in the mouth with a tightly closed esophagus.

The essentials of sound production are somewhat similar in both normal and esophageal speech. In the former, exhaled pulmonary air passes through the narrow glottis between the vocal folds. In the latter, the air trapped in the upper esophagus is expelled through the closely approximated surfaces of the cricopharyngeal sphincter, or pseudoglottis, or else from any area where a narrow opening can vibrate (Martin, 1950), and in turn it is sent into the pharynx. The sound formed in this way is molded into speech by the lips, teeth, cheek, tongue, and palate.

In esophageal speech training great emphasis has been placed on the ability to master the belching of air. The patient is trained to belch prior to laryngectomy, and he learns how to sustain the belch for conversion to articulate speech. The breath is held while belching.

The major difficulty has been to get enough air into the esophagus. This problem has stimulated the development of several technics.

Air can be derived by swallowing, insufflation, or by injection. Swallowing is least preferred. It is not ordinarily practiced by the patient who has become proficient as an esophageal speaker. In the insufflation method the patient fills and empties his esophagus with a quick diaphragmatic breath in and out while articulating plosive syllables. In this technic there is the disadvantage of having to pay too much attention to breathing during early training. The injection method seems to be the most preferable. The patient masters the intake of air by compression of air in the mouth and attempts to achieve a succession of syllables. An effort is made to obtain voice on the syllable. Consonants are readily practiced in monosyllables. Eventually, thoracic expansion occurs automatically, prior to speech. A small group of patients can never master the process, but most patients acquire an acceptable speech.

Conley et al. (1958) have presented a new surgical technic for the vocal rehabilitation of the laryngectomized person. A mucosal tunnel is created through the wall of the cervical esophagus so that there is a controlled communication between the trachea and the esophagus. A special plastic tube can be fitted into the mucosal tunnel. The tube is so built that air can enter the esophagus, but food and saliva cannot pass onto the neck or into the trachea. The method is still experimental. It is stated that patients can usually speak on the first effort. The quality of the voice is basically that of pharyngeal or esophageal speech, but there is better air control and supply.

Artificial Larynges. For the group which cannot learn esophageal speech, two kinds of devices called artificial larynges are available. The first variety is air-driven and is a reed type. A flexible rubber tube passes from the tracheal opening into the mouth. Just below the oral end of the instrument there is a metal reed which changes the upwardly directed air into a buzz or into tones within the normal voice range. The sounds are converted into speech by the existing natural speech molds such as the resonators and articulators.

The second device is electrically driven. It consists of a battery-operated vibrator over which a diaphragm is stretched. The instrument is pressed usually against the outside of the throat at about the level of the excised thyroid cartilage. The diaphragm is made to vibrate, and it produces sound waves that pass through the throat tissues and into the open mouth where they are articulated by the lips and tongue into a muffled and mechanical speech. The voice is monotonous and unnatural.

Artificial devices are bulky, conspicuous, and subject to damage. They do not produce a normal or pleasant voice.

SUMMARY

Laryngeal pathology takes many forms. These are classified as disorders of phonation.

The interior of the larynx is examined by many technics, ranging from simple laryngeal mirrors to devices providing motion pictures of laryngeal activity, as well as the visualization of the fold vibrations in slow motion.

The quality of the laryngeal tone is changed by any interference with free vibration of the folds or by conditions permitting unused air to escape between the folds. Tone quality is changed all too frequently in hoarseness, which is one of the most common of all throat disorders. Hoarseness is associated with many underlying causes.

Laryngeal pathology is sometimes related to anomalies of development. Paralysis of the folds is associated with lesions in the upper or lower motor neuron system. The effect upon the muscles is determined by the kind of neural lesion that exists.

The larynx is surgically removed if malignant lesions are present. Artificial speech can be learned. It is usually accomplished by expelling the air in the esophagus through narrow openings which can vibrate and by molding the sounds into intelligible speech with the articulators. Mechanical larynges are also available.

Chapter 9

THE VELOPHARYNGEAL MECHANISM: THE PALATE

The larynx produces audible sounds from exhaled air, but these sounds do not constitute speech as we hear it. Supraglottic structures resonate characteristically to the incident laryngeal tones and add specific qualities to them. The tongue, lips, and teeth then shape the final sounds, and in this way the individual voice acquires its unique characteristics or vocal quality.

In the process of voice production the velum and the pharynx assume great importance. Together they constitute a coupled velopharyngeal mechanism in which the pharynx is significant in the activity called resonation. The velum is not a resonator per se but is classified with the articulators. However, it helps regulate resonance in the oral and nasal cavities by its movements.

The process of resonation and the structure of the hard palate and soft palate (velum) constitute the subject matter of the present chapter.

RESONANCE AND CUL-DE-SACS

Borden and Busse (1929) defined resonance as the reflection of the condensation phases of a large number of air waves such that they are focused at or close to the narrowed outlet of a cavity. The physical instruments or bodily structures used to intensify the sounds or produce a resonant quality are called resonators.

Anderson (1942) defined resonance as an amplification of sound of such a reflection and concentration of sound waves that there is a significant increase in the energy output of the vibrating structures. He noted that although the total number of overtones of a speech sound and their relation in pitch to the fundamental are chiefly a function of the basic structure of the vibrating body, the relative intensities of these overtones are greatly dependent upon resonance. Anderson's concept of resonance is seen in the later literature. Hahn et al. (1952) defined resonance as the process of reinforcement and amplification of the fundamental and its overtones, which originate in the vocal folds.

176

Resonance may be physically defined as the prolongation and intensification of sound caused by the transmission of its vibrations to a cavity. It is, in a sense, the drumlike reverberation obtainable from a cavity filled with air. It is a vibrant sound, as distinguished from a dull sound. The latter is a flat, colorless, uninteresting sound representing a decrease or absence of resonance. Physically, resonance in a single cavity is like the sound produced by blowing over the mouth of an empty bottle. In the speech apparatus we do not necessarily deal with single or empty cavities, and the statements made in this paragraph do not describe the biological facts.

For many years resonance was claimed to produce significant amplification of the sound in addition to imparting a given shading to the quality of the resonated sound. Thus McBurney and Wrage (1953) state that without resonance amplification the vocal-fold tone would be inaudible even a short distance away. Berry and Eisenson (1956) caution against relating resonance to increasing vocal intensity and cite literature to the effect that the intensity of sound at the mouth is only about twenty per cent of its value at the larynx. Also, the resonating structures could add discordant partials to the sound by excessive tenseness in the mouth, nose, and throat. They also point up the recent objection to regarding the resonators as the chief determinants of voice quality. It may be preferable to refer quality to adjustments in the larynx.

Essentially, air is resonated much as organ pipes of various lengths resonate the sounds formed in their vibrational system. Reinforcement may occur when the laryngeal vibrations cause latent air in the supraglottic spaces to vibrate in tune with one or more partials of the incident waves. Damping occurs through selective absorption of the energy of certain tones by soft surfaces or else through neutralization of the energy by other movements in the same space. Some partials travel upward undiminished, while others are variably damped. Heffner (1950) says that most of the total energy of any speech sound lies in its fundamental and first harmonic. The resonators do not reinforce or modify with equal strength all the partials in the usually compound speech tone. The relative nature and strength of the partials are varied almost indefinitely in the changing oral cavity.

Resonance is produced in three ways (Hahn et al., 1952; McBurney and Wrage, 1953), and all methods may operate independently or simultaneously. In the first method, sound waves in a tube are reflected when hitting a surface, and the reflections change with the hardness and smoothness of the surface and also with the size of the tubal opening. This reflective resonance is the chief method of modifying the fundamental tone.

A second kind of resonance is that which occurs when sounds brought into contact with bodily structures produce a responsive vibration of these structures. This is forced or sounding-board resonation. Its role in speech appears to be minor.

A third principle is that of sympathetic vibration. If two resonators are tuned to the same frequency and one of them is sounded in the vicinity of the other, the silent one will pick up the vibrations. We shall discuss this again in Chapter 13. In the vocal cavities an air column may vibrate in sympathy with a frequency sounded at the opening of the cavity. If the vocal cavities could assume only one particular form, they would vibrate sympathetically to a narrow range of frequencies. This modification would occur because their capacity to respond would be determined by the cavity volume and by the shape and size of its apertures. Since the mouth and pharynx have variable but controllable sizes and shapes, they can selectively respond to a broad range of overtones. This is less true for the relatively fixed nasal chambers.

A distinction has been made above between resonance, as it applies to the forced vibration of bony and cartilaginous structures, and cavity resonance, which occurs within the recognized resonating cavities. Resonators in general are of two types, the cavity or the sounding-board type (Kantner and West, 1941). The latter may be represented by the piano or by placing a sounded tuning fork on a table; it is observed in the body by resonance in the chest walls, hard palate, bones of the cranium, and elsewhere. Cavity resonance is found in musical horns, and in the body it is produced in such cavities as the nose, mouth, pharynx, and larynx. It should be noted that cavity resonance is the form usually meant when the unrestricted term resonance is employed. It is also emphasized that resonance and quality are not synonymous; a voice having a disagreeable quality may not be lacking in resonance, although it may possess too much of the wrong kind.

Akin (1958) calls the pharynx, mouth, and nasal passages the primary resonating cavities. She notes that an inflexible tongue or relatively stationary mandible influences resonance and produces a throaty voice. A set of relaxed, open resonators generally leads to a pleasant vocal effect. Rubicheck (1952) contends that faults in voice quality result from a disproportionate use of any one of the above cavity resonators. For example, nasality is said to imply too many nasal reinforcements for the amount of mouth and throat overtones.

Fletcher (1953) notes that there is a contribution to speech from structures not usually designated as speech organs. The sounding-board type of resonance illustrates this. The bones of the face may contribute to resonance. The ribs and sternum may be felt to vibrate and be heard by the stethoscope to do so during phonation. Such vibrations are transmitted through the surrounding tissues. The facial bones are particularly active as sounding boards at medium and high frequencies, whereas the sternum and neighboring bones tend to vibrate at lower frequencies. The contribution of the chest at low frequencies is illustrated by the change of voice heard in an experimental subject placed knee-deep and then neck-high in water. According to Akin (1958), the vibration of the thoracic walls is not important in vocal resonance if the normal ratio between the chest and oral sounds is maintained.

The vibrations of the vocal folds, after being resonated by the various cavities, are collected within the restricted exit of the mouth or of the nose. The differential emphasis upon nasal or oral resonance is determined by whether the laryngeal tones can pass freely through the nose or the mouth or whether one of these chambers has been narrowed so that the air is being shunted through the path of least resistance. An individual learns to close his mouth or nose just to the proper degree for pleasant and acceptable speech. Cerebrospinal control over the voluntary muscles in the involved areas, particularly the palatal muscles that raise or lower the velum, provides this facility. Pathologically, the mouth or nose may be constricted through a variety of causes.

The concept of the cul-de-sac is implied in this discussion. If air is blown through a horn having a hollow diverticulum, the tone of the horn is altered. The diverticulum, or blind pouch, is the cul-de-sac. The sound emitted from such an instrument is blended from both the horn and the pouch. The same principle holds for the mouth and nose openings. Air from the pharynx is sent into either the mouth or the nose depending on the muscular action, and it is fractionated in a specific ratio between the mouth and the nose.

In nasal sounds the fauces leading to the mouth is narrowed, and the mouth acts as the cul-de-sac. The nose becomes the cul-de-sac in sounds chiefly involving oral resonance. In the nasal sounds Hahn et al. (1952) state that the entire nasal cavity is used for M, a smaller part for N, and only a small posterior pocket is used for NG. In cleft palate the speech is nasal because there is a change in the ratio between nasal and oral resonance.

In the oral (nonnasal) English sounds the soft palate is directed toward the pharyngeal wall. There is possibly a simultaneous protrusion of the pterygopharyngeal muscle (Passavant's cushion). The exhaled air cannot readily enter the occluded nasopharynx and is preferentially directed into the oral cavity. The closure of the nasopharynx is said to be produced by a palatopharyngeal sphincter. This machinery involves several muscles to be described in the text, including the superior constrictor muscle of the pharynx, the levator palati muscle, and the glossopalatine and pharyngopalatine muscles of the palate.

Berry and Eisenson (1956) emphasize that although the velum and pharynx close the entrance to the nose for all except nasal sounds, this closure is not complete but variable. In some bass resonant voices the nasopharynx could be kept open most of the time without producing nasality and, in fact, even enriching the timbre of the voice. This concept seems to minimize the classical view (Russell, 1931; West et al., 1937) of the importance of the cul-de-sac. Van Riper and Irwin (1958) state that although one should not expect velopharyngeal closure to be

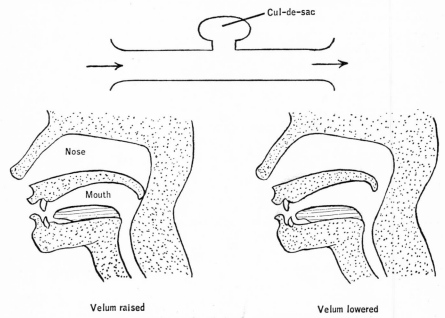

Velum raised   Velum lowered

Fig. 9–1. Partition of air between the mouth and nose.

airtight in the production of nonnasal sounds, one should not conclude from this that the degree of closure is unimportant.

Resonation is involved in the concept of optimum pitch, which is the general pitch level of an individual at which he can best emit full, resonant, and rich tones. The level is discoverable for a given person by trial and error (Hahn et al., 1952). At the optimum pitch, phonation is very efficient with a minimum of muscular action. Only the muscles used to produce tones are tensed.

THE HARD PALATE

The hard palate is the bony anterior part of the partition which separates the oral and nasal cavities. It is bounded in front and on the sides by the alveolar and tooth-bearing arch of the upper jaw (maxilla) and in back by the pendulous soft palate. The boundary between the hard and soft palates is easily determined by pressing a finger against the roof of the mouth behind the central incisors and sliding the finger posteriorly until the roof tissue is found to yield. The hard palate is generally vault-shaped, and the soft palate is veil-like.

The bony framework of the hard palate is penetrated by canals and foramina. The incisive canal is in the median plane, anteriorly. This canal connects the hard palate with the nasal cavity. The greater palatine foramina are located at the posterior corners of the hard palate, opposite the root of the last molar tooth on each side. They represent

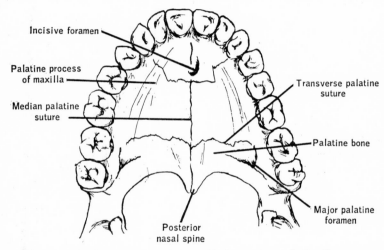

Incisive foramen

Palatine process of maxilla

Median palatine suture

Transverse palatine suture

Palatine bone

Major palatine foramen

Posterior nasal spine

Fig. 9–2. The hard palate seen from below with the mucosa and other tissues removed.

the lower part of the pterygopalatine canal, which is an extension of the pterygopalatine fossa above. It will be seen later that nerves and blood vessels utilize these passageways.

The hard palate is covered by a membrane which represents the mucous membrane fused with the periosteal covering of the bone. In surgery of the cleft palate the entire mucoperiosteum can be readily separated from the bone. The palatine mucous membrane is continuous with that which lines the surrounding areas. This membrane is very thick, especially at the alveolar margin where it becomes continuous with the gums or gingivae. The continuity facilitates the spread of dentoalveolar abscesses to the vault of the palate.

Sharp (1956) divides the hard palate structurally into three zones. There is a peripheral zone which is continuous with the dense gingiva and whose surface texture is firm, resistant, and smooth. A second or central zone extends along the center of the palate and covers the entire length of the structure. In the front part of the central zone irregular branching ridges, or rugae, cross the palate transversely. The rugae are composed of dense connective tissue overlaid by a cornified epithelium. Between the central and peripheral zones there is a third or intermediate zone in which the mucosa is firmly adherent to the periosteum of the palate.

The functions of the hard palate are reflected in its structure. A loose and movable mucosa would not favor the function of crushing food between the palate and tongue. Anteriorly, the palatal rugae facilitate contact between the palate and the tongue. These ridges tend to disappear in old age.

The epithelial surface just behind the rugae is a region of considerable tactile sensibility which aids responses to taste upon tongue contact. Loss of taste in wearing a denture may result from loss of touch and a decreased power to evaluate the texture of the food. This same tactile sensitivity allows, through feedback into the nervous system, the accurate formation of speech sounds requiring palatal-tongue contact.

Beyond the alveolar arch, which provides sockets for the teeth, the hard palate is more or less acutely arched with wide individual variations in the height and breadth of the vault. The topography of the hard palate is important in that it is used in the description of many speech sounds. Oral resonance depends to some extent upon the shape of the hard palate, since it can be modified by a low or by a high, narrow vault. The density, rigidity, and tension of the palate also affect resonance.

THE SOFT PALATE

The soft palate is the mobile and muscular posterior section of the partition between the oral and nasal cavities and between the mouth and pharynx. It is attached anteriorly to the hard palate, laterally to the side walls of the pharynx, and it curves downward and backward into the pharynx.

The soft palate is variously called the velum palati, velum pendulum palati, septum palati, valvula palati, and claustrum of the palate. The velum is often synonymous with the soft palate, although it is more generally considered to be the lower portion of the soft palate that hangs down like an incomplete curtain. The framework of the entire soft palate is the palatine aponeurosis, a fibrous sheet to which several muscles are attached. The aponeurosis is best developed in the anterior portion of the velum, where practically no muscle fibers exist.

The velum is of considerable importance in speech since it changes the size of the apertures between the pharynx and the mouth and between the pharynx and the nose. It can vary the degree of oral and nasal resonance. When it is relaxed, as in quiet respiration, it is obliquely dependent and partially obstructs the aperture between the pharynx and the mouth. This port can be narrowed further by the active contraction of the glossopalatal and pharyngopalatal muscles, which pro-

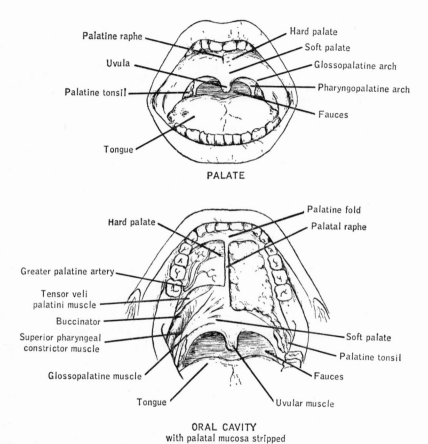

Fig. 9–3. Top: Composition of the soft palate. Bottom: Structures related to the hard palate seen after removal of the mucosa.

duce a riding-in of the palatal arches, or pillars of the fauces. For example, the velum is lowered in producing nasal tones, whereas it may be elevated by such actions as yawning or panting. Relaxation and depression of the arches may thus be opposed by tension and elevation.

The soft palate can rise variably in accordance with certain sounds. For example, it rises very little in the AH sound (as in are) and hardly touches the pharyngeal wall. It rises progressively and hits the pharyngeal wall with increasing force for the vowels, OH, A (as in late), EE, and OO.

The unpaired uvula is a cone-shaped structure of variable size, projecting downward from the center of the free lower border of the velum toward the fauces. It contains glands, connective tissue, and some muscle fibers. A definite uvula is present only in monkeys and man.

The uvular or azygus muscle (musculus uvulae) is frequently paired and consists of slender slips which originate from the posterior nasal spine and the palatine aponeurosis. The fibers run through the soft palate. As they come in medially from both sides, they fuse before attaching to the mucous membrane of the uvula. The uvular muscle shortens the uvula and brings the structure upward and backward.

The uvula is active in swallowing. Its movements are accessory to the ascent of the paired palatopharyngeal arches. Such movement shuts off the nasopharynx from the oropharynx, thus directing food downward.

The uvula is said to be important in helping the other parts of the palate to protect the openings of the Eustachian tubes. It has been thought to direct mucus drainage from the nasal chambers toward the base of the tongue. Accumulated secretions on the nasal floor in acute infections are aided in expulsion into the mouth by uvular movement during expiration. The uvula may become involved in generalized inflammations of the fauces and pharynx. Edema of the uvula may result from faulty or excessive use of the voice. An inflamed uvula interferes with deglutition and respiration.

In addition to its function in swallowing, in preventing middle ear disease, in massaging and moistening the posterior pharynx, and in aiding removal of material from the pharynx and root of the tongue, the uvula prevents excessive nasality of voice (rhinolalia aperta) by controlling the resonance of the air column just over the larynx. The uvula has attained phonetic significance in that it can be employed to make trilled sounds such as the uvular R sound.

The uvula may be abnormally long or thick, bifurcate or double. The long uvula can act as a foreign body in the pharynx, and it can impair the use of the soft palate in producing vowels. Van Riper and Irwin (1958) state that a long uvula is a rare cause of excessive nasality. The long, moist structure can cling to the rear of the tongue and be freed too slowly to prevent the air from being directed through the nasal chambers.

The long or redundant uvula is not ordinarily excised unless malignancy or protracted annoyance is present. In current practice incision has given way to antibiotic management. In shortening an elongated uvula which is causing annoyance, care is taken to preserve the uvular muscle. Uvular resection (staphylectomy) may lead to disturbances of speech and deglutition.

The uvula may shorten after tonsillectomy if excessive pillar-tissue removal has produced scar formation and contraction.

All told, the uvula is a highly functional structure, and it should not be regarded as a degenerate or vestigial remnant of vertebrate phylogeny. Actually, it has not made its biological appearance until a relatively recent time. It is absent in mammalian animals as high as the opossum.

The fauces (isthmus of the fauces) is a port between the mouth and pharynx. It is bounded superiorly by the velum, inferiorly by the root of the tongue, and laterally by the palatal arches.

The glossopalatal arches (anterior pillars of the fauces) are a pair of prominent folds located in the right and left lateral pharyngeal wall. Each contains a glossopalatal muscle covered by mucous membrane.

The pharyngopalatal arches (posterior pillars) are directly behind the anterior arch on either side. Each contains a pharyngopalatal muscle covered by mucous membrane. The posterior arches diverge from the anterior arches to produce on each side triangular fossae, or depressions, in which the palatine tonsils are held.

Tonsils. The tonsils are a series of lymphoid masses forming a discontinuous ring called Waldeyer's ring, which surrounds the entrance to the oropharynx. Small collections of lymphoid tissue fill the intervals between the discrete larger masses.

The palatine (faucial) tonsils are paired, soft and bulging submucosal lymphoid masses. They are enclosed between the anterior and posterior palatal arches on each side in a space called the tonsillar fossa. Their shape is variable, but they are typically oval and flat. Their size is so variable that they may hardly be visible or may be large enough to obstruct much of the throat. They are relatively and, in some instances, actually larger in children than in adults, but they shrink significantly after puberty.

A part of each tonsil is embedded, while the remainder projects and is visible upon inspection. The medial or pharyngeal surface is free except anteriorly. Mucous membrane covers the medial surface, and it presents many orifices leading into crypts that branch and penetrate the tonsillar substance. The cells of the surface, as well as those lining the crypts of the palatine tonsils, are stratified epithelium, like the cells that line the mouth. Mucous glands are abundant. Their ducts open onto the free surface and into the crypts.

The lateral surface of these tonsils is covered with a fibrous capsule which is continuous with the pharyngeal wall. This tough capsule, which encloses the unexposed area of each tonsil, fixes the organ in place.

The tonsils do not completely fill the tonsillar fossa. There is a small space superiorly called the supratonsillar fossa. This space is filled with loose areolar connective tissue. If the fossa becomes abscessed, pus may be delivered through this site.

The palatine tonsils are the best-known members of the tonsillar ring. They are perhaps the most frequent cause of tonsillar pathology. These are the structures meant when the unrestricted term tonsils is used.

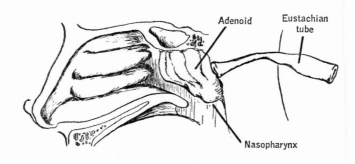

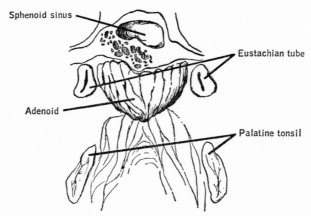

Fig. 9–4. Top: Lateral view of nasopharynx to show the pharyngeal tonsil. Bottom: The adenoid viewed directly after removing all structures anterior to it.

The unpaired pharyngeal tonsil (adenoid) is a lymphoid mass at the superior end of the pharynx, situated chiefly on its posterior aspect. This structure is also most prominent in children, and it shrivels or disappears in adults. In the hypertrophied state during childhood it is called the adenoids (pleural).

The pharyngeal tonsil is composed of several lobules, which are particularly evident during its enlargement, but it has only one area of attachment to the roof of the pharynx. Actually, this structure belongs to the pharynx. The cells of the surface of this tonsil and its follicles are ciliated columnar epithelium like the main part of the nose.

The lingual tonsil is a collection of lymph follicles covering the entire surface of the root of the tongue, lying directly below the mucous membrane and imparting a nodular appearance to this area. The lateral ends of each of these aggregations meet the lower poles of the palatine tonsils.

Just in front of the lingual tonsil is the foramen cecum, which marks the oral opening of the remnants of the thyroglossal duct, which in development led to the thyroid gland. This could be of clinical significance if a thyroid mass should grow at this point or if a cyst from the thyroglossal duct should persist there.

The lingual tonsils are not as large as the palatine tonsils, and they also do not have a complex crypt structure. They are rarely acutely infected concurrently with the palatine tonsils.

The tonsillar ring is a first line of defense against bodily infection. Parts of this lymphoid ring affect the character of speech chiefly because of their active defense reactions which involve inflammation and edema.

The exact functions of the tonsils in health have never been proved, but several views exist: (1) they protect against bacterial invasion; (2) they are endocrine glands; (3) they are blood-forming organs; (4) they are exposed lymph nodes for secretion or excretion; (5) they provide antibodies; and (6) they protect the bronchial tubes against infection.

Hypertrophy (excessive size increase) of the palatine tonsils is perhaps the most common type of tonsillar pathology, especially in children. Excessive enlargement may decrease the size of the fauces and partially occlude the mouth from the oropharynx. The next most common disorder is acute infection. Organisms and mucosal cells fill the follicles or crypts, showing up as white dots at the openings of the follicles. Repeated attacks lead to infection in the Eustachian tube, middle ear, mastoid air cells, upper respiratory passages, brain, or even in distant organs. This view of focal infection should be kept in mind, even though it may not be statistically as serious as was formerly believed. Pus-forming staphylococcal bacteria are the most frequent invaders, followed by the less frequent but more dangerous streptococcal organisms.

Enlarged adenoids can block off the nasal cavity from the pharynx and distort nasal resonance. Snorting and snoring are characteristic sequelae. Rhinolalia clausa, in which the voice loses its characteristic nasal resonance, may result from excessive closure of the posterior nasal passages by the hypertrophied adenoids. Enlarged adenoids may close the openings of the contiguous Eustachian tubes, and the resulting inability to equalize pressure in the middle ear can lead to deafness. The adenoids are said to contribute mechanically to distortion of the palate, narrowing and arching the vault of the mouth. Adenoids also encourage mouth breathing.

The problem of when tonsillectomy is really indicated is far from solved. It depends primarily upon the seriousness of the infection and not upon the distortion of oral or nasal resonance. The tonsils and adenoids form part of a discontinuous ring, and the mere largeness of the components of this ring means nothing in itself and may even be symptomless. Throughout infancy and early childhood the incidence of respiratory infections is high, and if tonsillectomy is done then, it may unjustly be credited with reducing the frequency of such infections. It may be that the tonsils help establish immunity toward respiratory infections and recede when this has been accomplished.

Adenoids and tonsils differ considerably in their relative need for removal, and many of the reasons claimed for tonsillectomy are really reasons for the adenoidectomy. The symptoms due to adenoid pathology are related to obstruction and infection. Repeated earache, deafness, otitis media, and other symptoms of tubal blockage are relieved more by adenoidectomy than by removing the tonsils, which lie a little distance away.

During convalescence from tonsillectomy and adenoidectomy, the tonal quality of the voice can change but generally returns to normal. After adenoid removal there may be hyperresonance. This condition may require some relearning in the activity of the muscles involved.

Pathology of the lingual tonsils is often overlooked. These tonsils also may become hypertrophied and in turn can influence the palatine tonsils above them and the epiglottis below them. If excessively large, the lingual tonsils interfere with deglutition and speech. Tremble (1957) asks for more attention to this area because of the possibility of malignancy.

Muscles of the Soft Palate. Five muscles act upon the soft palate. These muscles include depressor-relaxers (glossopalatinus and pharyngopalatinus), elevators (levator veli palatini and musculus uvulae), and an elevator-tensor (tensor veli palatini). Elevation is exemplified in swallowing in which the nasopharynx tends toward occlusion. Depression is exemplified in normal respiration in which the nasal port is kept open. The levator, tensor, and uvular muscles belong to the palate alone. The others are, in addition, a part of the lingual and pharyngeal mechanisms.

The *musculus uvulae* has already been described. It is coordinated with the levator and tensor muscles in elevating the posterior aspect of the uvula. This muscle shortens the uvula while it is raised by the levator.

The paired *levator veli palatini* (soft palate elevator, levator palati) is a pencil-thick muscle located in the superior lateral pharyngeal wall lateral to each posterior naris, or choana. It originates from the petrous part of the temporal bone and the cartilage of the auditory tube. It passes downward and medially and attaches to the palatine aponeurosis in which its fibers blend with those of the opposite side. It enlarges the fauces by lifting the soft palate upward and backward. It also elevates

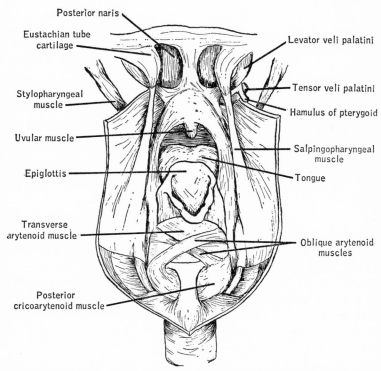

Fig. 9—5. Muscles of the palate and pharynx seen after reflection of the pharyngeal constrictors.

and widens the pharyngeal opening of the Eustachian tube during swallowing. This muscle forms the major mass of the soft palate.

The paired *tensor veli palatini* muscle (soft palate tensor, tensor palati) is a ribbon-like mass anterior and lateral to the palatal elevator. It arises at the base of skull, on the medial pterygoid lamina, on the inferior surface of the sphenoid, and on the cartilage of the Eustachian tube. It passes downward and forward and ends in a tendon which goes medially into the soft palate. The fibers insert upon the posterior border of the palatine bone and fuse partly with the fibers on the other side. The muscle tenses the anterior portion of the soft palate, which then serves as a fixed band to which the other palatal muscles are attached. It also assists the levator in raising the soft palate and in carrying it posteriorly to the pharyngeal wall. The tensor is relaxed in speech for all English sounds except the three nasal resonants.

The paired *glossopalatal* (palatoglossus) muscle is also called the constrictor of the fauces, and it extends between the soft palate and each side of the tongue. It forms with the mucous membrane the glossopalatine arch. It originates from the anterior aspect of the velum and it goes downward, forward, and laterally. It inserts into the side and dorsum of the tongue. Diamond (1952) states that the fibers bend transversely to enter the median septum of the tongue, so that they aid in forming a more or less circular sphincter. These fibers are then said to continue as transverse intrinsic tongue fibers. The muscle may draw the tongue upward and backward. In reverse, it draws the glossopalatine arch down and medialward. These actions decrease the anterior aspect of the faucial port.

The paired *pharyngopalatus* (palatopharyngeus) is a long, thin muscle forming with the mucous membrane the pharyngopalatal arch. It originates from the soft palate, passes laterally and downward, and inserts in common with the stylopharyngeus on the posterior border of the thyroid cartilage. At its superior end some fibers continue upward as the salpingopharyngeal muscle. The latter passes laterally to the velum and ends in the Eustachian tube near its orifice. The chief action of the pharyngopalatal muscle is to bring together the pharyngopalatal arches, an action which depresses the soft palate and narrows the posterior faucial port. In reverse, the muscle raises the larynx and the lower pharynx, as in the first stage of swallowing. This elevation is assisted by the stylopharyngeus muscle.

In résumé, these muscles are important in preparing the individual for speech. The soft palate becomes tensed. The levator veli palatini lifts the palate upward and backward and brings it close to the posterior pharyngeal wall. At the same time the superior constrictor muscle of the pharynx helps to constrict the pharyngeal lumen. There is controversy as to whether the posterior wall of the pharynx moves forward to narrow the lumen, or the lateral walls move forward, or the mucosa bunches up. At any rate the nasopharynx is narrowed to a degree varying with the sound. The elevation of the soft palate is also variable according to the sound, and it reaches its maximum height during blowing movements. The details of the entire dynamics involved in velopharyngeal closure and relaxation are still to be clarified.

These activities help separate the oral from the nasal cavity, and they allow the oral pressure necessary for speech to be built up. In cleft palate the air pressure essential for explosive consonants, such as P, is unobtainable since the oral and nasal cavities cannot be separated.

Innervation and Blood Supply. The tensor veli palatini muscle is innervated by the internal pterygoid nerve, derived from the mandibular division of the trigeminal trunk. The uvular muscle is supplied by the spinal accessory nerve, which reaches the muscle by way of the pharyngeal plexus. The other muscles of the group may also be innervated by the spinal accessory, but this is not conclusive. These muscles are possibly also controlled through the sphenopalatine ganglion and the palatine nerves. The term palatopharyngeal sphincter is used to designate the combined action of the levator veli palatini, superior pharyngeal constrictor, and other muscles. This action can fairly completely separate the oropharynx from the nasopharynx. This status is necessary during speech and blowing to obtain good efficiency with the least output of breath force while minimizing partial escape of the blast through the nose. The nasal resonants are exceptions to this statement.

The nerves controlling the blood supply, sensation, and secretion for the palate go through the sphenopalatine ganglion. This is a nerve cell enlargement having sensory roots from the maxillary division of the trigeminal nerve and motor plus sympathetic roots from the pterygoid or vidian nerve. The ganglion lies in the pterygopalatine fossa, which is a small triangular space deeply located among the facial bones directly below the apex of the orbit of the eye.

The sphenopalatine ganglion innervates the palate through several palatine nerves. The nasopalatines leave the pterygopalatine fossa through the sphenopalatine foramen and descend along the nasal septum. They penetrate the hard palate through the incisive foramen on each side, and they innervate the anterior section of the hard palate. The posterior palatal region and the entire soft palate receive three branches from the sphenopalatine ganglion; these nerves are the posterior palatine, the small posterior palatine, and the accessory posterior palatine. Since all the nerves from the ganglion contain somatic sensory fibers from the maxillary nerve, autonomic efferents from the facial nerve, and sympathetics from the superior cervical ganglion, the mucous membrane of the nose and palate therefore has pathways to mediate general sensations of heat, cold, and pain; it also has secretory impulses for glandular activity and vasomotor impulses to control the diameter and blood pressure of its blood vessels.

The soft palate and the posterior section of the hard palate are supplied by the posterior or descending palatine arteries. These originate from the internal maxillary artery. The palatine vessels descend through the posterior palatine canals along with the posterior palatine nerves. They enter the palate through the greater palatine foramina and travel forward in the angle between the horizontal and vertical processes of the maxillary bones. The same arteries supply the tonsillar region.

When a cleft palate is repaired, the posterior palatine vessels are protected to maintain nutrition to the tissue flaps involved in repairing the cleft. The operation which attempts to repair a defect in the bone is called a uranoplasty. Where the cleft is approximated in the soft tissue, the operation is a staphylorrhaphy.

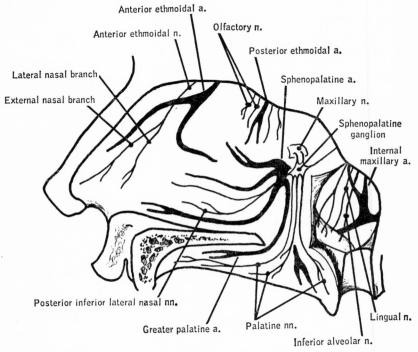

Fig. 9—6. Vessels and nerves of the palatal area seen in a sagittal section of the skull.

The premaxillary or front portion of the hard palate obtains its blood from the anterior palatine arteries. These are terminal branches of the nasopalatine vessels, which in turn originate from the internal maxillary artery. The nasopalatines enter the nose from the pterygopalatine fossa through the sphenopalatine foramen and travel downward along the nasal septum to enter the oral cavity through the incisive (anterior palatine) canal. The nasopalatines supply the nose and paranasal sinus region before sending branches down into the anterior palatal area. These anterior palatine vessels anastomose with the anteriorly directed twigs of the posterior palatine arteries.

The veins of the palate follow the arteries, and they are tributaries of the pterygoid plexus.

The lymphatics drain the anterior portion of the hard palate by entering the anterior facial lymph vessels. These vessels in turn drain into the submaxillary and upper deep cervical nodes. The tongue uses the same route (Sharp et al., 1956). The lymphatics drain the hind part of the hard palate and the entire soft palate by taking a posterior route along the branches of the posterior facial vein into the anterior-superior deep cervical lymph nodes. The latter also drain the base of the tongue and the posterior sublingual area.

DEVELOPMENTAL ANATOMY

Palatal development is an aspect of the development of the face and skull. This will be partly described in later sections dealing with the mouth and the nose. Some general facts are discussed at this point.

The stomodeum, or primitive mouth, is visible about the fourth week. It becomes surrounded by the frontonasal and the paired maxillary and mandibular processes.

The frontonasal process is above the mouth. It becomes separated by the appearance of paired olfactory pits into a lateral nasal process on the outer side of each pit and median nasal processes between the pits. As will be shown later in the text, the lateral nasal processes eventually form the lateral parts of the nose. The fusion of the two median nasal processes produces the septum and medial parts of the nose. The bridge of the nose comes from the frontal or upper part of the frontonasal process.

The median nasal processes help form the premaxillary region. A philtrum, or middle part of the upper lip, and also the upper incisor bony region will be produced when the median nasal processes fuse together.

The maxillary processes produce the cheeks as well as the remainder of the upper lip not formed by the philtrum. They also form the floor of the nose, a considerable portion of the upper jaw, and most of the palatal region except for the premaxillary incisor area.

The mandibular processes give rise to the lower jaw, or mandible, and also to the lower lip. The maxillary processes and the mandibular processes merge with each other at the corners of the mouth.

In view of time, the earliest fusion involves the median union of the paired mandibular processes. This occurs late in the fourth week. In the sixth week, the frontonasal process has been separated by the developing olfactory pits into the median nasal processes and the lateral nasal processes. In the fifth and sixth weeks, the eyes are separated from the mouth by the central extensions of the maxillary processes. The maxillary processes then fuse with the lateral nasal processes. This activity joins the cheeks with the sides of the nose and, by forming a nasal floor, separates the stomodeum into nasal and oral chambers. At that place where the maxillary and lateral nasal processes fuse on each side, a nasolacrimal groove is seen. This later becomes a nasolacrimal or tear duct. It drains fluid from each eye into the nasal cavity on the same side.

In the seventh week, the median nasal processes fuse with each other in the mid-line and with the lower part of the maxillary processes laterally. The premaxillary bones bearing the incisor teeth form in that section of the upper jaw which is of medial nasal origin. The maxillary bones bearing all the other upper teeth form in that section of the arch coming from the maxillary processes. Thus the middle part of the upper jaw comes from the original nasofrontal process, and the lateral parts come from the maxillary processes.

In the sixth week, the olfactory pits are shallow invaginations, but during the seventh week they are extended so that they open into the mouth just behind the premaxillary region. Their external openings are the nostrils, and their posterior openings are the choanae, or posterior nares.

The palate is coincidently being completed by a hard palate replacing the soft membranes. The activity involves a permanent separation of the nasal from the oral cavities by the ingrowth of bones into the roof of the mouth. This is called secondary palate formation. This secondary roof of the mouth forces the choanae to open much more posteriorly so that the crossing of food and air, which is called the pharyngeal chiasm, is transferred from the mouth to the pharynx.

In this palatal formation, the premaxillary, maxillary, and palatine bones produce plate-like extensions; these grow medially and meet in the mid-line. The hard palate begins in the sixth week with a central growth of palatal plates which have come from the maxillary process on each side. Fusion anteriorly with the premaxilla occurs in the seventh week, and complete mid-line closure occurs in the tenth week. The lower part of the nasal septum reaches the dorsum of the tongue until the secondary palatal plates fuse medially and separate these structures. The palatal plates fuse not only with the nasal septum, but their progressive median fusion continues posteriorly. At the ninth week, the anterior three-fourths of the septum are joined with the upper portion of the palate, and the posterior septal fourth is left free. In less than four months the nasal and oral cavities are completely separated by both hard and soft palates. It is seen that the tongue first lies between the palatal shelves and then descends as the shelves grow in medially.

For a diagram illustrating the facial development, see Figure 1–11.

COMPARATIVE ANATOMY

In fishes and amphibians, the secondary palate of the higher verte-brates, which separates the oral cavity from the respiratory passage, is not present. A hard palate becomes a constant structure in reptiles, birds, and mammals, and the posterior nares open into the pharynx rather than into the mouth, as in fishes. The secondary palate begins in the turtle (Nelsen, 1953). Although well developed in crocodiles, it is less sturdy in birds.

In fishes, the nasal pits are blind and have no relation to a pharynx or to the function of breathing. In amphibians, the pharynx has made its appearance as a short and simple tube called the pharyngeal chiasm in which both food and air cross.

The velum has appeared in birds. Among mammals, there is a sig-nificant development of a movable velum. The highest mammalian order of primates acquires the soft palate pillars, or arches. There is a view that the mammalian velum should not be regarded as a structure which separates the mouth from the pharynx but as one which separates the pharynx from the nasal cavities (Jones, 1949).

PATHOPHYSIOLOGY

Cleft palates of various types and degrees constitute an important anomaly of the oral region. They result from failures of unknown etiology occurring in embryonic development when many bilateral processes should have fused. The failure occurs typically in the first twelve weeks of development, the most critical period being in the second month.

A cleft may involve the lip but not the palate, the palate but not the lip, or both. Any section of the palate may become cleft, and the ab-normalities usually follow the lines of development. A normal palate should complete itself by or before the twelfth fetal week. If it does not do so, anomalies result. Some of the causative factors may (with question) be failure in maternal nutrition, uterine conditions preventing joining of the palatal ridges, heredity (through recessive genes), heavy radiation during pregnancy, and deficient oxygen supply. Berry and Eisenson (1956) state that 30 to 50 per cent of the causes can be traced to genic factors.

The most frequent anomaly is the single harelip, or cheiloschisis, which is generally on the left side. The failure is between the maxillary process and the lateral expansions of the median nasal process. Patten (1946) notes that the term harelip is a misnomer since the cleft of a hare is a mid-line one, whereas the human cleft is to one side of the mid-line. The double harelip is a common anomaly. It is called a wolf snout if it is accompanied by a palatal cleft and a projecting premaxilla.

In the more posterior failures, the hiatus (gap) is mid-line and involves the lack of median fusion of the lateral palatal shelves. There is the rare failure of the median nasal processes to fuse together, resulting in a median cleft of the upper jaw. A similar median cleft may rarely occur in the mandible through lack of fusion of the paired mandibular arches.

Speech with cleft palate is in a sense the opposite of that with nasal obstruction. Excessive nasalization is said to result from the defect or absence of the velum with failure to close the velopharyngeal valve. This explanation may not be correct. It will be noted in a later discussion that the causes of nasality are still unclear. In cleft palate the vowels and plosives become nasal, but the ordinarily nasal sounds are least affected.

Surgical closure of the lip and palate is done at different times. The cleft lip can be closed by plastic surgery between two weeks and three months. There is considerable disagreement as to the proper time to undertake surgery of the cleft palate. Early surgery minimizes speech defects, but it may unfavorably affect the shape of the head and also increase the risk of death. Some surgeons operate as early as six months, but many will operate only upon the two or three-year-old child.

Attempts to close the palate by drawing the tissues together (staphylorraphy) have not been overly successful because of the scarcity of tissue in this region and the necessity to overstretch what is available across the gap. The tissue too often pulls away from the suture. There are surgical procedures, such as the push-back method, in which the palate is closed first. In a second operation the blood vessels are stretched out, and tissue is pushed back into the soft palate.

A contribution by the prosthodontists is a lightweight plate, or obturator, which is essentially a plug that fills in the gap in the palate. It may be temporary or permanent. Plastics are commonly used in obturators.

Although surgery and other means are available to repair the palate or to compensate for the defect, the speech therapist plays an essential role in the subsequent social rehabilitation.

Presumptive evidence that vitamin therapy in the first trimester of pregnancy may prevent cleft lip and palates in infants born to mothers who have already had a deformed child has been presented by Conway (1958).

One of the developmental abnormalities of the hard palate is an extremely high palatal arch. This may obstruct the nasal passages and produce an aberrant nasal quality of speech. If the tongue were at the same time too small or too firmly bound down to the floor of the mouth, then speech sounds requiring contact of the tongue with the palate would be faulty. For example, if the tongue in a high palatal arch fails to contact the palate properly or if air escapes from the sides, an influence would be exerted particularly on the letter s, which might even be missing.

In a congenitally short soft palate there is not enough elevation and retraction to occlude the nasal port as needed, and excessive nasal resonance can result.

Paralysis of the soft palate musculature, which is attributable to one of several neurological causes, prevents separation between the nasopharynx and the oropharynx during swallowing; this allows food to regurgitate into the nasopharynx. Speech is difficult and may have a hollow character like that of cleft palate individuals.

SUMMARY

The nature of the vocal tone is influenced by resonance, which affects the amplification and quality of the sounds. When the supraglottic vibrations reach the restricted exit of the mouth or the nose, the degree of nasality imparted to the tone depends upon the nature of the passages through which the vibrations travel.

The soft palate has an important control over the entrances into the mouth and nose, and it thus controls the nasal quality of the sound. The muscular components of the soft palate prepare the individual for speech. They can elevate, depress, or tense the palate, and they can bring it posteriorly to the pharyngeal wall. Certain of these activities allow the oral pressure necessary for speech to be built up.

The tonsillar ring becomes concerned pathologically with the speech function because of its geographic location in the palatal region.

The rich blood and nerve supply to this entire region has been emphasized.

The comparative anatomy of the palate explains why it develops as it does in man. In all human embryology there tends to be a repetition of racial history.

Specific anomalies in palatal embryology can lead to cleft palates of various types and degrees.

Chapter 10

THE VELOPHARYNGEAL MECHANISM: THE PHARYNX

The pharynx, or throat (throttle, gullet), is a single musculocutaneous tube common to the digestive and respiratory systems. It is situated posterior to the nose, mouth, and larynx and anterior to the cervical vertebrae. It is cone-shaped and about 5 inches long. The upper end, or base, is just below the body of the sphenoid bone at the base of the cranium. The lower end, or apex, is continuous with the esophagus at the level of the lower border of the sixth cervical vertebra.

The tube is wider from side to side than from front to back. The latter diameter is greatest in the nasopharynx, just inferior to the cranial base, and it becomes smaller as it descends. The transverse diameter is abruptly constricted below; otherwise its width is fairly uniform.

The pharynx has three coats. The internal coat, or lining, is a mucous membrane. The middle coat is fibrous and is called the pharyngeal aponeurosis. The outermost coat is muscular. All these structures will be described in this chapter.

The pharynx is a tube whose diameters can be actively changed. It is also subject to elevation and depression through muscular action. The changing shape of the cavity influences speech resonance. The sound is altered by varying not only the diameters but also the tension of the walls. Depending upon conditions at the places where the pharynx joins other cavities, its coupling with such cavities is affected, and an influence is brought to bear upon the resonance of the entire vocal system. The pharynx may be the principal resonator of the human voice.

The pharyngeal tube should be kept patent for proper resonance. Its effectiveness in collecting sound waves and directing them into the mouth is decreased by crowding backward the dorsum of the tongue or by producing excessive tension of the constrictor muscles which form the posterolateral pharyngeal walls. An elevated tongue dorsum can be one of the causes of a guttural quality of the voice. A narrowing of the palatal arches between the mouth and pharynx can produce a muffling effect in the vocal tone.

Gray and Wise (1946) emphasize the unlimited possibilities of tonal variations made feasible by the coupled resonating system of the mouth and pharynx. An open tube is adapted to the resonance of a wave whose fundamental is twice the length of the tube. A closed tube is adapted to a wavelength four times the length of the tube and of its odd-numbered partials. The larger the cavity of a resonator the lower the pitch to which it is adapted; also, the larger the opening the higher the pitch, and the longer the neck of the opening the lower the pitch.

With this in mind, one then notes (Gray and Wise) that the mouth can act either as a closed or open tube or that the pharynx can have one or two outlets, because the soft palate can open or close the pharyngeal connections with the nasopharynx. Since these adaptations are made more complex by alterations of tube length and diameter, aperture diameter, and length of neck of aperture, the number of different fundamentals and partials to which the pharynx is adapted for resonance is very great.

Anderson (1942) says that the role of the pharynx in resonation is more difficult to evaluate than that of the mouth or nose, but that it is especially important to provide resonance for the fundamental and the lower overtones. This is said to give the voice a mellow, rich, and full quality.

The texture, as well as the size and shape, of the pharynx and its apertures affects speech quality. A hard-surfaced resonator emphasizes the higher partials, or overtones, so that a pharynx tightly constricted by its muscles takes on a metallic, strident, and tense tone. On the contrary, a soft surface, provided by relaxed throat muscles, increases the responsive range while damping the resonator. This in effect gives relative prominence to the fundamental and lower partials.

The pharynx has other functions more vital than resonance and speech. One such function is in digestion. Of the three classically differentiated stages of swallowing food (deglutition), the second involves rolling the food into a bolus, or cohesive rope, and transmitting it through the pharynx. This is done by voluntary muscles which are activated reflexly through a deglutition center in the medulla. The pharynx is also a passageway for respiratory gases. The ciliated epithelial cells of the nasopharynx help keep the respiratory tract clear by pushing foreign material toward the mouth. The nasopharynx functions as a ventilator of the middle ear and the Eustachian tubes. It also serves as a drainage canal for the nose and lacrimal ducts.

DIVISIONS OF THE PHARYNX

The superior division, the nasopharynx, is a cube-shaped cavity just posterior to the nasal cavities and superior to the level of the soft palate.

It has an average size about that of a walnut. It belongs with the nasal fossae as a part of the respiratory rather than the digestive system.

Unlike the remainder of the pharynx, its cavity is permanently open. During swallowing the nasopharynx is separated from the oropharynx by the soft palate and uvula, which are pushed against the contracting posterior pharyngeal wall.

Anteriorly, it communicates by the 'paired choanae with the nasal cavities. In its lateral walls there are the openings of the Eustachian tubes. The cartilage of the Eustachian tubes elevates the mucous membrane on each side into a cushion, or torus. The pharyngeal tonsil, or

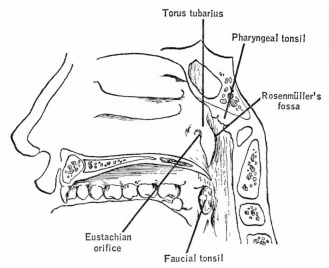

Fig. 10—1. Structures in the nasopharynx.

Luschka's tonsil (adenoids when diseased), is a prominence on the posterior wall. Just above the tonsil in the median line is a small diverticulum called the pharyngeal bursa.

Just above the level of the nasal floor in the lateral walls of the nasopharynx is a distinct depression called the fossa of Rosenmüller. This is a landmark for the opening of each Eustachian tube, which lies both below and anterior to it. This fossa, or deep pocket in the superior aspect of the nasopharynx, is occasionally involved as a hidden trap because of its depth. Infection can arise therein, and it may be the origin of many head colds and nasopharyngeal infections. Malignant growths in the fossa metastasize (spread) rapidly.

The walls of the nasopharynx contain a tough, fibrous membrane, the pharyngeal aponeurosis. This is a sheath which forms the middle coat of the pharyngeal wall. It is sandwiched between an internal mucous layer and a more external muscular layer. The pharyngeal aponeurosis (pharyngobasilar fascia or lamina) is definite in the nasopharynx but is less well defined below. Because the superior constrictor muscle fibers are missing above, there is a weak spot in the wall which the aponeurosis fills in. The muscles appear below this area, and the aponeurosis is not needed. It is the chief structure by which the pharynx is attached to the base of the skull.

The pharyngeal aponeurosis may serve as a tendon of insertion for the constrictor muscles. The general muscular coat of the pharynx lies external to this fascia. The muscles are in turn covered by a buccopharyngeal fascia. The latter is a covering of the upper alimentary canal. It covers the pharynx and is prolonged below to the hind surface of the esophagus.

The posterosuperior aspect of the soft palate forms an incomplete floor for the nasopharynx. An opening called the pharyngeal isthmus exists posterior to this floor. It is this space which is closed during swallowing, as well as in much speech activity, when the soft palate is brought toward the posterior wall of the pharynx.

Although the anteroposterior diameter of the nasopharynx changes very little from its dimensions at birth, the length of this compartment doubles in the first six months after birth.

The middle pharyngeal division called the oropharynx or mesopharynx is directly below the nasopharynx and lies posterior to the mouth and tongue. It extends vertically from the soft palate and pharyngeal isthmus above to the level of the hyoid bone below, and it communicates anteriorly through the fauces with the mouth. The important structures within it are the palatine tonsils and their pillars, the lingual tonsils, and the uvula. The epiglottis protrudes into it. The posterior wall becomes involved in inflammations, local muscle disturbances, and in abscesses within the retropharyngeal space.

The inferior subdivision, the laryngopharynx, decreases abruptly in width and becomes continuous with the esophagus at the level of the inferior border of the cricoid. Its anterior wall is formed partly by the posterior wall of the larynx. It communicates in front with the larynx through the epiglottis. The aryepiglottic folds are its lateral boundaries.

The laryngopharynx contains the valleculae, which are depressions produced by a median glossoepiglottic ligament, and a lateral glossoepiglottic fold on either side. The valleculae are perhaps better visualized as lying between the tongue and the epiglottis. In some persons, pills get lodged in these pockets.

When the epiglottis deflects food or fluid to each side of itself, the material travels into a right and left pyriform sinus. Each sinus is like a trough which can be eliminated when the larynx rises as in swallowing. The pharynx can be anesthetized by cocainizing the floor of the pyriform sinus, below which the superior laryngeal nerve travels.

The terminology of the pharyngeal divisions has been subject to change because of objections to static anatomical relationships (Bosma,

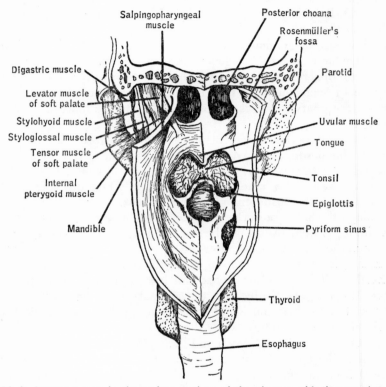

Fig. 10–2. Structures seen in the various sections of the pharynx with the constrictors resected.

1957). The newer concept calls the area above the palate the epipharynx, that between the lower surface of the soft palate and the valleculae the mesopharynx, and that from the valleculae to the opening of the esophagus the hypopharynx. In this functional view, the boundaries dynamically shift with the position of the soft palate and the epiglottis.

PHARYNGEAL MUSCLES AND MOVEMENTS

Movements of the pharyngeal divisions and the neurophysiological regulation of the movements are described in some detail by Bosma

(1957). Huber (1958) gives a concise description of the musculature. Motor performance in the pharyngeal area of several species of animals has been clarified by multiple-channel electromyography, among other technics (Duty and Bosma, 1956).

The pharynx is not a quiet, motionless passageway. Early in swallowing, it is pulled upward and dilated to receive the bolus of food. The active muscles are the palatopharyngeus (pharyngopalatine), stylopharyngeus, salpingopharyngeus muscles, and the suprahyoid group of

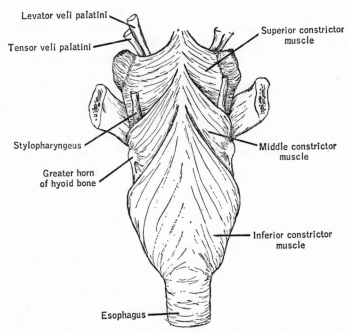

Fig. 10–3. The intact pharyngeal musculature viewed from behind.

muscles. After receiving the bolus, the pharynx descends and constricts. This action pushes the bolus into the esophagus. Descent represents, to a great degree, relaxation of previously activated elevator muscles. Constriction results from active contraction of specific constrictor muscles.

Elevation of the organ crowds and narrows the opening through the epiglottis into the larynx to help prevent food from entering the lung passages. The epiglottis also has some part in this protective action.

The muscles form much of the framework of the lateral and posterior walls of the pharynx. They are arranged in an outer and inner layer which are not readily separable throughout. The outer layer is arranged circularly and is comprised of three constrictor muscles. These muscles change the diameter of the tube. The inner layer is roughly longitudinal, and it includes the palatopharyngeus, salpingopharyngeus, stylopharyngeus muscles, and other irregular muscle bundles. The inner muscles function in elevation, depression, expansion, and contraction of the pharynx.

The *superior pharyngeal constrictor* (paired) is a broad quadrilateral mass containing fibers which, for the most part, curve backward and upward. It has several origins including the pterygoid and hamular processes, the pterygomandibular raphe, the posterior end of the mylohyoid line on the medial area of the mandible, and the root of the tongue. The fibers run posteriorly and fuse at a median pharyngeal raphe with their fellows of the opposite side. The uppermost fibers fail to meet at the base of the skull, and the interval left free is filled by the pharyngeal aponeurosis.

At the level of the soft palate some of the uppermost constrictor fibers become intimately associated with the soft palate musculature. This connection forms a complex sphincter locally active in that region.

The superior constrictors do not have a broad attachment at the skull base, but they are suspended from a central area, leaving a variable free area on each side called the sinus of Morgagni. The levator and tensor veli palatini muscles and also the cartilaginous part of the Eustachian tube run through this space.

The *middle pharyngeal constrictor* (paired) partly overlaps the superior constrictor from behind. The muscle arises at the major and minor horns of the hyoid bone and along the adjacent part of the stylohyoid ligament. The fibers diverge widely from their origin as they curve backward and medialward to blend with those of the opposite side along the posterior median raphe. The only horizontal fibers are the middle ones. The upper ones ascend obliquely to cover the superior constrictor, and the lower ones run beneath the inferior constrictor.

The *inferior pharyngeal constrictor* (paired) overlaps the middle constrictor posteriorly, and it is the broadest and thickest of the constrictors. It originates from the sides of the cricoid and thyroid cartilages, and its fibers curve backward and medialward to insert along the posterior median raphe. While the lowest fibers are horizontal, the highest ones rise obliquely to reach their insertion, which overlies much of the middle constrictor muscle.

Valsalva in 1717 called the horizontal muscle fibers arising from the cricoid cartilage at the lower end of the pharynx the cricopharyngeus muscle. Some investigators think of this muscle as an esophageal section of the inferior constrictor muscle (Batson, 1955). Chevalier Jackson (1915) referred to the structure as the cricopharyngeal pinchcock. In normal swallowing this sphincter opens while the inferior constrictor proper contracts. The muscle is probably best regarded as a sphincter of the esophagus. Huber (1958) says that this section does not go to the median raphe but blends into the esophageal musculature.

The *stylopharyngeus* muscle (paired) appears on the lateral wall of the pharynx as a slender, flattened cylinder. It arises on the styloid process of the temporal bone. Its fibers go down medially to insert partly in the constrictor musculature and partly in the posterior border of the thyroid cartilage. The glossopharyngeal nerve on its way to the tongue

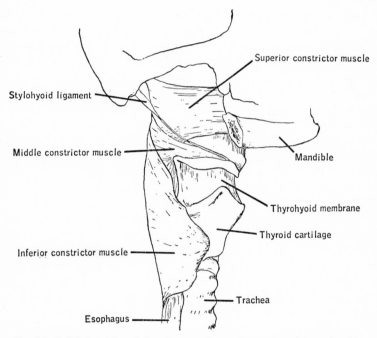

Fig. 10–4. Relationships of the pharyngeal constrictors viewed from the side.

crosses over this muscle. The stylopharyngeus expands the pharynx laterally and also elevates the pharynx and larynx. The front to back dilation of the pharynx during its ascent is caused by the forward carriage of the larynx and the tongue.

Other muscles associated with the pharynx include the salpingo-pharyngeal and pharyngopalatine. These muscles are described elsewhere in this text, and they are especially important in deglutition. In brief, the chief pharyngeal muscles that are used in swallowing are the constrictors, the stylopharyngeus, salpingopharyngeus, and pharyngo-palatine.

The reader is referred to the previous chapter for a discussion of the muscles which shut off the oropharynx from the nasopharynx above and from the oral cavity in front.

We have, under laryngeal physiology, stated that the larynx gradually descends through fetal and early postnatal life. After birth, this descent causes the fibers of the pharyngeal constrictors to be oblique in the position of rest. When the pharynx elevates during swallowing, these constrictor fibers become more circular, and then act as a sphincteric mechanism.

NERVES AND VASCULAR SUPPLY OF THE PHARYNX

The motor nerve supply is chiefly through the pharyngeal branches of the vagus nerve. These rami generally include two on each side, originating from the nodose ganglion and running to the pharyngeal plexus. The existence of this plexus has been noted in Chapter 7. The plexus is on each side of the pharynx, adjacent to the middle constrictor. It is formed by an intercommunication of the vagus pharyngeal rami with others from the glossopharyngeal nerve and from the laryngopharyngeal branch of the sympathetic nervous system.

The plexus sends out motor fibers. Those fibers going to the salpingopharyngeus and pharyngeal constrictors come through the vagus nerve, and those to the stylopharyngeus come through the glossopharyngeal nerve.

The sensory nerves from the mucous membrane of the pharynx also come in through the pharyngeal plexus and are branches of the glossopharyngeal nerve.

The total sensory distribution of the glossopharyngeal nerve includes the root of the tongue, the posterior and lateral walls of the pharynx from the inferior part of the nasopharynx to the epiglottis, the glossopalatal and pharyngopalatal arches, the Eustachian tube apertures, the tympanic membrane, and parts of the soft palate and uvula.

The blood supply of the pharynx comes primarily from the ascending pharyngeal, ascending palatine, and tonsillar arteries, any one of which may be missing. The ascending pharyngeal artery is a branch of the external carotid, and the other two arteries are branches of the external maxillary artery. These vessels supply the constrictor muscles, the stylopharyngeus muscle, the mucous membranes, and such structures as the soft palate, palatine tonsils, and Eustachian tubes.

The veins form a plexus which empties into the lingual and pharyngeal veins.

The lymphatics are especially abundant in the upper pharynx and around Waldeyer's tonsillar ring. Those vessels located in the nasopharynx drain into lateral retropharyngeal nodes or into internal jugular-vein nodes. They supply the pharyngeal tonsil, pharyngeal roof, posterior wall of the oro- and nasopharynx, and the uppermost lateral nasopharyngeal walls. The lymphatics of the hard and soft palates and of the middle region of the pharynx drain into retropharyngeal, deep lateral cervical, or submaxillary nodes. The lymphatics of the arches and faucial tonsils empty into the subdigastric or internal jugular nodes. These same nodes also receive the lymphatic drainage of the anterior portion of the lower pharynx, the posterior drainage of which goes into the lateral retropharyngeal or internal jugular nodes.

PASSAVANT'S CUSHION

Passavant in 1869 described a cushion that projects forward into the pharynx originating from the posterior and lateral walls of the nasopharynx. Although he observed it in a patient with cleft palate, he stated that it is essential for normal speech.

The cushion, or bar, is formed by contraction of muscle fibers that course around the pharynx from the palate in a horizontal direction. These fibers are part of the palatopharyngeus muscle, which has fused posteriorly with the superior constrictor muscle. Townshend (1940) states that the palatopharyngeus has been considered to be a muscle that originates from the palate and travels nearly vertically downward to fuse with the pharyngeal musculature. Thus when muscle fibers were observed originating from the palate but traveling posteriorly to fuse with the upper portion of the superior constrictor, they were considered to be part of the superior constrictor muscle. Earlier anatomists included with the palatopharyngeus all fibers going from the palate to the pharyngeal wall.

The fibers of the palatopharyngeus which encircle the upper portion of the pharynx are seen in all mammals. The chief difficulty has been to assign these horizontal fibers to one definite muscle.

Passavant's bar appears considerably smaller in a normal person than it is in the individual with cleft palate. In the latter the closure of the nasopharynx is brought about by the strong contraction of muscles forming the palatopharyngeal sphincter. In such instances there is excessive obstruction to the oronasopharyngeal passage, and this alters breathing and resonance. In the normal person the closure of the nasopharyngeal valve is effected chiefly by the highly movable soft palate, so that the importance of Passavant's cushion is questionable.

In the previous chapter we discussed how the mutual approach of the velum and the posterior pharyngeal wall is involved in speech sounds. In swallowing, palatal closure is brought about forcibly by several muscles, including the palatal levators, the superior constrictor muscle of the pharynx, and the palatopharyngeus muscle. In speech, the superior constrictor may possibly help to elevate the ridge of Passavant, narrowing the nasopharynx anteroposteriorly and laterally. Cessation of speech often is attended by a sensation of relaxation in the posterior pharyngeal wall.

Passavant's theory that the bulging of the superior constrictor muscle on the posterior pharyngeal wall just above the level of the velum helps to produce a palatal flap necessary for intelligible speech has been both supported and denied (LeJeune and Lynch, 1955). Even the existence of Passavant's cushion has been questioned (Calnan, 1954). Hagerty et al. (1958) state that except when Passavant's phenomenon occurs as a process essential to closure, it is doubtful whether the forward movement of the posterior pharyngeal wall is significant in the production of speech sounds. These views do not invalidate the observations that a phenomenon of this kind apparently exists in association with a cleft palate.

MICROSCOPIC ANATOMY

The pharynx is divided to an epipharynx, mesopharynx, and hypopharynx, and each area may have some preferential functions which may be correlated with the histological specialization of its lining wall. Where blind pouches exist and there is need for cleaning machinery, a ciliated columnar epithelium tends to be laid down. In this general region the epipharynx and the ventricle of the larynx are blind pouches which must be kept clean. In areas of friction and movement, such as in the mouth, most of the pharynx, and over the vocal folds, a stratified squamous epithelium is laid down. Mucous glands predominate in the stratified squamous lining, but seromucinous glands are more common in the pseudostratified columnar epithelium.

In the epipharynx there is a pseudostratified ciliated columnar lining rich in mucous and seromucinous glands. This arrangement is also found on the nasal surface of the uvula. Where the function is not respiratory but one involving deglutition, the epithelium is nonciliated, stratified squamous in type. This variety is extended onto the oral surface of the uvula and variably onto the nasal or dorsal aspect of the soft palate, where friction occurs in swallowing.

All parts of the mesopharynx and hypopharynx retain the stratified squamous lining. The epiglottis has a mixed character such that squamous epithelium covers its anterior surface and the upper half of its posterior surface, while the lower half of its posterior aspect has a covering that is pseudostratified ciliated columnar.

The pharynx is considered to be a first line of defense against infection. This view is based upon the presence of many lymphocytic cells throughout the entire tube. These cells lie in a fibrous network of the reticuloendothelial system.

The pharyngeal mucosa is continuous with that of the nose, mouth, larynx, and Eustachian tubes.

DEVELOPMENTAL ANATOMY

In the early embryo the digestive tract appears as a tubular fore-gut and hind-gut. The fore-gut dilates to form the pharynx, which is thus first a part of the digestive system. The respiratory relationships of the pharynx are seen about the fourth fetal week, when a series of ridges separated by grooves develops along each side of the head. These ridges have an evolutionary significance corresponding to the respiratory gill arches for breathing in fishes, and they are termed branchial arches. We shall discuss these arches again in the text; some general facts are described at this time.

In the human embryo of one month there are five pairs of branchial arches produced by thickening of mesenchyme in the lateral walls of the pharynx. Each arch has a cartilage framework upon which muscles and nerves develop. As seen externally on each side, furrows appear between each arch so that the arches are fairly distinct from one another.

In fishes, the external furrows on each side invaginate, or push inward, toward the pharynx. Simultaneously, a corresponding series of internal pharyngeal pouches evaginate, or push outward. These oppositely directed processes meet, and the barriers break down between them. This process produces a series of openings, or gill slits, from the pharynx to the exterior. The slits are found between each cartilaginous arch.

Such a complete process does not occur in man. The furrows rarely perforate by inward extension. If they do, they produce a persistent fistula from the pharynx to the exterior through which fluid may drain.

The pharyngeal gill system would be of no use in pulmonary respiration. Since it is only an ontogenetic recapitulation of vertebrate evolution, it is transitory. Within perhaps two weeks the branchial arches disappear. The arches, pouches, and associated elements actually do not vanish but change into several structures modified for terrestrial rather than aquatic existence. There is some question about the exact fate of any given structure, and the following account is controversial.

In regard to the arches, the first forms the maxilla, the mandible, a portion of the tongue, and also the malleus and incus bones of the middle ear. The second arch forms the lesser cornua of the hyoid bone, the stapes, the styloid process, and perhaps the styloid ligaments. The third arch produces part of the epiglottis and the greater cornua of the hyoid. The fourth arch forms part of the epiglottis and also the ary-tenoid, corniculate, and cricoid cartilages of the larynx. The fifth arch may also contribute to the larynx.

The evaginating internal pharyngeal pouches, or grooves, which are formed in the late fourth week, also have many derivatives, some in common with the arches. The first pouch forms the paired middle ear chambers and possibly the Eustachian tubes, and it may contribute to the palatine tonsils. The second pouch also contributes to the palatine tonsils and to Waldeyer's ring. The third pouch produces the thymus gland and helps produce the parathyroids. The fourth pouch also contributes to the parathyroids. The fourth or fifth pouch produces the ultimobranchial bodies that either become enveloped by the thyroid gland or else atrophy completely.

The floor of the pharynx, like its lateral walls, produces or helps produce important structures, which include the thyroid bud, the tongue, and the glottis.

Prior to the bony development surrounding the pharyngeal area, a mass of glandular tissue appears, part of which remains in the vault of the pharynx to differentiate into the pharyngeal tonsil. The remainder is cut off from the pharynx and roof of the mouth by the growing sphenoid bone, whose body forms the superior boundary of the pharynx. This isolated glandular mass lies on the under surface of the brain, and it becomes incorporated as a part of the pituitary gland.

COMPARATIVE ANATOMY

Lower animals up to mammals hardly show a definite pharynx, and the transition from mouth to esophagus is very abrupt. This circumstance is partly explainable by the small size of the larynx and by the failure of the epiglottis and its folds to appear. Even in most mammals the pharynx is short. The human pharynx is relatively spacious, and this state is related to the embryological descent of the larynx after it appears as a diverticulum in the floor of the pharynx.

In phylogeny, the pharynx changes more radically than any other bodily region. This is because of the transition of vertebrates from water to land with the corresponding loss in function of the pharyngeal gill slits. In this evolution we have noted that the pharynx modifies to many derivatives including the tonsillar ring, the parathyroid, thyroid, and thymus glands, and several other structures.

In the lungfish, or Dipnoi, air is breathed in the dry season, and these animals develop a passageway from the external nares to the choanal openings leading to the pharynx. A pair of lungs forms whose entrance is guarded by a sphincteric larynx. A glottis appears for the first time.

In the air-breathing amphibians, the glottis must be kept open. The pharyngeal gill arches, which no longer have to support gill openings, become modified to supporting glottic cartilages. In newts, the cranial sector of the fifth gill arch becomes the arytenoids, which help open the laryngeal aperture. The caudal part becomes the cricoid cartilage, which keeps the larynx open.

The pharyngeal gill slits of snakes, birds, and mammals are visible as clefts only in embryonic life. The oral cavity achieves a sharp separation from the pharynx first in reptiles through development of the hard and soft palates. The mammalian pharynx is not very different from that of reptiles or birds; Waldeyer's tonsillar ring and the cervical endocrine structures are prominent.

APPLIED ANATOMY AND PHYSIOLOGY

There are many pathological conditions of the pharynx. For a survey of the disorders of this region, refer to Seltzer (1950) and Hollender (1953). Some selected aspects of applied anatomy and physiology are discussed in this section.

The anatomy of the space behind the pharynx, which is called the retropharyngeal space, is of interest because of pathology. Abscesses occur there, especially in infants and children. The space separates the pharynx posteriorly from the vertebral column. The loose connective tissue within the space permits the pharyngeal elevation and descent entailed in swallowing.

The original view that the area behind the pharynx is one space has been refuted (Davidson, 1949). There appear to be four potential spaces called peripharyngeal, parapharyngeal, postvisceral, and prevertebral. The term retropharyngeal may well be eliminated, and the exact space involved specifically designated.

The retropharyngeal space is only a potential cavity, since the region is actually filled by the loose areolar tissue of the prevertebral fascia. Its vertical extent reaches from the base of the skull above to the farthest point of the cervical fascia below. Its anterior wall is the posterior wall of the pharynx. Posteriorly it is attached to the spine by connective tissue. Its lateral boundary is another compartment called the pharyngomaxillary fossa. The retropharyngeal space contains many lymph nodes, and their breakdown in lymphadenitis characterizes retropharyngeal abscess. These nodes tend to involute during childhood.

Ordinarily, very little of the pharynx can be observed through the normal nasal passages. One can usually look posteriorly into the throat through a space close to the nasal floor. A test, which is especially valuable in children for visualizing the adenoids, is to have the patient say "twenty-five," during which the soft palate should rise and fall. Hypertrophied tissue is indicated if the palate fails to move or if its amplitude of motion is relatively small compared to normal controls.

The pharynx is often examined without using elaborate instrumentation. The posterior nasopharynx is conveniently studied with a nasopharyngeal mirror and reflected light. The mid-portion of the tongue is firmly held down with a tongue depressor, and the mirror is carefully introduced behind the soft palate, avoiding contact with the uvula, tongue, and posterior pharyngeal wall to eliminate the gag reflex. The nasopharynx is brought into view by rotating the mirror so that its reflector surface is directed toward the subject's forehead. Where the gag reflex is too easily elicited, the uvula and soft palate are treated by the physician with a local anesthetic.

The pharynx can also be examined roentgenographically to demonstrate tumors and inflammatory lesions, since these alter the pharyngeal air shadows.

Several diseases of the pharynx are bacterial in origin. The pharynx can harbor potentially pathogenic microorganisms, and the nasopharynx and faucial tonsils may constitute the bacterial centers of the respiratory tract. The presence of pharyngeal anomalies, tumors, diverticula, etc., points up the presence of other categories of disease.

Inflammation of the mucous membrane and underlying tissues of the pharynx may produce pharyngitis (sore throat), which is a common cause of a harsh, husky voice or hoarseness. This is the most frequent disorder of this region.

Acute pharyngitis may occur upon exposure to cold and wet, especially in debilitated persons. The infecting organism is bacterial or viral, but there can be other causes. There is irritation of the throat, the feeling of a lump in back of the throat, and an inflamed mucous membrane covered with whitish mucus.

Chronic pharyngitis may be a sequel to the acute form or may be a result of prolonged irritation from many causes, including excessive or faulty use of the voice. Neglect in treatment may lead to involvement of the Eustachian tubes and produce middle ear deafness, or it may heighten susceptibility to laryngitis, tracheitis, and bronchitis. There is persistent irritation and expectoration of mucus with voice fatigue and hoarseness. The throat shows venous engorgement and inflamed follicles.

Diseases of Waldeyer's ring are another aspect of pharyngeal pathology. The significance of these diseases in speech has already been discussed.

The motor aspects of function may also become deranged. Paralysis or weakness of the muscles of the pharynx, making complete closure of the nasopharynx difficult, has a diverse etiology. It is expressed primarily as a disturbance of swallowing or by a cough because of failure to propel food and secretions in the proper direction. The characteristic sign of organic pharyngeal lesions is painful swallowing, or dysphagia. In severe lesions of the hindbrain, dysphagia may be accompanied by paralysis of the muscles of the palate and pharynx and by alterations in the voice.

The glossopharyngeal nerve is important in the sensory aspects of pharyngeal function. In disorders of the sensory fibers of this nerve, there may be several sequelae. Examples are hypersensitivity (hyperesthesia) with an excessive gag reflex, hyposensitivity (anesthesia) involving varying degrees of loss of pharyngeal sensation, or perverted sensations (parathesia) in which the patient often complains of bizarre stimulation of the pharyngeal area. Severe pain can attend a glossopharyngeal neuralgia.

In connection with the nasopharynx, a statement concerning the Eustachian tubes may be made at this point. These structures will be considered in detail in the final chapter of the text.

The orifices of the Eustachian tubes are in the lateral nasopharynx behind the posterior ends of the inferior turbinates. The cartilage ridge, or torus tubarius, which bounds each orifice superiorly and posteriorly, can be seen shining through the mucosa of the tube openings in a mirror examination of the nasopharynx. The border of the tube orifices is deficient in front and below. It has been stated previously that deep pharyngeal recesses called the fossae of Rosenmüller are located above and behind the openings of the tubes, and these fossae extend laterally beneath the petrous bone. This general region is of clinical significance because lymphoid tissue may proliferate and narrow the openings of the tubes. This could produce deficient ventilation of the middle ear.

In the infant, the Eustachian openings are level with the nasal floor, and they rise only later to a permanent site behind the inferior turbinates. Children are particularly susceptible to invasive nasopharyngeal infection since their tube openings are in a line with nasal secretions traveling posteriorly from the nasal floor.

SUMMARY

The pharynx is a common digestive and respiratory passageway. It may be the principal resonator of the voice. It should be kept open for proper resonance. The coupling of the pharynx with the mouth and nose makes an enormous variety of tonal variations possible. Pharyngeal resonation is influenced by the size, shape, texture, and coupling of the tube.

The pharynx is arbitrarily divided to three vertical regions, each having distinct contents.

The tube is subject to active elevation and depression and also dilation and constriction. These changes are linked with the swallowing of food and with the qualities of the vocal tone.

The sensory fibers of this region belong to the glossopharyngeal and the motor fibers to both the glossopharyngeal and vagus nerves. The blood supply comes chiefly from the ascending pharyngeal, ascending palatine, and tonsillar arteries. Lymphatics are rich particularly in the upper pharynx and tonsillar region.

The problem of Passavant's cushion has been considered. Its involvement in normal speech is less conclusive than in speech with cleft palate.

The pharynx is a dilation of the embryonic fore-gut. Its paired bilateral branchial-arch transitions recapitulate the racial history. A study of comparative anatomy reveals the progressive stages in the lower vertebrates. The pharynx changes more radically than any other bodily region because the transition of vertebrates from water to land necessitated a change from gill respiration to a new pulmonary air system.

Chapter 11

THE NOSE AND SINUSES

In the present chapter the general structure, function, and development of the nose and paranasal sinuses and the involvement of these structures in speech will be described.

IMPORTANCE IN SPEECH

The nasal cavities are subdivided into many variably sized air spaces, and they should not be considered as a pair of large nasal chambers. The subdivisions of the nose tend to classify it as a multiple resonator. Its resonance cannot be as readily varied as that of the velopharyngeal apparatus since its upper bony walls are immovable. Its lower, fleshy walls can be moved, however, by external muscles.

The exact importance of the nose in the speech apparatus is still uncertain. In some regards it is less important than once thought. For example, the causes of nasality are not necessarily localized within the nasal chambers. Berry and Eisenson (1956) note that a discordant nasal twang may result from excessive tension of the pharyngeal constrictors, the pharyngeal arches, the levator palati muscles, or from tension anywhere in the supraglottal region.

On the other hand, the evidence of certain pathology indicates that the nose offers a relatively important contribution to speech. In the disorders, or dyslalias, caused by deformities of the nasal passages, distinct speech defects called rhinolalias are produced (West et al., 1957).

Hahn et al. (1952) state that the nasal cavities are the least adjustable and least versatile of the resonators and that they may serve chiefly as supplemental sympathetic resonators for high-frequency overtones.

The paranasal sinuses, which are diverticula, or recesses, of the main nasal cavities, have been said to contribute to general resonance, although their influence is ordinarily slight or even doubtful. The sinus contribution is relatively fixed and perhaps may be thought of as a part of the nasal resonance component of speech. The bones of the skull

215

surrounding the air sinuses are fairly thin and may add a forced vibration to the tone.

SKELETAL FRAMEWORK OF THE NOSE

The nose and its cavities are developed by the fusion of several bones and cartilages. There is an external integument and an internal mucous membrane.

The bones of the external nose are the nasals and the frontal processes of the maxillary bones. The maxillaries form not only the principal framework of the cheek but help form the lateral aspects of the external nose. When the small nasals undergo medial fusion, they produce the bridge of the nose in the superior facial region. The point above this, where the nose is continuous with the forehead, is the root. The lower free angle is the apex. The alae nasi are the rounded lower sections of the lateral surface.

The nasal cartilages are prominent in the lower part of the external nose. They include the cartilage of the septum, the paired lateral and paired major (greater) alar cartilages, and several minor (lesser) alar cartilages.

At the inferior section of the nasal septum there is a central post, or columella, which separates the right and left nostrils. The columella is developed in the embryo from a depressed part of the medial nasal process. The cartilages which enter into its construction include the lower part of the septal cartilage and the medial parts of both greater alar cartilages. The bony anterior nasal spine also helps form the columella.

The cartilage of the septum fills in the anterior space left deficient by the recession of the perpendicular plate of the ethmoid bone. This cartilage fuses posteriorly with the ethmoid bone. It connects above in front with the nasal bones and also with the lateral cartilages. It meets the medial crura of the greater alar cartilages below. Its lower border also connects with the vomer and the palatine processes of the maxillary bones.

The major alar cartilages shape the form of the nostrils and the nasal tip. Each major cartilage is a thin, flexible structure, so curved that it forms the medial and lateral nasal wall of its own side. There are thus the medial and lateral crura. The paired medial crura along with adjacent soft tissue form a movable structure called the septum mobile nasi. This appears in the lowest part of the nasal septum. The cartilage of the septum does not extend downward as far as this level. One can easily move the flexible septum mobile nasi voluntarily.

Stovin (1958) discusses the importance of the septum mobile nasi. It serves as a shock absorber for the lower nose. It is also concerned with the facial expressions elicited by speech and laughing, so that its mobility is important to facial appearance.

Each lateral crus of the major alar cartilages meets the frontal process of the maxillary bone in its posterior section. Within the membrane that connects the crus and the frontal process are several minor alar cartilage plates.

The lateral nasal cartilages are attached above to the nasal bones and to the frontal processes of the maxillary bones. They meet the greater alar cartilages below. The lateral cartilages are continuous above with the septal cartilage but slightly separated from it below.

Converse (1952) has briefly reviewed the anatomy of the nasal cartilages and their role in surgery. They are important in nasal physiology since their movements help maintain an adequate airway. Thus in facial paralysis, in which the cartilages are fixed because of muscle paralysis, there is an inadequate airway on the paralyzed side.

The muscles of the external nose are small and not very important. One or more of them are occasionally absent. They lie in pairs on each side of the nose. The procerus muscles cover the nasal bones, and they wrinkle the skin over the root of the nose. The nasalis muscles have an alar portion, which draws down the nasal wings, or thickened lower section of the sides of the nose. There is also a transverse portion, which constricts the nostrils. Two separate muscles on the sides of the alae dilate the nostrils. These are the dilator naris anterior and the dilator naris posterior muscles. The nasal septum is drawn down by the depressor septi nasi muscle. The nasal muscles are included in the facial muscles of expression which form a part of the speech mechanism.

The nasal cavities, or fossae, are divided by a central structure called the nasal septum. It usually deviates, because of repeated trauma, toward one nasal cavity, generally to the left. This deviation can affect nasal resonance.

The anterior part of the septum is mainly cartilaginous. This section is received in a triangular wedge of bone. The crest of the nasal bone and the frontal spine help form the anterior aspect of the septum. The perpendicular plate of the ethmoid bone forms its middle section. The vomerine and the sphenoid bones form its posterior aspect. The perpendicular ethmoid section becomes fused below with the upper anterior border of the vomer. Actually, the vomer extends forward from this fusion, and this anterior extension then fuses above with the lower margin of the septal cartilage of the nose. The septum nasi is completed below by the maxillary and palatine bones.

The ethmoid bone extends upward into the anterior part of the cranial cavity. This forms a projection resembling a cockscomb in the anterior cranial fossa, and it is thus called the crista gallae. A perforated sieve-like area, the cribriform plate, surrounds this projecting spur and serves for the passage of the olfactory nerve from the upper olfactory areas of the nasal chambers into the rhinencephalic or smell areas of the fore-brain.

The ethmoid bone is T-shaped, the upper horizontal cross limb being formed by the horizontal cribriform plate and its extensions. This constitutes the partition between the cranial and the nasal cavities.

The upper lateral extensions of the horizontal portion of the ethmoid bone appear on each side as a labyrinth or lateral mass. Each mass is a group of thin-walled cavities, arranged in an anterior, middle, and

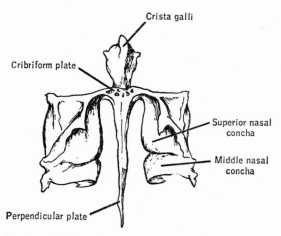

Crista galli

Cribriform plate

Superior nasal concha

Middle nasal concha

Perpendicular plate

Fig. 11–1. Nasal septum in natural disarticulated appearance seen from in front.

posterior group of ethmoidal cells or paranasal sinuses. The labyrinth on each side folds in medially to produce a pair of oblique shelves, the upper and the middle turbinates, or conchae. Inferiorly on each side an independent bone, the inferior turbinate, similarly projects shelf-like into the nasal cavity.

These three pairs of very light and spongy conchal processes divide each nasal chamber into three paired chambers, which extend from the front to the back of each nostril. The passages on each side are called the superior, middle, and inferior meati. Each meatus communicates with the air in front by an anterior naris and with the nasopharynx in back by a posterior naris, or choana. The meati receive, in localized regions, the canals which drain the various paranasal sinuses.

The turbinates increase the available mucous membrane surface within the small nasal chambers. Most of this surface deals with respiratory activity. In animals with considerable olfactory acuity, the turbinates may be greatly enlarged and are rolled up into scrolls.

The roof of each nasal fossa is very narrow from side to side. It is formed from back to front by the sphenoid, ethmoid, and frontonasal bones.

The floor of the nose, which ordinarily is a complete partition between the nose and mouth, is formed by the palatine and maxillary

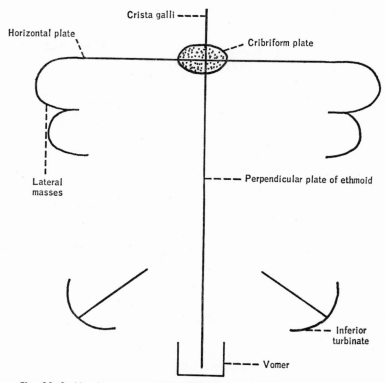

Fig. 11—2. Nasal septum and its extensions in diagrammatic front view.

bones. The superior surface of the palatines forms the posterior section of the floor of the nose. The inferior surface of the palatines forms the back part of the hard palate. The anterior border of the palatines fuses with the maxillary bones. The maxillaries comprise approximately the anterior three-fourths of the hard palate. Except for openings, or foramina, to transmit nerves and blood vessels, all the processes normally fuse together in the mid-line and elsewhere. Failure of palatal fusion results in cleft palate.

The mucous membrane of the septum and of the nasal cavities generally contains many mucous glands. The upper third is the olfactory area, which contains the tiny filaments of the olfactory nerve. The lower two-thirds form respiratory epithelium, which contains a richer supply

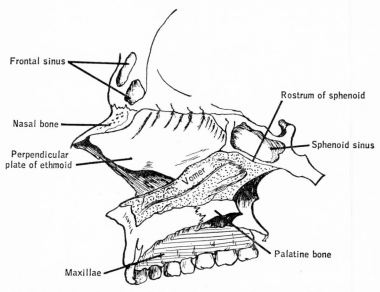

Frontal sinus

Rostrum of sphenoid

Nasal bone

Sphenoid sinus

Perpendicular plate of ethmoid

Vomer

Palatine bone

Maxillae

Fig. 11—3. Sagittal section of the skull showing paranasal sinuses and the nasal septum.

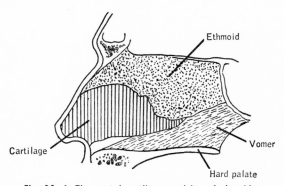

Ethmoid

Cartilage

Vomer

Hard palate

Fig. 11—4. The septal cartilage and its relationships.

of glands. Histologically, the respiratory lining is pseudostratified, ciliated, and columnar. The membrane is especially thick and vascular over the turbinates, somewhat less thick over the septum, and thin elsewhere including the inside of the paranasal sinuses.

BLOOD AND NERVE SUPPLY

The blood supply of the nose and its sinuses is important from the standpoint of pathology following infection of the mucosa. The arteries are derived from both the internal and external carotids. The internal carotid sends branches through the ophthalmic artery. The external carotid utilizes its internal and external maxillary branches, chiefly the sphenopalatine branch of the internal maxillary artery.

The blood supply of the turbinates, meati, and septum comes from the sphenopalatine branch of the internal maxillary artery. The roof of the nose and the ethmoidal and frontal sinuses are supplied by anterior and posterior ethmoidal branches of the ophthalmic artery. The pharyngeal branch of the internal maxillary artery supplies the sphenoid sinus. A branch of the superior labial artery plus infraorbital and alveolar branches of the internal maxillary artery supply the maxillary sinus.

The facial artery, a branch of the external maxillary, travels along the sides of the nose and supplies its skin and dorsum. The nostrils receive blood from the facial artery and also from a septal branch of the superior labial artery.

The venous drainage exists under the mucous membrane as a cavernous plexus, emptying chiefly through the ophthalmic, anterior facial, and sphenopalatine veins. The "swell bodies" (erectile tissue on both sides of the septum which adjusts its thickness according to atmospheric changes) represent the venous plexus in full development over the lower septum and over the middle and inferior turbinates.

The nasal mucosa contains an abundant network of lymphatics which are continuous with the lymph vessels of the nasopharynx and soft palate. There is an anterior set of trunks which drain into the preauricular, facial, and the submaxillary nodes. Trunks in the Eustachian tube area drain a large segment of the nose and paranasal sinuses, and these in turn end in deep cervical and retropharyngeal nodes. The various nodes may become involved in infections of the nose and sinuses.

Lymphatics of the external nose, the vestibule, and the mucosa of the anterior section of the nasal fossa travel up above the superior eyelid and drain into the parotid nodes. Other trunks from the sides and roof of the nose reach the parotid nodes by traveling across the lower eyelid. Still others from the front part of the septum and from the external nose drain into the facial or submaxillary nodes.

As a general statement, the lymph in the anterior third of the nose flows out to the external surface, but the lymph in the posterior two-thirds as well as in the sinuses flows toward the Eustachian region of the nasopharynx and eventually to deep cervical and retropharyngeal nodes.

Several nerves innervate the nose. The facial nerve sends motor fibers to the blood vessels and glands. Eggston (1947) states that efferent parasympathetic fibers for the mucosa of the nose and paranasal sinuses originate from cells in the reticular formation of the medulla, contiguous to the facial nerve nucleus. They pass from the medulla in the pars intermedia of the facial nerve and are distributed by the great superficial petrosal nerve to the sphenopalatine ganglion. Postganglionic fibers go from that ganglion to the mucosa, glands, and blood vessels of the nose, palate, tonsils, and lacrimal glands.

The "opposing" sympathetic efferents originate in several segments of the thoracic spinal cord, typically 1-T to 5-T, and pass as preganglionics to the vertical sympathetic chain. They ascend to the superior cervical ganglion at the level of the thyroid cartilage. Postganglionics then go superiorly and gain entrance chiefly to the trigeminal nerve, whence they supply nasal glands and blood vessels. The sympathetics are more vasoconstrictor than dilator, the latter tending to prevail in the parasympathetics of the pars intermedia. The erectile tissues of the nose are especially subject to vasodilation.

Eggston (1947) emphasizes the fact that the vasomotor nerves may produce immediate effects upon the diameter of the nasal passages and of the paranasal sinuses. Anger quickly produces swelling of the mucosa. Fear rapidly shrinks the membranes. These emotional effects are reflexly brought about by an action upon the vasomotor centers in the hindbrain.

On the sensory side, the ophthalmic and maxillary divisions of the trigeminal nerve innervate the nasal skin and mucosa for the general sensations of hot, cold, pressure, and pain. The anterior section of the septum and lateral wall of the nose receive the nasociliary branches of the ophthalmic nerve. The inferior turbinates and the inferior meati receive the anterior alveolar branches of the maxillary nerve. The posterior and superior aspects of the septum are supplied by the nerve of the pterygoid canal. This is also called the vidian nerve, which we have described elsewhere as being formed by fusion of the greater superficial petrosal nerve with the deep petrosal nerve. The vidian nerve runs into the sphenopalatine ganglion. The center of the septum receives the nasopalatine branches of the maxillary nerve. The innervation to the middle and superior turbinates comes from the posterior superior nasal branches of the maxillary.

The nose also receives the olfactory nerve for the special sensation of smell. This nerve leaves the sensory epithelium in the mucosa of the upper part of the nose. Its twigs penetrate the skull through the cribriform plate and reach the olfactory bulb. Central fibers pass from there to the smell areas of the cerebrum.

NASAL FUNCTIONS

The nose functions for smell and as a respiratory channel which filters, warms, and moistens the entering air. It serves also to modify the resonance quality of speech.

The humidifying power of the nose is indirectly involved in modifying laryngeal function. In the dry larynx, or laryngitis sicca, the incident air has insufficient moisture. Ordinarily the seromucinous glands of the mucosa within the nose may secrete as much as a liter of fluid per day. A lack of moisture is also a factor in destroying the action of the nasal hairs, or cilia, which normally aid in the removal of dust and bacteria.

The air is warmed by the radiator function of the mucosal blood vessels. These vessels open or close according to the air temperature, acting as a thermostat for the respiratory tract and perhaps allowing the paranasal sinuses to behave as heat insulators for surrounding cerebral structures.

The nasal mucosa is also linked, although obscurely, with endocrine function. Eggston (1947) speaks of the gonadotropic activity of extracts from the nasal mucosa and the paranasal sinuses of cattle. The erectile tissues of the nose develop in puberty. In animal castrates such tissues tend to involute. Endocrine influences are also suggested by the observation that menstruation and puberty may be associated with an increased incidence of nosebleeds.

THE PARANASAL SINUSES

Four pairs of accessory sinuses, all called paranasal, drain into the nose. They include the frontal, maxillary, ethmoidal, and sphenoidal air cells. All are lined by a ciliated mucous membrane continuous with that lining the nose. Disease thus readily spreads from the nose to the sinuses. There is considerable variation in the size and shape of the sinuses among individuals.

The frontal sinus is an irregular cavity in the frontal bone, behind the superciliary arches. The paired sinuses are separated medially by a usually deviated bony septum. Each sinus drains by a frontonasal duct into the middle meatus, or passageway below the middle turbinate.

The ethmoidal air cells are many, small, thin-walled, intercommunicating air chambers situated in the labyrinth of the ethmoid bone between the orbit of the eye and the nasal cavity and just below the cranial cavity. The number of cells varies from three to eighteen. They are divided into anterior, middle, and posterior groups. The anterior and middle groups drain into the middle meatus, the middle by one or two openings. The posterior sinuses drain into the superior meatus by one or more apertures.

The maxillary sinus, or antrum of Highmore, is a pyramidal cavity occupying the hollow body of each maxillary bone in the cheek area. These sinuses are the largest of the paranasal group. Each member lies lateral to the lower half of the nasal cavity below the orbit and above the molar and premolar teeth. The opening out of it, which is on its

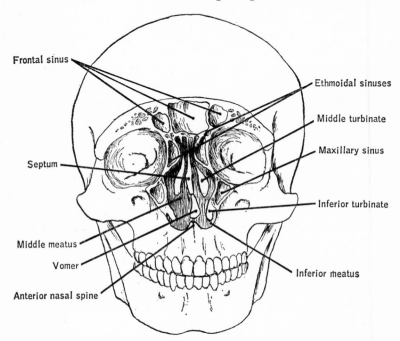

Fig. 11–5. Anterior view of skull showing nasal cavity and paranasal sinuses.

medial side, drains into the middle meatus. There may be one or two drainage canals into the nose, and these are frequently higher than the sinus floor. This presents difficulty in drainage. The secretions of the mucous membrane are propelled toward the opening in the medial wall by cilia. It is during inflammation, when the cilia cannot keep up with the quantity of secretion formed, that the bottom of the sinus collects fluid.

The sphenoidal sinus is a large cavity within the body of the sphenoid bone. This bone occupies the central part of the base of the skull. The sinus is just above and behind the nasal cavities, and it is above and a little anterior to the nasopharynx. It is divided more or less completely into halves by a central bony septum. Each half may be considered to be an individual sphenoidal sinus. On each side a duct runs to the corresponding nasal cavity, terminating in the sphenoethmoidal recess of the nose, a space above the superior turbinates.

A palatine sinus may be present, lying within the orbital process of the palatine bone and opening either into the sphenoidal sinus or into a posterior ethmoidal sinus.

FUNCTIONS OF THE SINUSES

Proetz (1941) says that the sinuses are developmental accidents which form as the facial bones grow away from the relatively stationary cranium. As an example, the maxilla grows inferolaterally to support the alveolar process, and the vacated space is filled by sucking in the nasal mucosa, which then lines the cavity so produced. This process could explain the position of the drainage opening in the upper medial part of the maxillary sinus. Boies (1954) says that the sinuses have no physiological function and are important primarily because of the complications of nasal disease originating in them.

The sinuses, on the other hand, have been claimed (without real proof) to do many things. Since they are cavities in the skull bones, they permit these bones to increase in size without adding too much weight. They add a mucus secretion to the nasal chambers, and they help moisten the incoming air. They equalize the barometric pressure of the air.

The general problem of the resonance function of the paranasal sinuses is still to be solved, and exact data are lacking. There is very little direct evidence that these cavities are important in resonance (Curry, 1940), but there is some indirect evidence. A stuffy nose and sinuses will change voice quality. The greater nasal cavities seem to be the more important agents, since a loss of vocal resonance need not occur in a chronic sinus infection without significant nasal involvement.

Greene (1957) differentiates the relative importance of the sinuses as resonators. The maxillary sinuses are stated to be important because they are large and open into the nose by fairly large orifices. The other sinuses, and also the Eustachian tubes and mastoid air cells, are small, closed-in, and waterlogged. Since they have inadequate communication with the external air, their resonating function is problematical.

Some of the difficulty in analyzing the problem lies in the need to differentiate the part played by resonance due to forced vibrations occurring in bony and cartilaginous structures from the part played by cavity resonance which occurs within the known resonating chambers. The former have been termed universal and the latter selective resonators.

DEVELOPMENTAL ANATOMY OF THE NOSE AND SINUSES

This subject is treated in a thumbnail sketch, since the development of related facial structures is described in Chapters 9 and 12.

The earliest sign of the developing nose in the early embryo is the olfactory placode, which is an oval thickening on each side of the front end of the head. About the fourth week a fold forms around the outer border of the olfactory placode, and small pits begin to form in the surface. The pits deepen, move toward one another, and come to lie together except for a narrow separating band of tissue. The nostrils develop from the pits.

Simultaneously with the nasal changes, outgrowths called the maxillary processes appear. They grow forward and medialward to join the nasal structures and produce a primitive mouth and nose.

The nasal pits by the thirty-fifth day have deepened to blind pouches above the oral cavity. The pits grow posteriorly and become continuous with the throat through the posterior nares. The anterior nares are never closed during development. Thickening of the walls above the mouth elevates the position of the nose. The nasal septum forms from the tissue between the nostrils.

By the end of the second month the external nose is broad and flat. The mid-line area develops early, and the inferior part descends to form the nasal tip.

The floor of the nose, or palate, develops as a part of both the face and the mouth (Chapters 9 and 12).

The paranasal sinuses begin in the third or fourth fetal month as small groups of cells which appear at different points in the mucous walls of the nasal fossae. These cells proliferate into the bones of the skull and form sacs at some distance from their origins, although they retain a permanent connection with the nasal chambers by one or more ducts. The mucous membrane of the nose continues along each duct as a lining of the sinuses.

The groove foreshadowing the maxillary sinus appears in the fourth fetal month, which is earlier than the other sinuses appear, but the structure is not fully developed until after the child gets its second dentition. The maxillary sinus at birth is still represented only by a groove. According to Woodburne (1957), the maxillary sinus exhibits a definite cavity at birth, and it is the only one to do so.

The rudiments of the sphenoidal sinuses appear in the fifth fetal month or later. They represent recesses of the nasal cavity which have been partly separated and enclosed within the sphenoidal conchae. The conchae comprise the anterior surface of the body of the sphenoid as well as the anterior part of its lower surface but not including its crest and rostrum. The sphenoidal rudiments actually do not extend into the body of the sphenoid until the seventh year or later.

The ethmoidal air sacs are present at birth, but they are very small.

The frontal sinus first appears during childhood at about the seventh year.

All the sinuses enlarge slowly until puberty, after which they expand and differentiate rapidly. Only the frontal and sphenoidal sinuses are radiologically visible at six or seven years of age.

PATHOPHYSIOLOGY OF THE NOSE AND SINUSES

All the sinuses can be visualized by ordinary diagnostic X rays with the head placed in specific positions, as described in routine manuals of X-ray technic. Their status is evaluated according to the resulting shadow densities and contrasts.

Transillumination is occasionally of some diagnostic value when disease of the sinuses is suspected. In this procedure the patient is examined in a dark room. To observe the maxillary sinus, an electric light is placed in the patient's mouth, and he closes his lips. The light can pass readily through a normal antrum, and it appears as a light crescent between the eye and the floor of the orbit. There is perception of light in the eye, and a redness of the pupil may occur. There is a failure of light passage where severe antral (maxillary sinus) disease exists. In a variation of this technic, the electric light is placed between the cheek and the back part of the alveolar (toothbearing) process posterior to the canine fossa; light readily passes through the floor of the orbit only in a normal antrum.

The frontal sinus is occasionally transilluminated, but with less frequent success, by directing the incident light against the roof of the orbit just above its inner canthus (angle). Again, the light is more easily transmitted if the sinus is normal, and the light will be seen in the forehead.

Transillumination is generally of limited significance because of developmental abnormalities of the bones and sinuses.

For examining the nasal cavities, a flashlight can satisfactorily bring out the conditions in the anterior nares and the anterior part of the septum. A nasal speculum and reflected light can be used to bring into view the posterior nares and the posterior part of the septum.

Some abnormalities of the nasal cavity and sinuses affecting speech are briefly listed herein.

Marked deviation of the septum.

Hematoma of the septum. This condition is usually traumatic and is followed by bilateral swelling and obstruction.

Polyps. These are saccular swollen masses of tissue covered with a boggy mucous membrane.

Foreign body.

Acute rhinitis. This condition is also called acute coryza or the common cold. The turbinates swell, and the mucous membranes are hyperemic (engorged with blood). A thin watery fluid, which later thickens, enters the nasal cavities.

Chronic hypertrophic rhinitis results from repeated attacks of acute rhinitis. It involves congested turbinates, thickened mucous membranes, and narrowed air passages.

Vasomotor rhinitis is characterized by mucous membranes and turbinates which are swollen but pale, and there is excessive watery secretion. This condition is generally considered an allergy.

Neoplastic rhinitis implies the presence of benign or malignant tumors in the nasal cavity. They act as any growth to interfere with breathing and speech.

Tuberculous rhinitis usually causes destruction of the septum of the nose with involvement of the sinuses. The symptoms resemble those of malignancy and syphilis.

Lupus is a chronic tuberculous condition of the skin which may involve the nose and destroy the septum and inferior turbinate, occasionally spreading to include the pharynx and larynx.

There are clearly several conditions called rhinitis so that it is not a disease but a symptom in which nasal secretions are increased. Concomitantly, the nasal mucosa shows some degree of swelling, which interferes primarily with breathing and secondarily with vocal resonance.

Nasality as a distinct speech deviation is one of the most frequent speech defects encountered. This and nasal resonance are not synonymous terms. Nasal resonance is the normal resonance added by the nasal passages to the exhaled tone, whereas nasality implies too much nasal resonance. The opposite condition is called denasality.

The only English sounds primarily nasal are M, N, and NG. It is also probable that some nasal resonance is expected in sounding certain vowels. In nasality the subject seems to talk through his nose, and the vowels are overnasalized. In denasality the vowels sound dull, and the nasal consonants show a lack of resonance, such as during speech with a head cold. The definition and acceptance of nasality are to a great extent subjective.

Nasality is in a sense a disorder of articulation, since the vowels are given distinctive qualities by the position of the articulators as well as by the size and shape of the resonating chambers. For example, the velum, which is an articulator, can lower improperly and permit nonnasal sounds to obtain nasal resonance. Actually, the velum does not completely occlude the nasal cul-de-sac even in normal speech. We have discussed this in Chapter 9.

Nasality or denasality are found under many circumstances. A point may be made of their occurrence as sequelae of certain disorders involving excessive patency of the nasal passages (rhinolalia aperta) or excessive closure of the nasal passages (rhinolalia clausa).

Rhinolalia aperta (hyperrhinolalia) may result from cleft palate, holes in the hard or soft palate, soft palate paralysis, faulty habits in the use of the soft palate, etc. The voice is hypernasal.

Rhinolalia clausa (hyporhinolalia) has both anterior and posterior varieties. The anterior type is organic and involves different degrees of obstruction to the passage of air in the anterior part of the nose. There are anatomical deviations such as polyps. The voice may sound as though the person had a plugged nose or a head cold.

The posterior type may be associated with organic lesions, such as adenoids or other growths in the nasopharyngeal region, or it may be functional. In the latter there may be permanent elevation of the soft palate during speech, along with contracted pharyngeal or tongue muscles.

The distortion of nasal sounds because of the absence of nasal resonance exemplifies denasality, or negative nasality, and it illustrates the fact that the voice without resonance is lifeless.

Some simple although inconclusive tests of nasal conditions may be tried. To check first for whether the air in a given person passes without obstruction through each nostril, hold a piece of paper so that its upper border is about 3 inches from his left nostril. Let him close his right nostril with a finger and gently exhale air for a few seconds through his open left nostril. If there is an unobstructed stream of air, the corner of the paper will be made to move visibly and smoothly. This procedure is repeated for the other nostril.

It may then be checked whether nasal resonance is being unduly involved in primarily nonnasal sounds. Cool a small mirror and dry it, then position it perhaps one-quarter of an inch below the nostrils of a subject. Have him speak aloud a sentence in which nasal sounds are not emphasized. If an appreciable film of warm air condenses upon the mirror, there is too much nasal involvement in the emitted breath stream.

A modification may then be tried to test whether sufficient nasal resonance is being imparted to what should be a set of nasal sounds. Holding the cooled mirror below the nostrils and above the mouth, have the individual speak aloud a sentence in which nasal sounds predominate. The mirror should then collect a more obvious film of condensed air.

The above tests must be interpreted with caution. Nasality can be fairly independent of the nasal emission. In that instance inferences concerning nasality should not be drawn from the nature of the nasal emission. The nasal cavities could be occluded and still vibrate with sufficient intensity to produce audible sounds that are nasal (West, 1936).

It was stated at the outset of this chapter that the causes of nasality are not necessarily localized within the nasal chambers. Van Riper and Irwin (1958) review the literature on the possible origins of nasality. Greene (1957) says that the most important factor causing nasality is not the degree of nasal air escape. Nasality is determined by the degree of tension found in the upper pharynx and also by the ratio of the size of the openings into the mouth and nose, relative to the size and shape of the air-filled cavities.

The resonating potential of the nasal cavities is influenced by humidity. This effect is reflected in the different degrees of swelling of the nasal mucous membranes and the turbinates.

In functional states, such as in fear, the mucous membrane may become dry, and the turbinates shrink. Moses (1954) makes the plea that voice problems involving inflammatory changes require not only medical treatment but often psychic therapy.

In regard to the paranasal sinuses, the most common disorder is sinusitis, which is an acute or chronic inflammation usually stemming from nasal disorders but also having an occasional traumatic cause. Mucopurulent discharge filling the nostrils or spread over its floor usually indicates sinusitis. In these conditions the pus or mucopus may spread to the nasopharynx with subsequent mucosal congestion.

Tuberculous infections and cancerous cells may spread into the sinuses. The nose is not the only avenue of transmission, since infected tonsils in the mouth and throat may be involved. Carious teeth below the maxillary sinus may spread infection into the antrum. Even chronic laryngitis may be associated with chronic sinus infections high above the larynx in the respiratory tract.

Eggston and Wolff (1947) may be consulted for a comprehensive discussion of the biological and pathological aspects of the nose and sinuses.

SUMMARY

The nose in speech activity is a multiple resonator whose relatively fixed structure restricts variability in its resonance function. The basic functions of the nose include respiration and then olfaction.

The nose is constructed from several bones which undergo fusions. These include the paired inferior turbinates, maxillaries, nasals, palatines, and also the unpaired ethmoid, sphenoid, and vomerine bones.

The median nasal septum is formed by the nasal bones and frontal spine anteriorly, by the ethmoid in the middle portion, by the vomer and sphenoid posteriorly, and by the maxillary and palatine bones inferiorly. Its anterior section has a triangular notch, which receives the septal cartilage.

The nasal cartilages provide not only support but mobility for the lower parts of the nose. They include the cartilage of the septum, two lateral and two greater alar cartilages, and a number of paired lesser alar cartilages.

The nasal blood supply is from the external and internal carotid arteries. The venous drainage exists under the mucous membrane as a cavernous plexus. There is a rich lymph supply.

The nasal mucosa is especially responsive to vasomotor nerve control. General sensation is mediated by the trigeminal nerve and smell by the olfactory nerve.

The paranasal sinuses, which are diverticula of the main nasal cavities, contribute only slightly to resonance. They help lighten the skull, and they act as air conditioners.

The development of the nose from the olfactory pits is described.

Chapter 12

THE STRUCTURES FOR ARTICULATION

GENERAL ASPECTS

Articulation refers to the activities of supraglottic structures which modify the phonated air. In its broadest sense it also refers to the acceptability of the sound to the listener.

Articulators are valves to stop the phonated exhaled air completely or to narrow the space for its passage. They shape, fuse, and separate the sounds transmitted to them. Articulators include such structures as the lips, teeth, hard and soft palate, tongue, mandible, posterior pharyngeal wall, and probably should include the inner edges of the vocal folds. The hyoid bone may be classified as an articulator (Van Riper and Irwin, 1958) in view of the effects of its movements upon consonants and vowels.

The tip of the tongue appears to be the fastest articulator, and the soft palate is probably the slowest. Perhaps the teeth and hard palate should be regarded as walls against which the articulators move. Contact of the tongue against the alveolar ridges in the front of the hard palate helps produce many consonants.

Froeschels and Jellinek (1941) linked the articulatory mechanisms with a kind of embryological theory for the origin of speech. Phonetic utterances made while chewing are said to be formed into articulated speech. They based this theory on the assumption that primitive man produced sounds while eating, and that in primitive man the connection between the vocal activity and the chewing function did not disappear in phonetic utterances. In animals and primitive tribes chewing is accompanied by various sounds. Original speech did not consist of single sounds but was a continuum. The early unity of chewing and speaking is said to be further corroborated by the fact that chewing activities are sometimes used to treat certain types of speech disorders. This eating-speaking theory is but one in a host of similarly inconclusive proposals.

Gray (1957) surveyed the minimum essentials of speech sound formation that produce intelligibility. Any sound, whether in isolation or in context, should be supported by adequate breath pressure and should be correctly formed. There must also be a sharp release or movement into the next sound formation. The clearness necessary for intelligibility is provided by the consonants, while much of the tonal quality of speech is given by the vowels. A dominant role is assumed by the articulators in shaping all consonants. They also assist in forming some of the vowel phonemes.

In the formation of consonants, the vowel sounds are interrupted to variable degrees in the mouth or diverted through the nose. The air does not flow through a wide-open mouth. The consonant machinery includes the mandible, lips, tongue, and velum. There are movements such as approach and recession of the jaws, protrusion of the lips, and approximation of the lower lip to the upper teeth. The tongue moves toward or to the teeth, palate, velum, or alveolar ridge. The velum rises or falls.

Although all vowels are voiced, which implies activity of the larynx, consonants can be voiced or voiceless. The latter term negates laryngeal activity. A changing relative importance of phonation and articulation in the formation of sounds is therefore indicated. Whispering involves articulation to a great degree. In English, whispering is almost fully as intelligible as loud speech, which implies that phonation is adjunctive, providing such parameters of speech as amplification, emotional setting, and inflection. In a language where inflection is necessary for intelligibility, whispering is ineffective.

In the description of the articulation of sounds, a simplifying system of classification had to be established. This is the province of phonetics. There have been three main approaches to this problem (Kantner and West, 1941). In the acoustic approach, sounds are classified by their effect upon the auditory mechanism in terms dealing with auditory sensation. Thus there are the vowels, semivowels, diphthongs, and consonants. The consonants in turn are subdivided to sonants and surds, and these are further subdivided into fricatives, sibilants, etc. The vowels, which are less clearcut, are described by such terms as long, short, high or low pitched, stressed or unstressed, strong or weak, more or less resonant, and more or less sonant.

In the placement or positional approach the geographic places of the articulators in producing the given sound are described. Thus there are front, mid- and back vowels, and there are palatal, velar, various labial, and other varieties of consonants. The emphasis is placed upon anatomy.

In the kinesiological approach, the positions of the articulators are similarly determined, but the movements of the machinery to accomplish such positions are also emphasized. The neuromuscular apparatus is brought into the description. Such terms as stop, glide, and continuant suggest movement rather than position or auditory sensation. They also suggest persistence, or duration, whose value is indicated as a continuant or a stop. A continuant sound is continuable as long as the breath holds out, but a stop (plosive) is instantaneous and finished.

To illustrate the usage of the classifications, let us run through a few sample descriptions of consonant formation. The reader is referred to standardized speech textbooks dealing with phonetics and articulation for an adequate and comprehensive discussion of this subject.

The sound P involves closure of the lips and a subsequent sudden opening of the mouth. This sound is called an unvoiced bilabial plosive, or stop. The release, or explosion, follows the increase in oral air pressure, or implosion. The P sound could also be described by stating that the exhaled air is stopped completely. This would then be a stopped consonant.

The involvement of the soft palate in articulation can be illustrated in the plosives. The increasing air pressure in the mouth is made possible not only by a closed oral port but also by closure of the posterior nares through elevation of the soft palate. Perhaps the first stage in the formation of such sounds in this velopharyngeal closure.

We can similarly describe the sounds F and v. These are called labiodentals from the fact that the lower lip lightly meets the upper incisors and sharply withdraws. The lip is the active agent. F is unvoiced, and its cognate, v, is voiced. From another standpoint, F and v are fricatives, or the air escaping through the mouth is only partially stopped with the velopharyngeal valve closed. These sounds are also called oral continuants.

Air stoppage depends upon the velopharyngeal mechanism. If the oral escape is minimized or prevented and the air is directed through the nasal passages, as in M or N, the nasal consonants are produced.

In the s and z sounds, air is forced through a narrowed oral port. s is an unvoiced fricative, and its cognate, z, is a voiced fricative. These sounds are also called hissing sounds, or sibilants.

s and z can be described anatomically. The tongue is the primary articulating agent. The velopharyngeal mechanism first closes. Then the mandible rises to approximate the upper and lower teeth. The lips retract, and the tongue tip is free, although the sides of the tongue occlude with the lateral dental surfaces as far forward as the labial incisors. This action allows air to travel in a small channel over the tip as well as through the narrow opening between the central incisors.

In consonant formation, the partial or total stoppage of air or its direction of flow are not the only variables. The time taken to dissipate the augmented air pressure is another factor. Thus in CH and Y, which are called affricatives, the air is partially stopped, but it need not be quickly released.

Dynamic bodily changes and movements, involving the activity of muscle groups and studied as the science of kinesiology, are seen to be of considerable importance in the explanation of how the individual phonemes are produced.

The articulatory adjustments for vowel phonemes are less precise. In the vowels the mouth is relatively open, yet there are constrictions of the mouth and throat which modify the volumes of these chambers and the size of their openings. In the front vowels the anterior part of the mouth narrows between the tongue-blade and the hard palate while the pharynx widens. In the back vowels the lips narrow, the tongue dorsum elevates toward the soft palate, and the cavity of the pharynx enlarges. In the neutral vowels the tongue is in a "resting" position.

Vowel production is particularly linked with resonation, which may be the chief factor in differentiating the vowels. Although vowels are produced by vocal fold vibration, it is possible to replace the laryngeal sound. Thus, vowels can be produced by whispering or be formed even in laryngectomized subjects. Hahn et al. (1952) state that to produce vowels, several conditions are ordinarily needed. The vocal folds vibrate. The velum rises against the posterior pharyngeal wall. There must be a relatively open passage from the vocal folds through the lips, and movements of the articulators must change the size and shape of the oral cavity.

For each vowel, the mouth, nose, and pharyngeal resonators take a given position and shape which permit selection and exaggeration of specific overtones. There are two unlike theories of vowel production, the harmonic and inharmonic theories (Fletcher, 1953). In the first, the vocal folds are said to produce a compound wave containing a fundamental and many harmonics, and the component frequencies are exact multiples of the fundamental. The bodily resonators magnify frequencies to which they are tuned, and this in turn determines the vowel quality. This is a steady-state theory, in which the waves pass in regular succession for short periods of time. In the inharmonic view, the vocal folds serve to excite transient frequencies characteristic of the vocal cavities. Irregular or nonperiodic puffs of glottic air excite the supraglottic air. In both theories, the vocal quality depends upon the natural periods and damping of the vocal cavities.

There is a more recent school of thought which deemphasizes the value of the previous classifications and holds that speech is not a succession of sounds in which each sound implies a specific corresponding position of the speech organs. Heffner (1950) says that speech is a continuum of movements and the isolated sounds and positions represent ranges of variation rather than fixed entities. The same sound is produced inconstantly; conversely, different sounds can be elicited by the same articulation. Sound is learned and expressed as a unit resulting from considerable integrated bodily activity. Even in the early literature (Travis, 1931), it was emphasized that it is inadvisable in therapy to reeducate only a limited group of muscles. The important goal is to establish a new total-reaction pattern.

There is little doubt of the validity of these contentions, but it is also true that speech is inescapably bound to a unique human structure and its correlative activities. All biological activities are more complex and dynamic than previously supposed, but the importance of their correlates in structure is in no wise diminished by this knowledge. We are simply confronted with the necessity of adding additional technics of analysis to our investigative armamentarium.

APPLIED PHYSIOLOGY

The largest percentage of speech defects are those of articulation. The term dyslalia has been used as a blanket word to cover disorders of the articulatory machinery. A dyslalic individual is one whose sounds are improperly produced, replaced by others, or entirely lacking. The causes may be central or peripheral and functional or organic. Some examples include low intelligence, auditory defects, motor deficiencies, cleft palate, retarded speech, irregular teeth, inactive tongue, and social and psychological causes.

Whether persons have real differences in anatomical structure at the basis of their articulatory disorders remains generally uncertain. This point will be considered again in the chapter. In functional articulation disorders, no systematic differences in the lips, palate, or tongue have been proved.

In disorders of the dominant cerebral hemisphere, there may be thick and slurred speech as a result of hemiplegia of such articulator organs as the cheeks, lips, and tongue.

Basal ganglia disturbances affect articulation. In progressive lenticular degeneration (Wilson's disease), the hypertonus and stiffness of all muscles, including those of the mandible, lips, pharynx, and tongue, lead to faulty articulation. The patient with Parkinson's disease usually has a slow and hesitating speech. The individual with chorea may have explosive and arrhythmic speech along with irregularities in respiration.

In a cerebellar lesion, phonation may suffer more than articulation. There is a lack of rhythmic correlation of respiration with speech, and even the strength of the breath stream suffers. The speech is labored, many syllables tend to be explosive, and facial grimaces are common. The speech may be slow and monotonous.

When the articulator muscles become paralyzed, as in progressive atrophy of the motor neurons of the cranial nerves leaving the brain stem (progressive bulbar paralysis), the speech becomes labored and eventually unintelligible.

West (1936) pointed out that when phonetic lapses are traceable to disorders of the articulatory muscles or of their lower motor neurons, it is useful in diagnosis to list the difficulty according to the fairly distinct neuromuscular unit involved in producing the given sound. The variety of the phonetic failure would help to diagnose the lesion.

In this grouping, the labial sounds are articulated by facial muscles innervated by the facial nerve. The lingual group is articulated by lingual muscles and the hypoglossal nerve. The nonnasal group, requiring velar closure, is supplied by palatal and pharyngeal muscles through the glossopharyngeal and spinal accessory nerves. The guttural group involves the palatopharyngohyoid musculature, supplied by the glossopharyngeal, vagus, spinal accessory, and the first three cervical nerves. The mandibular group, requiring either a wide or a narrow spread of the mandible, uses the muscles of mastication and the trigeminal nerve. Finally, all voiced sounds involve laryngeal muscles and the vagus nerve.

In practice, the technic of diagnosing defects in the articulatory mechanism involves, among the other things, a complete phonetic testing whereby the capacity to produce each speech sound is analyzed. This area is outside our scope. Rutherford (1956) outlines a technic for cerebral-palsied children, which very briefly but comprehensively illustrates the general methodology of an examination for speech integrity. Tests of adequate phonetic analysis, including a bibliography on the subject matter, are reviewed by Milisen (1957). For a general survey of the etiology, symptomatology, and therapy of disorders of articulation, consult Travis (1947) and Berry and Eisenson (1956).

A phonetic alphabet has been useful in some disorders of phonation. In this system speech sounds are represented by special phonetic symbols instead of conventional letters or orthographic symbols. This alphabet ideally attempts to have one symbol for one speech sound. This plan provides a stable system in which one letter does not represent too many sounds. In practice, the assumption is not actually correct that one sound has one symbol and vice versa.

There are a great many speech sounds, which vary considerably among languages and individuals. A rough estimate of these sounds is obtained from the number of symbols and all the variations in sound characteristics of each of the phonemes represented by these symbols.

What is heard as т, a phoneme or family of speech sounds, may be produced with the tongue tip in many positions in the oral cavity, thus varying the sound qualities.

Several factors produce variations in sounds. Significant examples include the inability to replicate speech patterns exactly, the influence of the preexisting position of the speech organs, individual variations, and the tendency to repeat environmental speech sounds. There is a definite position of the tongue, teeth, and lips for every sound, and these positions vary in accordance with the real nature and form of the sounds as they are spoken. The phonetic alphabet, which is based upon describable structural positions, can aid in correctly producing the acceptable sound of words. Although ordinary spelling emphasizes only one pronunciation of a word, the phonetic alphabet shows the variant pronunciations. It is applicable for teaching a foreign language or correcting an unwanted accent because it can designate any position of the articulatory organs.

A widely used system is the International Phonetic Alphabet (Kantner and West, 1941). The symbols used are not as a whole readily recognizable by a layman or by one just beginning the study of the science of speech. In this text the ordinary symbols of dictionary usage are employed throughout, and the student is referred elsewhere (Gray and Wise, 1946) for the technical phonetic symbols.

A simplified Northampton Chart (Yale, 1946), which is practicable in teaching the deaf and uses symbols recognizable by the layman, may give an elementary concept of the number of English speech sounds and how they are formed in isolation. The symbols used represent the most frequent spellings.

In vertical column 1 the vocal folds are in open position, but in column 2 they are vibrating. The sounds of column 3 are nasal, and they are the only English sounds having an open nasopharyngeal port. The sounds of vertical column 6 are associated with extended lips and sounds at the front of the tongue while phonated air passes freely through the mouth. In column 7 there is emphasis upon the back of the tongue and the lips are rounded. The sounds of column 8 are misfits. In column 9 the sounds are diphthongs or combinations of two vowels.

Other similarities among speech sounds are illustrated in the horizontal columns. In column 1 the lips are closed. In column 2 the tongue tip in most cases reaches the hard palate. In column 3 the back of the tongue touches the hard palate, or it rises in the posterior part of the mouth. In column 4 the tongue tip goes between the teeth. In column 5 the superior border of the lower lip meets the inferior borders of the upper teeth. In column 6 frictional noises at the edges of the front teeth produce a part of the sound. In column 7 similar events occur, but

SIMPLIFIED NORTHAMPTON CHART†

	1	2	3	4	5	6	7	8	9
	Consonants					Vowels			
	Breath sounds	Voiced sounds	Nasal sounds						
1	p	b–	m						
2	t	d–	n	l	r				
3	k	g–	ng						
4	t^1h	t^2h							
5	f	v							
6	s	z							
7	sh	zh							
8	ch	j–							
9	wh	w							
10	h–								
				y– x = ks qu = kwh		ee –i– a–e –e– –a–	o^1o o^2o o–e –o– aw	a(r) wr –u–	i–e a–e o–e u–e ou oi

† A dash after a letter in the consonant chart signifies that the sound is initial in a word or syllable.

SOURCE: By permission, The Clarke School for the Deaf, Northampton, Mass. As found in Caroline A. Yale, *Formation and Development of Elementary English Sounds*, Metcalf Printing and Publishing Company, Inc., Northampton, Mass., 1946.

the median groove of the tongue is wider and forms more posteriorly. In column 8 the tongue tip drops or explodes into positions such as those of column 7. In column 9 the lips are rounded. The H of 10 is without its own position and takes that of the succeeding sound, i.e., the O–E of hole.

Let us now briefly examine some implications of the so-called information theory. The need to develop the relationships between the physiological facts and the acoustical signal appears to be a central problem in speech. Much more will have to be known about the anatomy and the exact changes in the vocal tract before any strict relations can be established.

Many quantitative as well as qualitative facts concerning the acoustical signal have been derived from use of the information theory. The reader is referred to papers by Miller (1951), Licklider (1951), and to Wiener's presentation (1948) of the relation of time series to information and communication. A major problem in communication involves the amount of information conveyed by speech and the efficiency of the average speaker in producing the information.

The speech musculature has been said to produce about 5 syllables, or 12.5 speech sounds per second. If any one of 39 different speech sounds were randomly generated at 12.5 phonemes per second, the speaker is estimated to produce any one of 10^{19} different sequences of sounds per second, and a perfectly efficient listener could select any one of the possible referents. There are factors, however, which reduce the amount of information. The speaker is relatively inefficient in that (1) motivation may be limited; (2) not all speech sounds are articulated with equal ease or frequency; and (3) the speech mechanism cannot select many words per second. Another set of limiting factors depends upon the construction of the spoken language, in that (1) phonemes and different words are not emitted equally often; (2) there is a sequential dependency of phonemes; and (3) the verbal context restricts the number of words which may be chosen.

In a fully developed speech message individual words have a meaning only in context. The unit of meaning is one or more sentences. In isolation a single word has a meaning; it is an auditory or visual symbol of an object, with a meaning of an elementary nature. Meanings are communicated otherwise, as through gestures, exemplified in the manual speech of the deaf and dumb. The term propositional speech was coined by Hughlings Jackson to differentiate the communication of meanings from the expression of feelings, which have no propositional value. Logical abstract thought may also require concomitant internal verbal formulation, but this may not be needed for the more simple mental processes. Brain (1955) defines speech as the entire process by which meanings are comprehended and expressed in words, whereas articulation is a motor activity in which the formulated words are changed into sounds. In this view a disorder of articulation would involve no derangement in the correct formulation of words, but it would in the machinery of verbal sound production.

Travis (1957) discusses factors governing the accuracy and validity of the information derived from central nervous system automatons in terms of the cybernetic reactions involved. Speech lapses are said to be rarely the failure of pure automatisms but a result of breakdown of some speech synergy or an interference with such a synergy by the entrance of an automatism into the efferent circuit which frees the lower motor neurons of articulation.

The cybernetic analysis of speech, among other mental functions, may provide significant contributions. It is one way in which the activity of nerve fibers can be quantitatively treated, by the analogy that the nervous system operates similarly to an electronic calculating machine. Since neurons and synapses act as relays which are either on or off, the Boolean algebra of classes (particularly the algebra of propositions, which is based upon the choice between yes or no, on or off) is especially applicable to treating information. Simplification is made possible by using binary arithmetic, which uses the scale of two instead of the decimal scale of ten, since the number of alternatives presented at each choice is two.

The development of machines for the analysis and synthesis of speech sounds may be noted at this point. The reader is referred to a brief but interesting account by Carroll (1955) of some new devices which are helping to establish a field of experimental phonetics. This instrumentation is illustrative of the rapid entrance of communication engineering into the field of speech. For example, the sound spectrograph measures variations in vowel quality among dialects and permits the phonetic range of variation of a phoneme to be estimated. The speech stretcher plays back speech at a changed utterance rate without changing the original pitch. The electrical vocal tract synthesizes vowel sounds, which are quite naturalistic. Machines to convert speech to writing and to translate languages are in the making.

Speech elements have been artificially varied independently of one another to test the specific role played by each in speech by a device called the vocoder, first demonstrated by the Bell Telephone Laboratories in 1939. An oscillator replaces the larynx, and electrical filters replace the vocal resonators. The spectrum of the desired sound is obtained by filters, and the oscillations are converted to audible sound waves. Such parameters as the pitch can be varied at will.

Van Riper and Irwin (1958), in discussing the treatment of voice disorders, review a number of new instrumental methods used to improve voice quality. These methods make such factors as pitch variation visible and make possible the correct control of pitch. Nasality may be indicated and controlled. Intensity levels can be analyzed and corrected.

THE MOUTH

Speech Activity. The mouth articulates recognizable sounds. It also provides the free passage necessary to build up tone by addition of volume and resonance. Oral resonance has been considered previously, but some facts pertinent to articulation will be noted. The mouth is not only an articulator, but it is also the most movable and controllable of the resonators. This remarkable oral versatility is ascribable to the many associated structures within and about it such as the tongue, teeth, velum, pharyngeal walls, lips, cheeks, and mandible.

The muscles associated with the mouth continually alter their activity to modify the oral tone. In front, the orbicularis oris muscle of the lips alters oral cavity resonance by pursing and retracting. Along the sides, the mouth is enlarged or constricted by the buccinator, platysma, risorius, and zygomaticus muscles. The posterior opening is constricted by the glossopalatal muscles.

Oral resonance is also influenced by the hard palate through the rigidity, density, and tension of its structure and also partly through its shape (low or high, narrow vault).

The mouth is important as a resonator in forming vowels. It changes its size and shape to amplify certain partials in the laryngeal tone, and it imparts to the tone a quality described as a vowel sound. Through the associated changes in tongue positions and in the shape of the lips, the tonal quality is altered, and another vowel sound is produced.

In the building up of mouth pressure the velum helps to dam up the air by aiding closure of the nasal passages. This action gives sufficient force to develop high pressure consonant sounds, like к or g (West et al., 1937).

Developmental Anatomy. In describing palatal development (Chapter 9) it was noted that the essential elements for the formation of the face are usually present during the fourth week. Some additional details concerning facial development, with particular reference to the mouth, will be considered.

The anlage of the mouth appears in the ventral head region as an ectodermal pit called the stomodeum. This is bounded above by the projecting forebrain, laterally by the mandibular processes (and their developing extensions, the maxillary processes), and below by the mandibular processes. The pit is open in front, but it is closed in back by a buccopharyngeal membrane. This separates it from the fore-gut. During the third or fourth week the membrane, or stomodeal plate, ruptures at a point corresponding to the tonsillar region of the adult and forms the oral opening into the gut.

Several surrounding structures grow forward about the mouth to enclose it as the face and the jaws. At four weeks the stomodeum and the mandibular arch below it are the prominent landmarks of the face.

In the mid-line above the developing mouth there is an overhanging prominence. This is the frontonasal (nasofrontal) process, which projects from just below the forebrain to bound the upper border of the mouth. The process is derived from mesenchyme surrounding the cranial end of the notochord. The latter is a rod-like structure, ventral to the primitive nervous system of the embryo, which will define the primitive axis of the body and form vertebral elements.

A pair of olfactory pits, described elsewhere in the text as the primordia of the nostrils, divides the frontonasal process into a central section, the paired median nasal processes, which are between the developing nostrils, and the paired lateral nasal processes, which are lateral to the nostrils. This division occurs in the fifth week.

In the meantime, the maxillary processes, which have proliferated from the dorsal ends of the mandibular processes, grow inward toward

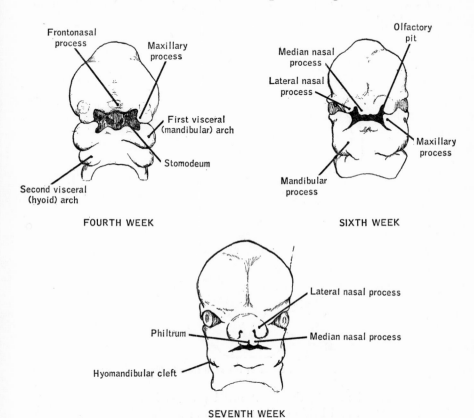

Fig. 12—1. Early development and fusion of the facial primordia.

the median line in the ventral aspect of the face. The medial tip of each maxillary process fuses with the lateral nasal process on its own side. The combined processes are pushed medially. A fusion then occurs with the expansions called globular processes, which develop on each side of the median nasal processes. The maxillary process on each side also merges laterally with the section of the mandibular arch that is located at the corner of the mouth.

These fusions have separated the oral pit from the olfactory pits.

These pits will open later into the cavity of the oral pit by paired openings called choanae, or posterior nares.

The anterior part of the mouth is bounded below by the mandible developing from fusion of the mandibular processes. It is bounded above by several fused processes. There are the median nasal processes and their paired globular process extensions in the mid-line. The lateral nasal processes are just lateral on each side. The fused maxillary and mandibular processes are forming the corners of the mouth.

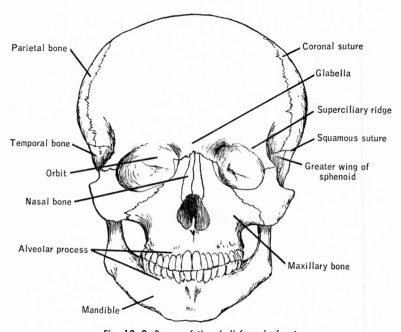

Fig. 12—2. Bones of the skull from in front.

In the second month, the frontonasal process has narrowed down to form the septum and bridge of the nose, and the face looks more human. The facial region is just about completed by the close of the third month.

The inward growth of the palatine extensions of the various processes to produce the secondary palate has been described in Chapter 9. This activity completes the mid-section of the oral cavity. The hind part of the cavity of the oral pit then opens into the pharynx. The gums and teeth are developed from the walls of the hind section.

The upper lip develops from tissue covering the frontal and maxillary processes. The lower lip develops from tissue covering the mandibular arches.

In rare instances the mouth fails to develop, a condition called astomia. The essential failure occurs in the ninth and tenth week. An excessively large mouth, called macrostomia, is a result of incomplete fusion of the mandibular with the maxillary processes; if these fuse excessively, they produce a tiny mouth, or microstomia. Ordinarily, the paired mandibular processes fuse to form the mandible in the fourth or fifth week. An incomplete fusion may leave a median cleft in the lower lip.

General Anatomy. The mouth is divided into a vestibule, or buccal cavity, and a larger oral cavity proper.

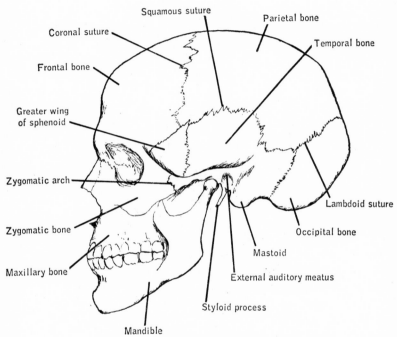

Fig. 12–3. Bones of the skull viewed laterally.

The buccal cavity is bounded externally by the lips and cheeks and internally by the outer aspect of the teeth and gums. Where there is a full dentition, the buccal and oral cavities in the resting position of the mandible communicate between the upper and lower teeth. In the occlusal position, when the teeth are in close contact, these cavities communicate through capillary clefts between the adjacent teeth in each jaw and also through a narrow opening behind the back teeth on each side.

The buccal cavity has many glands. The labial glands on the inner surface of the lip are mucous. Molar glands open from the cheeks to the buccal cavity opposite the back teeth. Stenson's ducts of the parotid salivary glands open opposite the second upper molar teeth.

The labial frenulum is a vertical fold of mucous membrane on the inside of the upper lip, and it connects the lip with the alveolar process. A similar but weaker structure is found in the inner median aspect of the lower lip.

In the oral cavity proper, the peripheral boundary is the alveolar process and the teeth. The roof is the hard palate, which separates the oral from the nasal cavity. The floor is muscular, and it is occupied by the tongue. The posterior wall is the dependent section of the soft palate which continues laterally into the arches of the palate. The mouth communicates with the throat through the fauces.

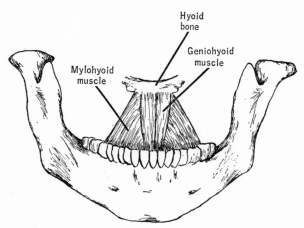

Fig. 12—4. The mandible and the muscular oral floor.

The tongue is held down in the floor by the frenulum linguae. On each side of this and parallel to the lower teeth is a crescentic sublingual ridge into which the ducts of Rivinus open from the sublingual salivary glands. Wharton's ducts from the submaxillary salivary glands open into the frenulum linguae near the lower central incisors.

Oral lubrication from the salivary glands is important to speech as well as to mastication and deglutition. With a decreased salivary flow, the movements of the lips, tongue, and cheeks against the teeth are accomplished less smoothly and efficiently. This condition handicaps speaking or singing.

The maintenance of the pliability of the oral mucous membranes is an action somewhat different from lubrication. It is called an emollient action, and it is brought about by the mucin content of the saliva. It allows free movement without frictional injury to the surface of the moving structures. Abrasions, inflammations, and increased sensitivity of oral membranes tend to follow a long-standing decrease in mucin resulting from suppression of salivary flow. The protecting and soothing effects of saliva upon the surface membranes, in contrast to its softening property, is termed its demulcent action.

Prolonged speech activity can result in some deficiency of salivary flow. This failure is explained by nervous and endocrine influences or even by simple evaporation of water.

There are three types of mucous membranes in the oral cavity. One type, which is sensory in nature, covers the dorsal surface of the tongue. A second variety lines the gingivae and the hard palate, and it is built to resist the strong pressures of mastication. The third type is an ordinary protective lining found in the lips, the cheeks, the alveolar processes peripheral to the gingivae proper, the floor of the mouth, under surface of the tongue, and in the soft palate.

Oral Blood Supply. The structures within and about the oral cavity are supplied by branches of the external carotid artery. These branches include the lingual, superficial temporal, external maxillary, and internal maxillary arteries.

The blood to the lips and cheeks comes chiefly from the external maxillary artery through its submental, superior and inferior labial branches. There is a lesser contribution from the internal maxillary artery through its buccinator, infraorbital, and mental branches. The superficial temporal branch of the external carotid sends the transverse facial artery to the cheeks.

The blood supply to the gingivae and teeth of the lower jaw and also to the oral floor comes from the lingual, external and internal maxillary arteries. The supply to the gingivae and teeth of the upper jaw and also to the roof of the mouth comes from the internal maxillary artery through the posterior and anterior alveolar, the greater palatine, and the long sphenopalatine branches.

The chief drainage is by way of the lingual veins into the anterior facial veins. In the upper mouth the pterygoid plexus drains into the internal maxillary veins.

Lymphatics in the anterior oral floor drain into the superior deep cervical nodes about the internal jugular veins or indirectly through the submental nodes into the deep cervical nodes. The lymphatics of the main oral floor drain into the submaxillary and upper deep cervical nodes.

The lymphatics from the tip of the tongue drain into the suprahyoid nodes and to a so-called principal node of the tongue located at the splitting of the common carotid artery. Lymphatics from the lateral tongue margins travel to the submaxillary and deep cervical nodes. The vessels of the vallate papillae go to deep cervical nodes. Lymphatics from the central mass of the tongue go to the submaxillary nodes but chiefly to the deep cervical nodes.

Oral Nerve Supply. The nerves are described in more detail with each organ. As a general statement, the motor nerves to the oral muscles include the facial nerve to the mimetic musculature, the mandibular division of the trigeminal nerve to the muscles of chewing, and the hypoglossal nerve to the tongue. On the afferent side, the oral mucosa, gums, teeth, and tongue are innervated by the trigeminal nerve for

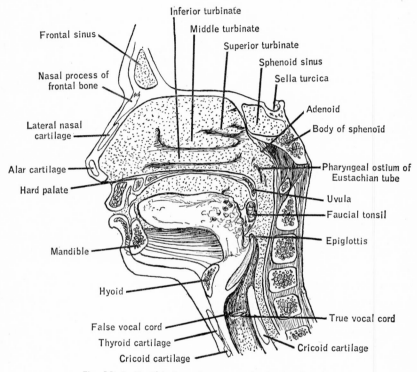

Fig. 12–5. Medial view of structures in the head region.

general sensation. Taste in the anterior tongue is mediated by the facial nerve, and in the posterior tongue, by the glossopharyngeal nerve. Distinct efferent autonomic fibers are carried in several nerves to the salivary glands and to the blood vessels and mucous glands of the mouth.

THE TONGUE OR LINGUA

Functions. The tongue is the primary and the most important organ of articulation. It works in conjunction with the mandible and other articulators. By modifying the shape of the oral cavity, it also acts as a resonator. During speech it assumes positions that relate it definitely to the language or dialect being spoken, and it produces most of the phonemes, or sound families, characteristic of connected speech.

Some phonemes, especially vowels, are primarily resonance phenomena. Other phonemes, like the unvoiced consonants, are mouth noises which bear no relationship to the laryngeal note. Still other phonemes, such as most voiced consonants, combine the mouth noises of their respective unvoiced partners with a laryngeal note.

The tongue has an important role in mastication, which is its chief biological function. It transfers food to the occluding teeth surfaces and helps mix the particles with saliva. It removes from the teeth food that is ready for swallowing. It facilitates crushing by pressing the food against the hard palate. This action is aided by the roughness of the tongue dorsum because of its papillae and by the hard palate because of its rugae, which prevent the food from sliding. Following deglutition, the tongue removes particles much as a mechanical sweeper. The dorsum of the tongue also functions for taste reception and for the selection of food through touch and temperature receptors.

Hudgins and Stetson (1937), by having subjects repeat simple syllables very rapidly, showed that the tongue is the most mobile of the resonators. In order of speed come the tip of the tongue, the jaw, the back of the tongue, and the velum and lips equally.

The tongue moves most rapidly for protrusion and retraction and less rapidly for lateral motions. Adequate salivary lubrication increases its facility, a dry mouth being associated with rather slow and clumsy movements (O'Rourke and Miner, 1951).

Comparative Anatomy. The tongue varies greatly among animals. It first appears as a definite organ in fishes, where it is seen as an elevation of the oral floor. In fishes it contains no muscles but rather a cartilage or bony framework derived from the gills and covered by mucous membrane. There is little movement or prehensibility to this structure, although extrinsic muscles can cause it to vary its position and thus help in swallowing food.

A new tongue appears among amphibians in the more evolved salamanders, and it develops intrinsic muscles which bring about variations in shape. This tongue is protracted by the genioglossals and retracted by the hyoglossals. In the anuran frogs and toads, the tip of the tongue at rest is held posteriorly toward the pharynx, and it is quickly thrust out in capturing insects or other food.

In the reptiles, the tongue action ranges from very limited protraction in turtles to the great protrusion in snakes. The carnivorous reptiles, such as crocodiles, have a flat, immobile tongue, since food is only retained in the mouth fleetingly.

The tongue of birds is well developed from vestiges of the nonfunctional embryonic gill arches. Extrinsic muscles are built upon the arch framework.

Among mammals, the anterior and posterior tongue divisions become distinguished by a V-shaped groove called the sulcus terminalis. At the center of the backward-pointed V lies a small pit, or foramen cecum. This pit marks the position of a thyroglossal duct through which, in the embryo, the thyroid gland is for a time continuous with the tongue.

The mammalian tongue is highly mobile and prehensile, and it serves many purposes. It is well formed and mobile in the carnivores, but it is best developed in the herbivores for grasping herbage. Although the oral cavity of man has suffered a relative decrease in phylogeny, the human tongue is relatively large. Whether or not this development is because of its activity in speech is speculative.

Developmental Anatomy. The anterior part of the tongue appears at about four weeks in front of the thyroglossal duct as a central swelling, or tuberculum impar, in the floor of the mouth. The inner aspect of the first (mandibular) arch on either side produces lateral lingual swellings which grow and entirely surround the central swelling. All of these primordia form the anterior two-thirds of the whole tongue.

The posterior aspect of the tongue develops behind the thyroglossal duct, and it represents the primary tongue of the lower vertebrates. It arises from the ventromedial ends of the second (hyoid) arches.

The paired second arches fuse to a single swelling called the copula, and this is the future root of the tongue. The mesoderm of the third arch later contributes to the completion of the tongue.

The general connective tissue of the tongue is produced by the branchial mesoderm underlying the epithelium. The muscles seem to be formed by the ventral migration of muscle blocks (myotomes) from the occipital region. The overlying epithelium of the tongue differentiates and becomes multilayered, in which process it develops the dorsal papillae containing taste buds.

General Anatomy. The tongue is a muscular organ located in the floor of the mouth to which it is attached at its base and at the central portion of its body. The root is posterior and is connected with the hyoid bone, the epiglottis, the soft palate, and pharynx. The apex extends anteriorly to the lower incisor teeth. The inferior surface is connected with the mandible, and the mucous membrane is reflected from this surface to the floor of the mouth to form a median fold, the frenulum, which loosely binds down the tongue.

The upper surface, or dorsum, is bisected by a longitudinal median sulcus which runs back to a pit, the foramen cecum. On either side of the pit a groove called the sulcus terminalis runs laterally and forward and separates the anterior two-thirds of the dorsum from the posterior one-third. The anterior section forms the body, or corpus, and the apex. The dorsum shows many punctiform (specifically positioned) projections, or papillae, which contain the taste buds. The pharyngeal surface, or root dorsum, contains many prominences produced by accumulations of lymphatic tissue collectively comprising the lingual tonsils. The freely movable areas of the tongue include the apex, sides, dorsum, and a portion of the inferior surface.

The mucous membrane is stratified squamous epithelium. This lining is similar to that of the mouth in general. The mucosa is closely adherent

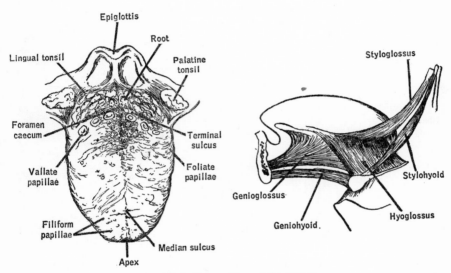

Fig. 12–6. Composition of the tongue.

to the underlying muscle on the anterior dorsum and on the free margins, but it is freely movable behind the sulcus terminalis.

Muscles. The directive movements of the tongue are produced by muscles. Anatomically, the muscles are described individually, but it is only through their combined actions that speech sounds are actually articulated.

There are many factors in addition to muscles which determine the inherent mobility of the tongue. The freedom of motion in the tip is determined by the frenulum. A constitutionally large tongue, which is not frequently found, could interfere with speech. The neural capacity for precise regulation is also important, and there are other restrictive factors. The presence of a tumor could act like a foreign body to produce thick, unintelligible speech.

The tongue muscles are extrinsic or intrinsic. The former originate from the skeleton, but the latter are located entirely within the tongue and produce internal changes in shape.

The intrinsic muscles are longitudinal, transverse, and vertical.

The *superior longitudinal* muscle (unpaired) lies directly beneath the mucous membrane and extends throughout the dorsum from root to tip. It arises posteriorly from the septum and the submucosa, and it inserts in the skin along the borders and tip of the tongue. Its actual origins and insertions are indefinite. It works with the inferior longitudinal muscle to shorten the tongue. As a consequence, the organ becomes thicker and wider. It can bulge the tongue upward in a longitudinal direction, and it can retract and curl the tongue tip.

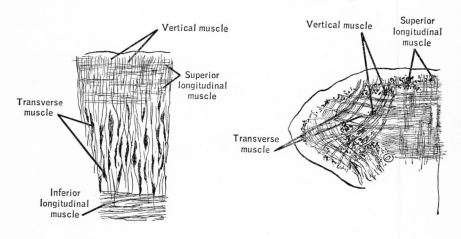

VERTICAL VIEW   HORIZONTAL VIEW

Fig. 12–7. Microscopic enlargement of intrinsic tongue muscles.

The *inferior longitudinal* (paired) is a rounded muscle traveling longitudinally between the genioglossus and hyoglossus muscles through the lower and lateral tongue. It originates at the mucous membrane of the root of the tongue. The fibers go downward and forward and converge to a bundle which goes apexward with the hyoglossus and styloglossus muscles. Most of the fibers pass forward to insert in the mucosa of the inferior lingual surface, but some go upward to the mucosa of the dorsum. The muscle shortens the tongue from front to back. It can also depress the tip if this area has been elevated.

The *transverse* muscle (paired) forms much of the fleshy part of the tongue. It contains horizontal layers which fan out as they travel laterally toward the dorsum and to the lateral tongue margins. Some fibers originate from the dorsal septum, while others perforate it. The muscle does not reach either the dorsal surface or the tip of the tongue.

The transverse muscle narrows the tongue and thereby protrudes it. It may bulge the organ upward. The lateral margins become lifted to help produce a tongue groove.

The *vertical* muscle (paired) constitutes with the transverse muscle much of the flesh of the tongue. The presence of vertical fibers has been questioned. They originate from the mucosa of the dorsum, whence they sweep downward and laterally to insert into the mucosa of the inferior surface. The muscle flattens the tongue.

There are several extrinsic muscles which act in synergism with the intrinsic ones to produce tongue mobility.

The *genioglossus* (paired) is a flat, triangular muscle which spreads fan-like toward its insertion. It is the strongest of the extrinsic muscles, and it forms most of the substance of the tongue. It originates from the mental tubercles at the posterior or inner aspect of the mandibular symphysis. The lowest fibers travel horizontally to the tongue base and insert into the body of the hyoid bone. Most of the fibers radiate to the dorsum, where their insertion extends from the tip to the base.

The middle and lower sections of the muscle are concerned primarily in protruding the tongue. The organ is also elevated. The upper fibers bring the tip back and down. The middle fibers can also depress the median part of the tongue, making a concavity in its dorsum to receive food.

The *styloglossus* (paired) is an elongated muscle stretching from the styloid process to the apex of the tongue. It originates not only from the styloid process of the temporal bone but in small part from the stylomandibular ligament. It passes downward, medially, and somewhat anteriorly to end in the tongue near the base of the glossopalatal arch; there it turns almost horizontally and travels to the tip. An inferior group of fibers penetrates the hyoglossus fibers and goes medially into the substance of the tongue. The muscle retracts and elevates the whole tongue.

The *palatoglossus* muscle (paired) has been described previously as a depressor of the soft palate. Acting from a fixed soft palate, it elevates the posterior section of the tongue. The fibers of insertion of the palatoglossus and styloglossus are blended.

The *hyoglossus* muscle (paired) is a quadrilateral sheet of fibers which extends from the hyoid bone to the side of the tongue. It originates from the upper border of the greater hyoid cornua and from adjacent portions of the hyoid body. The fiber bundles go vertically up to the tongue and interlace en route with the horizontal fibers of the styloglossus muscle. Some writers call those fibers which originate from the lesser hyoid cornua the chondroglossus muscle.

The hyoglossus draws the tongue downward and backward. Acting in reverse, it can elevate the hyoid, but this is a secondary function. Note the antagonism between the depressor function of this muscle and the elevator activity of the other extrinsic muscles. In retraction, however, it can act with other muscles in opposition to protruding fibers of the genioglossus muscle.

Blood and Nerve Supply. The tongue blood comes chiefly from the lingual branch of the external carotid, and there is a supplementary supply from the ascending pharyngeal and the external maxillary arteries. The lingual artery goes forward on each side to the apex. The veins drain into the internal jugulars. The lymph vessels begin in a network in the submucous coat and in the muscular substance, and they drain into deep cervical glands, as described previously.

The tongue is innervated by the trigeminal, facial, glossopharyngeal, vagus, and hypoglossal nerves. The trigeminal nerve (lingual branch of the mandibular nerve) mediates general sensation. The glossopharyngeal nerve (lingual branch) mediates taste at the root, while the facial nerve (chorda tympani branch) does this at the body and apex. Small, questionable, taste areas on the cheeks and at the root are claimed to be innervated by the vagus nerve (superior laryngeal branch).

The lingual muscles proper receive motor fibers through the hypoglossal nerve. The palatoglossus muscle is innervated by the accessory nerve through the pharyngeal plexus; any involvement of the vagus nerve is problematical.

The hypoglossal fibers originate in the hypoglossal nucleus of the medulla and emerge from its ventral aspect. The rootlets unite in the anterior condylar foramen, and they leave the skull. In the neck the nerve travels downward and forward. In the region of the hyoid bone it turns medially and passes beneath the digastric and stylohyoid muscles. After going between the hyoglossus and mylohyoid muscles, it reaches the tongue.

The main trunk of the hypoglossal nerve gives off a descending ramus which runs down the neck with the vagus, meeting a cervical descending branch primarily from cervical nerves C-2 and C-3. This union forms a loop, or ansa hypoglossi, which supplies the omohyoid, sternohyoid, and sternothyroid muscles. Diamond (1952) says that the descending branches to the infrahyoid muscles are not produced from the twelfth nerve but from communicating branches of C-1 and C-2.

Dynamic Tongue Positions. Through a technic called palatography, information is obtainable as to how the tongue and palate come into active contact. A thin, powdered artificial palate is fitted to the roof of the mouth, an isolated sound is produced, then the artificial palate is examined to find where the surface powder has been removed by contact with the wet tongue.

The fact that the tongue may act in conjunction with the palate may be illustrated in the phonetic analysis of consonants such as G and K. For one thing, cleft palate patients have difficulty with these sounds, and they are termed posterior linguapalatal sounds to indicate that the back of the tongue rises against a depressed soft palate when the sound is started. They are produced quickly with pressure from a closed position. G is voiced, and K is unvoiced. To sound K, the back of the tongue becomes lowered and the soft palate raised. In sounding G, the vocal

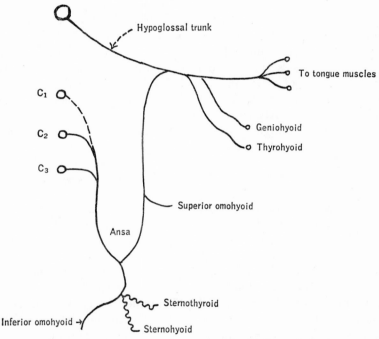

Fig. 12—8. Diagrammatic representation of the hypoglossal fibers to the tongue and neck muscles.

folds force a short vibration against the K position, with subsequent blending into the succeeding vowel. In both consonants the tongue is primary and the soft palate secondary.

The relative positions of the articulatory organs are also studied by X-ray photography. A technic has been developed to obtain synchronous recordings by the X-ray motion picture camera, the cathode-ray oscilloscope, and the phonograph. This method gives an analysis of the articulator movements and sound waveform, and it provides an audible record (Curry, 1937).

An early attempt to ascertain the forms and sizes of the speech cavities and to determine the positions and relations of the various structures as they appear during vocal activity was that of Russell (1931). He obtained a comprehensive series of X rays as well as data from a laryngoperiscopic study of the vocal fold and of internal laryngeal function. Through such attempts to know more about the living positions of the speech organs, the facts pertaining to speech production might become more firmly grounded.

Carmody (1941) studied by X-ray films the positions of the tongue in relation to the palate during speech, and he concluded that there is a mean anatomical position for each speech sound. He extended this study to the pharyngeal region and established tables giving the length and breadth of the pharynx for the vowels and consonants.

A graphic scheme commonly used to show the position of the tongue in forming vowels is the cardinal vowel diagram (West et al., 1941). It involves a set not of regular vowels but rather a set of vowels placed at arbitrary positions to make them identical for all people, thus acting as reference levels. All vowels are describable from this in terms of tongue positions, as higher, lower, farther front or farther back than the corresponding cardinal vowels.

For a description of a diverse group of instruments used for analyzing tongue activity, as well as for speech diagnosis, therapy, and research in general, consult Steer and Hanley (1957).

Probably no description of lingual activity would be complete without noting that any gross movement of the tongue may be dependent upon the position and movement of the hyoid bone. In this sense the hyoid bone can be classified as an articulator.

The hyoid can be elevated and simultaneously brought either forward or backward. It can be depressed and simultaneously tilted either forward or backward. It may possibly be pulled backward horizontally. Any one of these movements has an effect upon lingual sounds which is still to be definitely ascertained.

Applied Physiology of the Tongue. At present there are no established standards to evaluate the size, shape, and mobility of the tongue. Fairbanks and Bebout (1950) tried to correlate the size and shape with superior and inferior speakers, but they could not find any real differences.

Size, shape, and mobility are involved in correct lingual activity. The coordination of this activity is effected at the lower motor neuron level by the hypoglossal nerve.

Travis (1931) tested motor coordination in a rough way by kymography. The subject places his tongue against a Marey tambour, and then he rhythmically and rapidly protrudes and retracts his tongue. The movements are transmitted by the recording needle of the tambour to a moving kymograph drum or similar recorder. Normal records are compared with those of a subject with defective articulation and evaluated in terms of the rhythm, force, and ability needed to maintain the speed of motion.

Coordination of tongue movements is usually sufficiently obvious simply by listening to the articulated sounds. As an illustration, a highly complex integration of tongue movements is necessary in forming the consonant s and in differentiating it from SH. This is one reason why s is a sound to be acquired late by a child. The incorrect formation of this sound is called a sigmatism. The deviation is of some interest in that it may be a relatively sensitive barometer of central nervous system damage.

There are many kinds of lingual disorders; some selected examples are presented briefly.

O'Rourke and Miner (1951) emphasize that apart from local causes the tongue expresses many disorders of systemic origin. These conditions include blood diseases, metabolic disorders, etc. In this sense the tongue is a barometer of much internal function. Locally, when the teeth deteriorate, the tongue is adaptively set into greater compensatory activity. This activity is carried on in a medium favoring local lesions of the organ.

In hypothyroid states, such as myxedema, the tongue may enlarge, and this may be accompanied by a slow, thick speech. A large tongue may be found in severe cervical infections. It may also be enlarged congenitally.

In hemiplegia, the tongue when protruded deviates markedly to one side. This is observed similarly in lesions of the hypoglossal nucleus or of the nerve trunk, such as in bulbar paralysis. Unilateral paralysis need not impair articulation.

A tongue displaying tremor may indicate such conditions as nervousness, alcoholism, hyperthyroidism, and dementia paralytica. If the tremor is hesitating, it is suggestive of prolonged infection, debilitating conditions, or senescence.

A tongue that cannot protrude beyond the teeth even by force is not free enough for proper speech. In a tongue-tied individual, where the frenulum is binding down the tongue, there is an especial effect upon a sound such as s. The defect is evidenced by having the subject protrude the tongue maximally, whereupon the frenulum retracts the tongue in the middle.

Lisping is a disorder of the sibilant consonants. s and z are sounded incorrectly. Sometimes SH and ZH and also CH and J are sounded incorrectly. In correct articulation the tip of the tongue is raised so as to almost touch the teeth ridge, leaving a narrow channel through which air passes. In lisping, the tip of the tongue is placed between the teeth or against the edge of the upper front teeth. This position produces a frontal or lingual lisp, which is the usual type. In the lateral lisp, air escapes from the sides of the tongue. There is faulty use of the lingual muscles.

THE TEETH

Structure. A tooth is composed of a crown, which projects above the gums; a root, embedded within the jaw socket; and a neck, or region of transition, between the crown and root. Each tooth contains a hollow pulp cavity which admits blood vessels and nerves. This cavity eventually narrows and the growth of the tooth ceases.

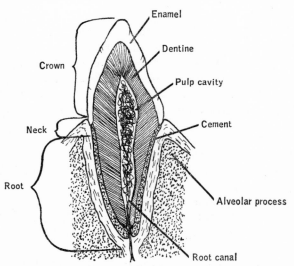

Fig. 12–9. Diagrammatic microscopic enlargement of a tooth.

Most of the solid part of a tooth is a very dense tissue called the dentine which deposits around embryonic cells termed odontoblasts. A solid layer of enamel covers over the dentine in the crown region. The protective coat around the dentine in the root area is a hard cement.

Number and Succession. The number of teeth is definite, limited, and differentiated according to position and function. The front teeth, which are incisors and canines, serve for gripping and tearing; the back teeth, which are premolars (bicuspids) and molars, serve for grinding and crushing.

The above facts are conveniently illustrated in a dental formula in which the adult or permanent dentition is expressed as $\frac{2.1.2.3.}{2.1.2.3.} \times 2.$

The figures in the numerator from left to right indicate respectively the number of incisors, canines, premolars, and molars on the right side of the upper jaw, and the figures in the denominator show the corresponding teeth in the right lower jaw.

The child has a temporary or deciduous set of twenty teeth, which are gradually replaced from about six years of age by the thirty-two permanent teeth. The first set of teeth has erupted by the second year of life. The permanent teeth originate with the first molars, which erupt just behind the last deciduous teeth. The permanent teeth are essentially established about the twelfth year.

The approximate ages for the eruption of the teeth are given below.

DECIDUOUS TEETH		PERMANENT TEETH	
Kind of teeth	*Months*	*Kind of teeth*	*Years*
Lower central incisors	6–9	First molars	6
Upper incisors	8–10	Central incisors	7
Lateral incisors and first molars	15–21	Lateral incisors	8
Canines	16–20	First premolars	9
Second molars	20–24	Second premolars	10
		Canines	11–12
		Second molars	12–13
		Third molars	17–25

The time of dental maturation has been used in speech therapy as one index of physiological maturity. In many cases the general bodily structures have not matured enough to make meaningful speech possible. Cretins and other feeble-minded children are physiologically retarded, and their dental development is similarly delayed.

Usually the dental status is not a practicable method of diagnosing maturity until at least seven years of age. For a complete schedule of dental maturation, the reader is referred to West (1936). The table of normals must be used only along with a careful history.

The relation of the upper and lower teeth to each other upon closing the jaws is called occlusion; this relation during movements of the mandible is called articulation. In occlusion there is a maxillary over-bite, since the upper arch has a greater diameter. The upper incisors and canines bite labial to (outside) the lower teeth, while the upper bicuspids and molars are shifted buccally. Normally the distal overlap of the upper teeth nearly disappears at the posterior part of the arches. In the temporary dentition the occlusal relationships are essentially similar to those of the permanent teeth.

The relationships of the jaws in occlusion have been described in Angle's classification. In his Class I, the normal occlusion described above holds, and this is called neutrocclusion. If the lower jaw is retruded in relation to the upper jaw, the condition is placed in Class II.

The term distocclusion applies to receding teeth and the lower jaw. Where the lower jaw is protracted, the condition is placed in Class III. The term mesiocclusion refers to protruding teeth and the lower jaw.

In phylogeny the masticatory apparatus is suffering progressive reduction. There is frequent absence of the third molars (wisdom teeth) and the upper lateral incisors. Where the molars of primitive man increased distally, they now decrease in size distally. With the reduced dental arches there has appeared a shortening of the jaws and an expansion of the brain and its capsule. As the masticatory structures have regressed in racial history, a concomitant reduction has occurred in the supraorbital ridges and in the prominent facial processes which once served for attachment of the larger chewing musculature.

Agencies Influencing Oral Tissues. Teeth, especially in the developmental stages, are affected by many agencies. The minerals and vitamins A, C, and D are important for development, although the teeth are less sensitive to these factors than are many other tissues. Although teeth are not overly responsive to vitamin A deficiency, they may suffer hypoplasia if there is deficiency of members of the vitamin B complex.

Some of the disorders of the softer oral tissues are nutritional. Swollen gingivae may result from ascorbic acid deficiency, and swollen tongue from a reduction of nicotinic acid. A loss of riboflavin can produce glossitis (tongue inflammation) or cheilosis (fissures at the mouth angles with lip desquamation).

The physical character of the diet influences the teeth and their supporting tissues. In this sense, diet has an effect of massage upon local circulation and brings about growth and keratinization of gingival epithelium from frictional contact.

Hormones have a marked influence upon the teeth in man and animals. In human hypothyroidism there may be a small dental arch, a poorly developed mandible, and a delayed eruption. In the hypopituitary dwarf there may be delayed eruption, loss of teeth, faulty dental arches, and malocclusion. In the opposite conditions of hyperpituitary acromegaly and giantism, the tongue enlarges and the lower jaw may become prognathic. The mandible is a bone which seems to be able to grow even in an adult.

The parathyroid hormone may play a role during tooth calcification. Injection of this hormone softens the alveolar bone and produces drifting of teeth with subsequent malocclusion.

Many pregnant women develop a gingivitis with bleeding and edema. The hormonal changes are speculative, but they probably involve the sex hormones of pregnancy.

Among other agencies affecting teeth, the premature loss of the first teeth or the retarded development of the second teeth produces faulty development and function of the jaws. The results are malpositions and disturbances of the eruption of teeth. If the developmental failure is severe, nasal and facial deformities may ensue, with disorders of breathing, chewing, and speech.

Tooth development is strongly influenced by related developmental processes. In cleft lips or palate the deciduous and permanent teeth in or about the pathological process may be deformed or missing. The premaxillary support of the incisors can be weakened in bilateral clefts of the lip and palate.

Dental Defects and Speech. The proper shape of the dental arches and the correct occlusion of the teeth may be essential for proper speech. There seems to be considerable difference of opinion about this statement. Carrell (1936) studied children with speech defects and said that they showed no real differences from the normal children in dental abnormalities or palatal malformations. Fymbo (1936) related the severity of speech defects to malocclusion. In another study inferior speakers were found to have a greater incidence of dental abnormalities (Fairbanks and Lintner, 1951). Bloomer (1957) says that although structural defects in teeth occur more frequently in persons with speech defects, this does not prove that dental abnormalities are primary causes of speech disturbances.

The teeth are structures which are needed to obstruct the free passage of air in certain sounds. Undesirable sounds can be potentially produced by malocclusions involving an inability to approximate the jaws properly, but these are usually compensated by the action of the tongue and lips (Van Riper and Irwin, 1958).

When the upper incisors protrude and rest upon the lower lip so that both lips approximate with difficulty, the labial sounds such as P, B, and M can be distorted. The quality of s is changed by protrusions of the upper teeth and by dental gaps.

Speech defects seem to be produced by the absence of teeth. In a loss of the upper incisors or in an open bite where the upper teeth do not touch the lower lip, F and v are distorted. If the lips do not come into contact, B and M are not sounded and even s and z can be difficult. Bloomer (1957) takes the somewhat contrary view that the absence of individual teeth in the adult is not a primary cause of articulatory defects.

The faulty position of even one tooth seems to be able to interfere with the position of the tongue. If one incisor is pulled backward, there may be hissing or whistling upon attempting to sound D and T.

Orthodontic appliances and dentures have produced distortions of speech. Subsequently there is the necessity to form new speech habits, especially those involving the tongue. Dentures that are too thick in the rugae area prevent the tongue from making a small air space. This interference occurs also with a large tongue or with narrow arches.

The effect of distorted teeth upon the personality is indirectly but emotionally linked with speech. Although difficult to assess, it is nevertheless a force in that it produces feelings of inferiority which lead to functional vocal disturbances.

THE MANDIBLE

The mandible, or lower jaw, is one of the primary articulators but it also influences resonance. A "tight" jaw adds to tonal flatness. Because the elevator muscles are stronger than the depressors, there may be a tendency to speak with a closed mouth or with muffled resonance. In cerebral palsy the jaw action may be ungraded and unpredictable, producing a distorted oral resonance.

Osteology. The body, or corpus, of the jaw is a roughly U-shaped arch, and the arch represents the fusion of two embryonic cartilage bones at the mandibular symphysis. The upper surface of the body carries the alveolar process. The arch continues on each side upward and backward into the mandibular ramus, and the two sides of the arch become widely separated posteriorly. The posterior border of the ramus meets the inferior border of the body at the angle of the mandible. The most anterior part of the body elevates externally in the mid-line to a prominence called the mental protuberance, or bony chin. An opening called the mental foramen lies just posterolateral to the chin, and it allows blood vessels and the mental nerve to pass from a canal inside the bone to the external surface on each side.

On the inner or medial aspect of the body, a crest called the mylohyoid line runs diagonally downward and forward to the region of the chin. This crest gives origin to the mylohyoid muscle, which forms the floor of the mouth. Just behind the symphysis there are one or two mental spines (genial tubercles) for the origin of the genioglossus muscles above and the geniohyoid muscles below.

The alveolar process on the upper border of the body consists of two bony plates, external and internal, which fuse and form the sockets for the teeth.

Each ramus is a quadrilateral and somewhat perpendicular plate which extends upward from the posterior part of the body. The superior border of each ramus displays two prominent projections, the anterior coronoid process and the posterior condyloid process, which are separated by a semilunar (sigmoid, mandibular) notch.

The coronoid process is a triangular spicule of bone which terminates in a spike or in a backward-curved hook. It is convex forward and concave backward. The temporalis muscle inserts upon it.

The condyloid process is the mandibular head (condyle, capitulum), which fits into the mandibular fossa (depression) of the temporal bone of the skull to form the temporomandibular joint. The condyle sits upon

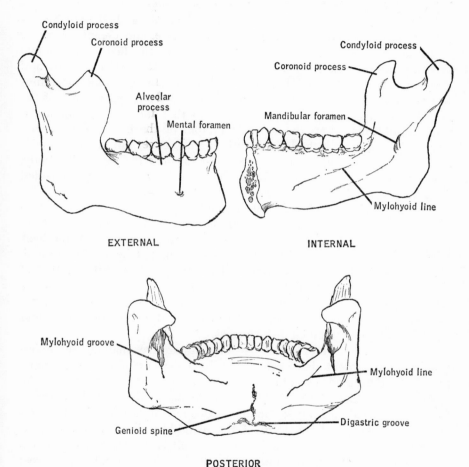

Fig. 12–10. The lower jaw bone seen in different views.

the neck of the condyloid process, and it is bent forward so that its articulating surface faces anteriorly and superiorly.

The ramus is overlaid by the masseter muscle on its external surface. It contains on its internal surface a mandibular canal which houses the inferior alveolar nerve and the blood vessels to the teeth. This canal begins proximally at the mandibular foramen and then travels downward and forward, becoming horizontal in its course under the roots of the molars. At the bicuspid region the canal divides, and a narrow channel continues toward the symphysis, while a wider mental canal goes laterally upward and backward to open at the mental foramen.

The bony changes of the mandible with age are externally conspicuous. The body of the bone at birth is simply a shell with incompletely partitioned sockets for the incisor, canine, and deciduous molar teeth, and the ramus is at an obtuse angle. In the first year the two separate arches fuse at the symphysis, then each arch elongates and deepens, while the ramus becomes less obtuse. In the adult the ramus has become nearly vertical, and the alveolar and subdental parts of the arch are of approximately equal depth so that the mental foramen is about equidistant from the top and bottom of the bone. The alveolar process regresses with the loss of teeth in senescence, and the mandibular canal with its mental foramen is brought up near the top of the body. The ramus again becomes obtuse and the jaw becomes protruded (prognathic).

The mandible is an important determinant of the growth and form of the facial skeleton. The growth of the upper and lower jaws anteroposteriorly gives the needed space for the temporal eruption of the back teeth. The growth in height of the jaws, stimulated by vertical growth of the mandibular ramus, is required for the free vertical eruption of the teeth. As bone develops in the jaws, it acts as a force to produce eruption. Mandibular growth at the condylar cartilage is necessary for the vertical growth of the upper face. Thus, disorders of mandibular growth contribute to facial disturbances.

The importance of a knowledge of comparative anatomy in understanding the present day form of the bony jaw or of the entire skull, as expressed through evolution and anthropology, is brought out in the writings of Weidenreich (Washburn and Wolfson, 1949). Although such factors as an abundance of iodine, calcium, and other materials influence the skull and the form of the mandible, the ultimate cause is more general. The history of the human skull is determined by the expansion of the brain and independently by the adaptation to erect posture. The size of the face reduces as the brain case expands. The adoption of erect posture changes both the form of the spinal column and the skull base. Brachycephalization, or the increase of the brain case in width observed in modern man, indicates a better adjustment of the skull to upright posture through the adoption of a more complete globular form. Some caution is needed in the tendency to ascribe too much to evolutionary causes. The prognathism of the jaw in certain modern races may result from relatively immediate factors.

Muscles. The mandible is important primarily in mastication, or chewing, and only secondarily in speech.

The muscles of the mandible operate in functional groups, just as they do elsewhere in the body. The chief movements are elevation and depression. The mandible can also be protruded and slightly retracted, and it has obliquely lateral motions. The last variety is for grinding food.

There are four muscles which are chiefly responsible for the chewing movements, and these are the ones generally classified as muscles of mastication. They include the masseter, temporalis, the external or lateral pterygoid, and the internal or medial pterygoid.

The mandible is elevated by three muscles which function primarily for mastication. They include the masseter, temporalis, and the internal pterygoid muscles.

The *masseter* muscle (paired) is the most superficial and stretches as a thick, flat, quadrilateral mass over the outer surface of the mandibular ramus. The muscle is incompletely divided to a superficial and deep part, both originating on the zygomatic arch and inserting upon the ramus or upon the angle of the mandible.

This muscle not only powerfully elevates the lower jaw, but it puts pressure upon the teeth, particularly in the molar area. The deep part of the muscle can retract as well as elevate, since its fibers go downward and forward when the mandible is protruded. The superficial part helps to protrude the mandible as well as elevate it.

The *temporalis* muscle (paired) is a triangular sheet originating from a large area on the side of the skull called the temporal fossa. The muscle travels deep to the zygomatic arch and converges toward the coronoid process of the mandible upon which it inserts as far down as the ramus of the jaw. Although the muscle is chiefly an elevator, its posterior fibers travel downward and forward, and they possess a retracting function. The retraction of the mandible may be accomplished primarily by the temporalis, although the digastric, geniohyoid, and other muscles contribute (Huber, 1958).

The *internal pterygoid* muscle (paired) is a thick, quadrilateral muscle roughly paralleling the masseter but lying on the medial surface of the mandibular ramus. It is somewhat weaker than the masseter. It originates mainly in the pterygoid fossa of the sphenoid bone, although its inner fibers originate from the medial surface of the lateral pterygoid plate. All the fibers run downward, backward, and slightly outward to insert upon the medial surface of the mandible near its angle. The muscle acts synergistically with the masseter to elevate the lower jaw. It can also help to protrude the jaw. Acting unilaterally, it pulls the mandible to one side.

The depressors include the mylohyoid, geniohyoid, the anterior belly of the digastric, and the external pterygoid muscles. The first three have already been considered in the suprahyoid group of extrinsic muscles, where they were described as raising the laryngeal apparatus when the mandible is fixed. When the hyoid bone is immobilized by the infrahyoid muscles, these suprahyoid muscles will depress and retract the lower jaw.

The *external pterygoid* (paired) is a thick, triangular muscle located deep to the temporalis. It originates in two heads. The larger inferior head arises from the lateral pterygoid plate, and the smaller superior head arises from the infratemporal surface of the greater wing of the sphenoid bone. Although the two heads are separated anteriorly, they

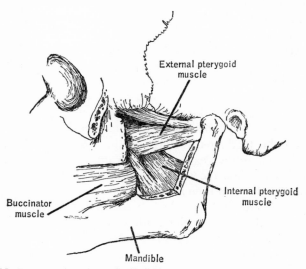

Fig. 12–11. Deep muscles of the mandible seen by cutting out a section of the bone.

fuse as they pass in front of the temporomandibular joint. The fibers travel backward and outward to insert upon the condyloid process of the mandible and also upon the capsule and articular disk of the temporomandibular joint. The muscle protrudes the lower jaw by pulling the mandibular head and articular disk forward, downward, and inward. When acting unilaterally, it draws the mandible outward.

The muscles of protrusion and retraction have been anticipated. The primary protruder is the external pterygoid. It is assisted by other muscles, including the internal pterygoid and the superficial part of the masseter.

The retractors have been described. They include the deep section of the masseter, the posterior fibers of the temporalis, and the suprahyoid muscles (mylohyoid, geniohyoid, and anterior belly of the diagastric).

The grinding movements of the mandible require compounded movements. To a great extent, they are accomplished by the external pterygoid and the posterior fibers of the temporalis.

The nerve supply of the mandible is the third or mandibular division of the trigeminal nerve. This nerve is primarily sensory to the mandibular teeth, but it gives off motor branches to the elevator muscles of mastication. These branches are the masseteric nerve to the masseter, several temporal branches to the temporalis, the internal pterygoid nerve to the same muscle, and the external pterygoid branch of the masseteric or buccal nerve to the external pterygoid muscle.

Applied Anatomy. If the muscles of the lower jaw do not function properly, mandibular action is distorted. The malfunction is observable in the instance where the jaw sags and saliva drools out of the mouth. The fault may reside in the muscles closing the lips as well as in the elevators of the jaw. The cause may also reside in a spasm of certain depressor muscles, like the digastric.

Difficulty with the motions of the mandible is also seen in pathology of the temporomandibular joint. Severe discomfort follows overclosure or any displacement of the mandible, and a loss of hearing acuity may result. Condylar displacement at the joint may produce the pain and other symptomatology by a traumatic degenerative arthritis rather than by any compression of the auriculotemporal or chorda tympani nerve fibers within the joint region. Overclosure disturbs muscular coordination, which in turn produces the chronic joint trauma.

The up and down motions are important in speech, and their function is tested by having an individual very rapidly and repeatedly open and close his mandible. About 5 cps in rhythm is a normal expectation.

There is a disorder termed an open bite in which the molar teeth occlude prior to approximation of the incisor teeth. This condition is ascribed to faulty jaw formation, dental abnormalities, or even ultimately thumb sucking. The air stream is not correctly impeded in front, and the sibilants are distorted. The handicap is often spontaneously palliated by blocking the opening with the tip of the tongue. The specific effect of an open bite upon speech would depend upon the size of the residual opening and also upon mandibular or maxillary prognathism.

A recessive mandible affects sounds requiring the proper position of the lips, incisors, and tongue. These sounds include P, B, M, S, Z, and TH. Prognathism has a similar effect.

LIPS, CHEEKS, AND THE MUSCLES OF EXPRESSION

The Lips, or Labia. The lips encircle the mouth orifice as a pair of fleshy folds whose contents include blood vessels, nerves, labial glands, and areolar connective tissue. They are covered externally by integument and internally by mucous membrane. There are glands directly underneath the mucous membrane. The connection between the lips is made at the corner of the mouth on each side by a thin fold called the labial commissure.

The skin of the lips terminates in a sharp line where a transitional area, the red or vermilion zone, lies between the skin and the mucous membrane. The vermilion epithelium is thin, and the cells contain eleiden. This substance increases their transparency so that the underlying capillaries show up with a red hue. The red zone may contain sebacious glands but neither sweat glands nor hairs.

The external integument and the internal mucosa are so tightly bound to the fascia over the great orbicularis oris muscle, or fleshy substance of the lips, that these membranes follow the muscle movements without folding. In the male the skin is thicker and firmer, which especially restricts upper lip mobility. In the resting mandibular position the lips are loosely approximated.

The lips of all mammals except monotremes are mobile, perhaps because of the primitive function of suckling. They are well developed in marsupials, which in later fetal life attach by their lips to the maternal mammae. There are no movable lips in the egg-laying fishes or in the reptiles and birds.

The lips have other functions. They are very sensitive to touch and temperature, and these sensations help in the rejection of unsuitable material. They aid in transferring food and water into the mouth and prevent the escape of food during mastication.

The lips are important articulators in speech. They form speech sounds such as the labial consonants, P, B, M, W, F, and V, and they also form certain vowels. Sounds would suffer a loss in quality if the lips were flaccid and immobile. Fairbanks and Green (1950) were unable to relate the dimensions of the lips and the size of the mouth opening to articulatory ability.

A few examples may be cited to illustrate labial activity in speech. The full closure of the lips followed by their immediate separation produces the sounds P and B. The velum assists the action by closing the nasal port. In lip closure without velar action, M is articulated. The P, B, and M are generally among the earliest and the easiest consonants to produce. They are primitive compared with the high frequency sounds like S, Z, SH, CH, J, and TH. In stutterers these primitive sounds can be troublesome. In a rounding motion with the velum blocking the nose, W and WH are sounded. To produce V and F, the lower lip presses lightly against the upper front teeth and interferes with the exhaled air, the nares being simultaneously closed. There is a difference, however, between the processes used to form v as compared with F. Both are continuant fricatives, which means that they take an appreciable amount of time to be produced and also that a pressure and friction are set up which result in a rushing sound. However, F is a breath or voiceless consonant, whereas v is vocalized and produces a vibration which can be sensed by placing the fingers upon the throat.

The lips should not be considered essential to the formation of all consonants. s and z are tongue and teeth consonants and do not require lip activity. In some cases, as in the R sound, the tongue is the primary agent and the lips are secondary. In the consonant L, which is formed essentially by the tongue, the lips only shape the vowel that directly follows. If the lip movements are substituted for the normal tongue movements, trouble with the L usually arises. Tongue-tip movements have been substituted for labial movements in facial paralysis (Palmer, 1948).

Lip action is tested very simply by pursing and retracting the lips, by moving the right and then the left lip corners, and by smiling.

A method to test the strength and rhythm of lip movements is described by Froeschels (1952). This is only an approximation in that the influence of extraneous muscles can not be eliminated. In this procedure a glass tube fixed to a small rubber ball, such as a device used to instill liquids into the eye, is attached at its free end to rubber tubing which is connected in turn to a Marey tambour that is free to write on a kymograph drum. The subject places the ball between his lips and compresses it rhythmically, which produces a rhythmic rise and fall of the tambour lever. This is a convenient ergometer which could allow rough comparisons of the lip movements of normal subjects and those with dysarthric (spastic) speech. This procedure is also feasible for testing the tip of the tongue, but in this instance the ball is inserted just behind the upper incisors.

Harelip has already been described as a congenital anomaly seen in the upper lip and resulting from failure of the structures forming the lip to fuse properly during fetal development. The defect is unilateral or bilateral. The failure shows several variations, such as a small fissure in the vermilion border of the lip, an extension of the cleft to the nostril, or a continuation of the fissure with an anteroposterior cleft through the hard palate. In harelip the sounds distorted are those involving the upper lip.

The Cheeks, or Buccae. The buccae, or cheeks, of man form the lateral aspects of the face. They are a fleshy mass composed chiefly of the buccinator muscles and also of the platysma, risorius, and zygomaticus muscles. Their external boundary is the integument. Their internal boundary is mucous membrane which fuses above and below with the gingivae or gums and behind with the mucosa of the soft palate. The mucous membrane is firmly attached to the buccinator fascia, and it thus closely follows the muscular movements.

The mucous membrane contains fairly thick epithelium which is stratified squamous and nonkeratinizing. This type occurs typically on wet surfaces where there is no absorption but where destruction of cells is favored because of continual friction. The deeper epithelial cells have to divide very rapidly to compensate for the cell losses.

A set of buccal glands are found between the buccinator muscle and the mucous lining. The ones which drain their secretion into the mouth in the region of the last molar tooth are called molar glands.

The duct of the parotid gland opens into the cheek opposite the second upper-molar tooth, and a raised papilla usually marks the orifice.

Sebacious glands may occur posterolateral to the mouth angles. They occasionally enlarge in older people, in which case they are seen as yellowish structures through the mucous membrane.

The buccal fat pad of Bichat (suckling pad) fills in the area between the buccinator and the chewing muscles. It is extensively developed in the infant, and it has been questionably implicated in suckling movements. It is more likely a mechanical cushion.

In the lower animals the mouth is large, but the cheeks are deficient. The necessity to keep the mouth closed and the loss of food minimized become associated with the appearance of cheeks. This aspect is illustrated in the prominent chewing habits of the herbivores. Whereas there are no cheeks in fishes and only rudimentary ones in reptiles and birds, the cheeks are well developed in monkeys, higher apes, and man. The phylogenetic appearance of the cheeks is also related to the muscular apparatus for chewing, which the cheeks assist by retaining food between the grinding teeth. Chewing is exclusively a mammalian property.

The cheeks are not very important in mastication. In the speech function they are used, like the lips, chiefly to articulate the labial consonants.

The Muscles of the Lips and of Expression. The muscles acting upon the lips and cheeks are part of the apparatus for facial expression, although additional muscles specifically performing the mimetic functions lie in other regions of the face. Facial expression as an independent activity can have an influence upon articulation and tone. Changes in the tenseness of the muscles involved may interfere with tone by influencing oral resonance (Moses, 1954).

The facial expressions can be more important than words in social interaction. Some investigators claim that facial expressions are associated with definite personality types (West et al., 1937). Typical facies have commonly been associated with specific diseases, such as the characteristically chronic anxiety expression of the child who has severely infected pharyngeal tonsils.

The various muscles of expression have in common their relatively superficial position in the subcutaneous fascia. This position contrasts with the deeper one of most other muscles. Also, these muscles have an attachment to or an influence upon the skin. They are highly variable in extent, shape, and strength among individuals. They are difficult to

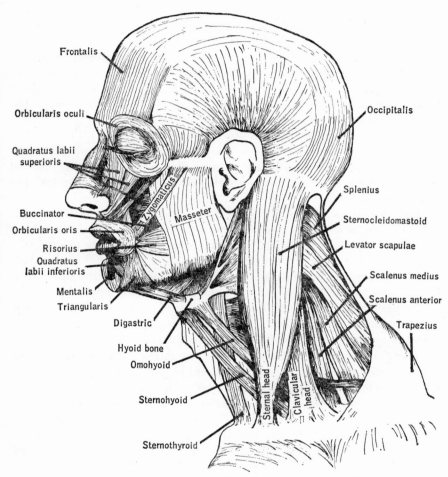

Fig. 12—12. Superficial muscles of the face viewed from the side.

isolate because of fusions and interlacing of fibers. Although small, they are among the strongest muscles in the body.

There are several muscles of the face which are classified strictly as muscles of expression. Most of them are superficial, and, except for the circular muscle of the lips, all are paired. The muscles of the nose may be included in the expressive groups (Mosher, 1951).

The facial muscles are arranged in separate groups. One group is composed solely of the platysma muscle. A second set occurs around the eyelids, a third around the ear, a fourth around the scalp, and a fifth around the mouth and nostrils.

The *platysma* (paired) is a wide, quadrilateral muscle covering most of the anterolateral surface of the neck, and it extends from the chest to the face, always lying between the superficial and the deep fascias. Its origin is from the skin and the superficial fascia in the superior chest and deltoid regions. It travels upward and forward. Some of its fibers attach to the lower border of the mandible and connect with the quadratus labii inferioris and triangularis muscles. The remainder of the fibers pass up into the face, and at the level of the lower lip these fibers cross each other. The most anterior and posterior fibers end in the lower lip, while the middle ones reach the upper lip.

The fibers ending in the mandible probably have very little influence in depressing the jaw. The muscle tends to draw the angle of the mouth downward and laterally, which changes the facial expression. Acting reversely, it elevates and wrinkles the skin over the clavicle and the deltopectoral region.

Most of the facial muscles act directly upon the lips, which makes these structures the most mobile part of the face. Changes in the shape of the lips affect oral resonance, and they also help complete the articulation of sounds. One set of lip muscles consists of parts of the orbicularis muscle, and it acts to close the lips. The other set opens the lips, and it is superficial or deep. The superficial activators of the upper lip are the quadratus labii superioris and the zygomaticus, while the deeper muscle of this region is the caninus.

In the lower lip the superficial muscle is the triangularis, and the deep muscles include the mentalis and the quadratus labii inferioris. The risorius and the buccinator muscles extend between the upper and lower lips to the mouth angle, the buccinator being the deeper.

The *orbicularis oris* (unpaired), or oral sphincter, is an oval ring of muscle fibers located within the lips and completely encircling the mouth. It has no direct attachment to the skeleton. It contains upper and lower fibers which are limited to one side, but these interlace with the opposite fibers at the mid-line.

The muscle primarily closes the lips, but it can narrow them while pressing them against the teeth. It can also protrude the lips and draw the lower lip up or the upper lip down. The muscle can perform these several actions because it is actually a collection of independent units and also acts in conjunction with other lip muscles.

The *quadratus labii superioris* (paired) is a flat, triangular muscle located above the lateral portion of the upper lip. It is formed of three heads. Each of these has an independent origin which extends from the side of the nose to the zygoma (cheek bone).

The *angular* head originates from the infraorbital margin and the frontal process of the maxilla. Its fibers run downward and somewhat laterally to insert at the ala nasi (wings of the nose) and the orbicularis oris.

The *infraorbital* head originates from the infraorbital margin. Its fibers converge as they run downward to insert into the skin, in which they travel almost to the vermilion lip region. Many of these fibers interlace with the orbicularis oris muscle.

The *zygomatic* head originates on the facial surface of the zygomatic bone. It travels downward and medially to insert into the skin of the upper lip and into the orbicularis oris.

Although in most cases the three heads are separated, their fibers of insertion converge near the mouth angle. Their common action is to raise the upper lip and also to elevate the corner of the mouth and the wing of the nose. The nostril is widened.

The *zygomaticus* (paired) is a flat, oblong muscle located superficial to the maxillary and zygomatic bones. It is one of the most developed and constant muscles of the middle face. It originates from the temporal process of the zygomatic bone and travels downward and medially to insert into the orbicularis oris and the skin at the mouth angle. It pulls the corner of the mouth upward and laterally. This action produces the expression of laughing.

The *caninus* (paired) is a flat, triangular muscle located above the corner of the mouth. It is deep to the middle quadratus labii superioris. Its origin, just below the infraorbital foramen, is at the canine fossa on the superficial surface of the maxilla. It goes downward and laterally toward the corner of the mouth where some fibers insert, while others end in the skin and mucous membrane of the lower lip. It elevates the corner of the mouth and may also help to close the mouth by elevating the lower lip. A sneering expression is ascribable to caninus activity.

The *risorius* (paired) is a flat muscle situated lateral to the mouth and superficial to the platysma. It is highly variable, and it may often be reduced to a few bundles or may even be missing.

It originates in the fascia over the masseter muscle and crosses horizontally and superficially to the corner of the mouth. Most of the fibers insert into the skin and mucosa of the upper lip and also into the mucosa directly lateral to the mouth angle. A few bundles terminate in the lower lip. The muscle retracts the corner of the mouth and produces an expression of grinning, threatening, or sneering.

The *buccinator* (paired) is the principal muscle of the cheek. It forms the lateral wall of the mouth and is deep to the remainder of the oral musculature. It arises (1) from the outer alveolar border of the maxilla in the molar region, (2) from the pterygomandibular raphe, and (3) from the outer alveolar border of the mandible in the molar region. Its fibers go forward to the corner of the mouth and enter both the upper and lower lips in which they interlace with those of the opposite side. The middle fibers decussate at the mouth angle in such a manner that the lower set goes to the upper lip and the upper set goes to the lower lip.

The muscle is covered posteriorly by the masseter and anteriorly by the muscles which converge upon the mouth angle. It is pierced by the parotid duct and by branches of the buccinator nerve.

The buccinator pulls the mouth angle laterally and posteriorly. It keeps the cheek stretched during any phase of oral activity. If it is paralyzed by a nerve lesion, the mucous membrane of the cheek cannot be tensed and becomes lacerated during chewing. The muscle can narrow the mouth opening and press the lips and cheeks against the teeth. This activity has given it the name of the "bugler's muscle."

The *quadratus labii inferioris* (paired) is a flat, quadrangular muscle located below the lateral portion of the mouth. It originates on the outer surface of the mandible between the symphysis and the mental foramen. It travels upward and medially into the orbicularis oris and into the skin of the lower lip. The deep fibers insert into the mucosa of the lower lip. There are some fibers which insert into the integument of the chin. The muscle draws the lower lip downward and slightly lateralward. This action produces an expression of irony.

The *triangularis* (paired) is a flat, triangular muscle located superficial and slightly lateral to the quadratus labii inferioris. It originates from the oblique line on the outer surface of the mandible. Along its origin, the fiber bundles alternate with those of the platysma. The fibers converge as they ascend to the corner of the mouth. They insert partly into the skin of the mouth angle and partly into the integument of the upper lip. The muscle pulls the mouth angle down. When both sides function together, the mouth is closed because of a depression of the upper lip. The expression of contempt is mediated by triangularis activity.

The *mentalis* or chin muscle (paired) originates from the incisive fossa of the mandible, just above the mental tuberosity. The medial fibers pass centrally and cross the mid-line to interlace with those of the contralateral muscle. They finally insert into the integument of the chin. The lateral fibers terminate in the skin on the same side. The uppermost fibers course superiorly to reach the lower part of the orbicularis oris muscle.

The muscle raises and wrinkles the integument of the chin. It also

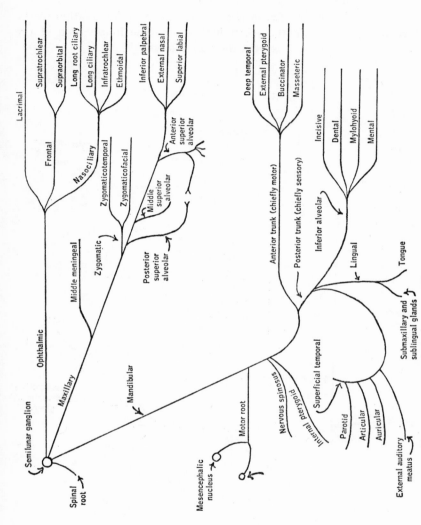

Fig. 12–13. Diagrammatic representation of the main branches of the trigeminal nerve.

275

protrudes the lower lip and turns it outward. The expression of doubt
or disdain exemplifies this activity.

The Nerve Supply of the Facial Region. The sensory innervation of the
facial region comes from the trigeminal nerve. The innervation of the
facial muscles of expression is from the facial nerve.

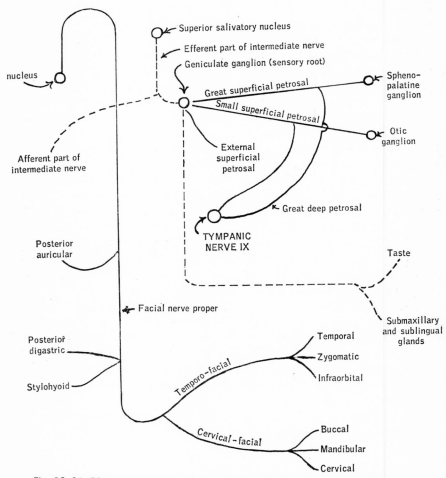

Fig. 12—14. Diagrammatic representation of the main branches of the facial nerve.

The facial nerve proper is primarily motor and goes to all the superficial muscles of the scalp, face, and neck and also to some of the deep
muscles in this area.

The trunk includes a smaller division called the intermediate nerve
(of Wrisberg). This division mediates taste from the anterior two-thirds

of the tongue, and it also sends autonomic efferents by way of the sphenopalatine, otic, and submaxillary ganglia to the lacrimal gland and to the submaxillary and sublingual salivary glands. The sensory fibers traveling in the intermediate nerve are received in the geniculate ganglion.

The facial nerve originates centrally in cells near the junction of the medulla and pons. From there it rises up to the fourth ventricle and emerges from the brain at the junction of the medulla and pons. It enters the internal auditory canal, where it sends out branches. It then passes through the facial canal in the petrous area of the temporal bone, where it presents an oval swelling called the geniculate ganglion. From this ganglion three small nerves arise. These are (1) the great superficial petrosal, which becomes joined by the great deep petrosal; (2) the small superficial petrosal, which is joined by a nerve from the tympanic branch of the glossopharyngeal; and (3) the external superficial petrosal, which is an inconstant branch that enters the sympathetic plexus surrounding the middle meningeal artery.

In the lower part of the facial canal, the facial nerve gives off additional branches to the stapedius muscles and to the auricular branch of the vagus. It also produces the chorda tympani, which contains parasympathetic salivary fibers and other fibers mediating taste.

The facial nerve subsequently emerges from the base of the skull through the stylomastoid foramen and passes forward through the parotid gland to supply the muscles of the face. Within the parotid gland there is an indefinite split to an upper temporofacial and a lower cervicofacial division.

When the facial nerve is subject to an extensive lesion, there is little or no power to raise the eyebrow, lip, cheek, and the skin of the forehead. There is also no ability to whistle or to close the eyelids firmly. All these defects are on the affected side. The mouth is pulled over to the normal side by the opposing healthy muscles. The face assumes a mask-like expression.

For a concise treatment of the oral and facial regions and their development, refer to Orban (1957).

SUMMARY

Articulators include the lips, teeth, hard and soft palate, tongue, mandible, and hyoid bone. They shape the consonants and assist in forming some vowel phonemes. The science of phonetics has established a simplifying system of classification to describe the articulation of sounds. Disorders of articulation do not necessarily imply real differences in the anatomical structure of the articulators.

The mouth is not only an articulator, but it is the most movable and controllable of the resonators. Its development and structure are described. The salivary glands open into the mouth and provide the lubrication needed for articulatory movements. The oral blood supply is from branches of the external carotid artery. The mouth receives a mixed innervation from cerebrospinal and autonomic nerves.

The tongue is the primary articulator. Its evolution, development, and structure are described. Its intrinsic muscles produce internal changes in shape. The extrinsic muscles act in synergism to produce the gross mobility of the organ. The tongue is supplied by the ascending pharyngeal, external maxillary, and lingual arteries. It is innervated by several cranial nerves. The articulatory positions of the tongue are detected by such technics as palatography and X-ray photography. Any gross movement of the tongue is dependent upon the position and movements of the hyoid bone.

The structure of the teeth is described. They are susceptible to many nutritional and endocrine influences during their development. The relation of dental abnormalities to speech defects is controversial. The static and dynamic spatial relationships of the upper and lower teeth, known respectively as occlusion and articulation, appear to have a significant influence upon speech.

Certain disorders of the mandible, involving its shape and structure, influence speech. The anatomy of the mandible is described. The muscles of the mandible operate in functional groups and provide for elevation, depression, protrusion, retraction, and combinations of these movements.

The cheeks and lips are important articulators. In speech the cheeks, like the lips, act chiefly to articulate the labial consonants. The muscles acting upon the lips and cheeks are part of the apparatus for facial expression. These muscles are mostly superficial, and they are arranged in separate groups around the sense organs.

The sensory innervation of the facial region is from the trigeminal nerve, and the motor innervation is from the facial nerve.

Chapter 13

THE EAR AS A SOUND RECEPTOR

THE EXTERNAL EAR

Sound is produced by a body vibrating in a medium such as air. When a sounding body like a tuning fork vibrates, alternate condensations and rarefactions of the air called sound waves radiate out from it. These waves may reach the auricle of the external ear.

The auricle, or pinna, is a concave cartilaginous structure which directs sound waves to the external auditory meatus, or canal. Its significance in man may be negligible, although it has been said to help localize sound and to have most of its effect on tones of high pitch. The human auricle may be considered a vestigial structure. Its muscles, which in lower animals direct the ears to the source of sound, are still present in man, but they are rarely functional.

The auricle develops essentially from six primordia, which accounts for the wide diversity in its shape. These variations, however, are only rarely abnormal. The primordia are mesenchymal derivatives of the first and second branchial arches.

The external canal, about 1 inch long, is composed essentially of cartilage which is entirely closed medially by the drum, or tympanic membrane. The canal in its inward course travels successively back, up, forward, and down.

Although the canal, or meatus, is present at birth, it is then only an imperfect ring which has come from a cartilaginous primary auditory meatus and also from an inner incomplete meatal plate. In the early embryonic stages an epithelial tube grows inward. The tube comprises the hollow primary meatus and the solid meatal plate, the latter being an extension of the former. The cartilaginous external canal develops from the primary meatus. The inner part of the canal comes from the meatal plate, which develops a lumen. The tympanic membrane comes from tissue embryologically located between the cavities of the meatal plate and the tympanum (middle ear).

The front and lower walls of the external meatus develop from the tympanic bone, while the back and upper walls develop from the mastoid process and the zygomatic arch. The elements fuse to a great extent in the second year of life, and the canal attains its definite form.

The drum membrane is not more than 0.1 mm thick, and it is elliptical, with approximate diameters of 9 and 10 mm. Its framework of thin fibrous connective tissue is covered laterally with skin and medially with mucous membrane. It is funnel-shaped with the concavity facing the external canal, and its direction is obliquely downward and inward.

The handle of the malleus, which is the most lateral of the three middle ear bones, is attached to the drum so that both vibrate together.

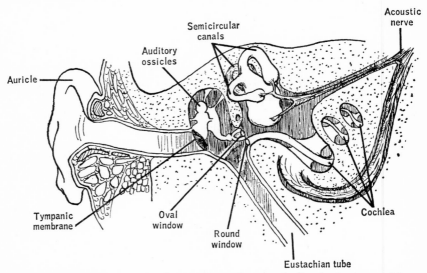

Fig. 13–1. Diagrammatic view of the entire auditory mechanism in the temporal bone.

The drum is extremely sensitive to sound waves, and it transmits all audible sound frequencies. Its vibrations are at the same rates as those of the sounding body, and the middle ear bones in turn faithfully follow these rates. A simple rupture of the drum could impair sound transmission, although perhaps not as much as once thought. Sometimes an extensive hole in the drum causes only a slight loss in hearing (Fowler, 1947). A few exceptional individuals who lost the drum as well as the malleus and incus retained hearing intensity within 20 to 30 db of normal.

It has been contended that the drum is not elastic enough to obey Hooke's law, which states that within limits displacement is directly proportional to the displacing force. The auditory response may thus fail to be linear, which results in the production of aural harmonics, or overtones. These are lower in intensity than the fundamental and may become masked, but they can modify the sound quality. Despite these statements, it is generally agreed (Wever, 1949), that except for high intensities of sound the drum does not significantly distort the form of the incident sound waves.

The bottom of the eardrum is higher than the floor of the external canal. Thus, wax and other substances do not rest against the drum but tend to accumulate below it on the wall of the external canal.

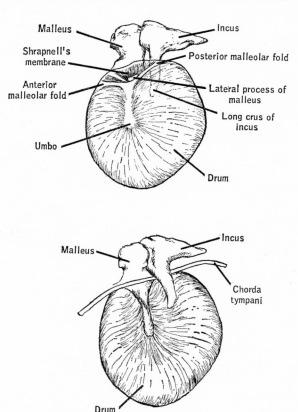

Fig. 13–2. The tympanic membrane. Outer and inner views.

The drum ordinarily works like the diaphragm of a microphone. The amplitudes of its vibrations are extremely small.

THE MIDDLE EAR

The middle ear is an efficient instrument to direct sound energy to the oval window, to match the impedance of the air to the inner ear, and to protect the inner ear from intense sounds.

Fallopius in the sixteenth century termed the middle ear chamber the tympanum. The chamber may be said to encompass the tympanic cavity, the antrum, and the Eustachian tube.

The tympanic cavity is an irregular space in the petrous bone. Its anteroposterior and vertical dimensions are each about 15 mm. Its transverse measurement is 2 mm at its narrowest portion. It extends upward into an epitympanic space which contains the head of the malleus and the body of the incus. This space, or attic, is separated from the middle

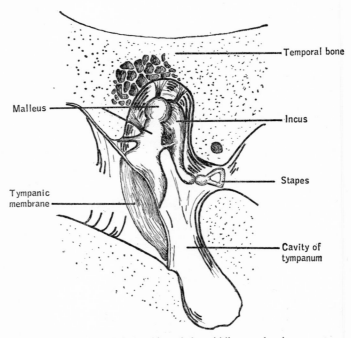

Fig. 13–3. Relationships of the middle ear chamber.

cranial fossa on the inner aspect of the skull by a thin bone called the tegmen tympani.

The aditus, which is a recess in the posterior wall of the attic, connects the main chamber with a tympanic passageway called the antrum. The middle ear communicates by way of the antrum with the air sacs of the mastoid process. The antrum develops before birth as an air sac produced by expansion of the tympanic cavity. The sac in turn proliferates small, hollow cells which project backward into the mastoid region. The antrum and air cells become lined with a mucous membrane which is continuous with the membrane of the tympanic cavity.

Although the air space of the middle ear is in continuity with the air spaces of the many bony cells contained in the mastoid process, this relationship does not have the same functional implications as that of the middle ear and Eustachian tube. The fact of continuity is of importance in pathology, however, where infection travels from the tympanic cavity to the mastoid.

The Eustachian (auditory) tube enters the anterior wall of the tympanic cavity on each side from the nasopharynx. It travels along an approximately 36 mm course. The anterior (pharyngeal) two-thirds is partly cartilaginous and partly fibrous, whereas the posterior third is surrounded by the temporal bone. The bony part is triangular in cross-section. The tube is flared out at both pharyngeal and tympanic openings. The tympanic orifice is too high to permit effective drainage of the

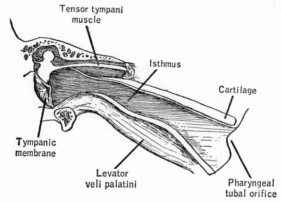

Fig. 13—4. The Eustachian tube, showing its flared ends.

middle ear, but it can be drained with the patient prone (lying on the abdomen), which places the anterior wall of the tube in a dependent position.

The pharyngeal end of the cartilage is just inside the mucosa of the nasopharynx. In that area it produces an elevation behind the pharyngeal opening of the tube called the torus tubarius. At the opposite end the place where the narrowest part of the tube is located in the temporal bone is called the isthmus. Clearly the tubal bore changes, narrowing down from a 9 mm diameter at the pharyngeal end to a constricted zone where the cartilage changes to bone. Then the tube reexpands to the flared orifice in the tympanum. The Eustachian tube of the infant is about half as long and is straighter.

The tube is lined by a mucosa which is continuous with that of the nasopharynx and of the tympanic cavity. It is a pseudostratified, ciliated columnar epithelium which contains a rich supply of mucous glands in the pharyngeal sector, especially near the tubal orifice. The pharyngeal part is also well supplied with lymphatic tissue and is sometimes called the tubal tonsil.

The tube permits the middle ear air to be equalized in pressure with that of the outside. This is necessary for proper movements of the drum membrane and for sound transmission. Thus, in an airplane ascent the drop in pressure may produce a temporary deafness which can be alleviated by opening the entrance to the canal through swallowing or yawning. Air blockage as a complication of inflammation, as it occurs in a head cold, may result in air absorption from the chamber. The inequality of external and internal pressures causes the drum to be pushed inward tightly, which may produce hearing impairment. Transmission of high tones seems to be especially impaired in the occlusion of the Eustachian tube, although not necessarily at first.

The Eustachian tube also functions to protect the tympanum against foreign bodies and nasopharyngeal infection. It accomplishes this by remaining variably closed except in activities such as coughing, deep breathing, sneezing, swallowing, and yawning. If the tube fails to open when it should, deafness and retraction of the drum may follow. Sometimes the tube is chronically patent. This condition may not affect hearing, but the voice may seem to the patient to have a disagreeable reverberation. In some instances the protective function of the tube is pathologically stressed in that the mucosa in the cartilaginous area may be thrown into folds which act like valves and obstruct the passage of air.

The drainage of normal and abnormal secretions out of the middle ear is still another function of the Eustachian tube.

It is noted above that the Eustachian tube is ordinarily closed and that it opens with yawning, swallowing, and with the contraction of muscles. The exact muscles involved are still open to question, and some views are now presented.

Guild (1955) described the probable machinery of Eustachian tube movements, and he involved the elastic tissue present in the tube in such movements. This tissue is said to counterbalance the action of the tensor veli palatini muscle, the latter serving to pull the lateral wall of the tube away from its medial wall and thereby open the tubal lumen. Closure has usually been regarded as a passive event which is caused by the pressure of neighboring structures. In Guild's view, closure is associated with active rebound of the elastic tissue.

Keogh (1957) described the opening and closing of the Eustachian tube as being brought about chiefly by contraction and relaxation of the palatal levators, assisted by the tensors and by the salpingopharyngeus muscle. When the levators contract, their structure rises in the opening of the tube and plugs its lumen. When the levators relax and the soft palate is depressed by the tensors, there is a transient opening of the valve-like slit in the anterior part of the tube. The suction caused by contraction and relaxation of the levators is a factor in draining the auditory tube of mucus.

The tube has been said to be opened, as during swallowing, by the salpingopharyngeus and dilatator tubae muscles. The salpingopharyngeus muscle originates from the inferior aspect of the tube close to its

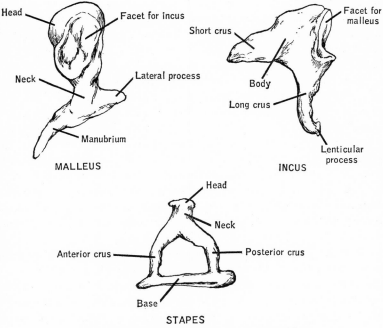

Fig. 13–5. The form of the disarticulated ossicles.

orifice and descends to fuse with the posterior portion of the pharyngopalatine muscle (which controls the opening between the mouth and throat). The dilatator tubae muscle originates from the cartilage sector of the Eustachian tube and passes downward to fuse with the tensor veli palatini muscle (which tenses the soft palate).

The three bones, or ossicles, of the tympanum are the malleus, incus, and stapes, which stretch in that order from the tympanic membrane to the oval window. They are interconnected by small ligaments and covered by mucous membrane which is continuous with that of the main chamber.

The oval window is on the medial wall of the middle ear at the entrance to the scala vestibuli of the inner ear. The stapes sends a foot-plate into the oval window which can push inward to displace the liquid, or perilymph, in the scala vestibuli. Because stapes fixation is stronger on one side than the other, its movement is not like that of a piston in a cylinder but rather like a pivot whose axis of rotation is at the lower posterior pole.

The ossicles vibrate as a single compound lever with a small amplitude, magnifying the force about ten times after losses have been taken into account. Attenuation of vibrations through fusion to an immovable joint leads to deafness. These bones can be bypassed in cranial bone conduction in which instance the waves travel directly to the inner ear.

That hearing could occur without the chain of ossicles does not deny their importance. They serve to deliver sound energy preferentially to the oval window. Otherwise, sound waves would enter the inner ear through the round window, and since in this instance they would hypothetically reach the sensory mechanisms in opposite phase to the waves entering through the oval window, they would reduce the effectiveness of the ossicle-borne waves. In this sense the round window decreases the maximum effectiveness of the auditory processes.

The ossicles collect energy from a relatively large area of air and bring it to a considerably smaller area at the stapes footplate. The tympanic membrane is most important in this process, since it receives sound energy over an area six to ten times that of the oval window. The force of vibrations reaching the oval window is six to ten times as great as it might be if the air entered the ear with the drum missing and if it reached the oval window directly.

The ossicles protect the inner ear against loud, low tones while still allowing passage of faint, low-frequency tones.

There is also a protective mechanism inherent in the normal air cushion of the middle ear. It guards against sudden large pressure changes or against loud, low-frequency sounds. This buffering effect, which is maintained by several factors, is known as the acoustic impedance of the ear. The stapes in loud sounds dissipates some energy by rotation on its transverse axis. Excessive vibration of the ossicles is moderated by muscle action as well as by the elastic cushion effect of the air within the chamber.

The ossicles change high-amplitude, low-pressure sound waves into those of lower amplitude and higher pressure. The stapes footplate moves only about one-half to one-third as much as the handle of the malleus, but the force of the stapes movement is two or three times as great as the force of the malleus. The greater force is necessary to produce pressure waves in the cochlear fluid, which possesses considerable inertia. In this sense the ossicles act as a pressure amplifier.

The stapes is the primary bone concerned in conduction hypacusis, which is a shift in the hearing threshold that can be corrected. Otosclerosis is the common cause. Disorders of the stapes usually involve its footplate. Lesions of the malleus and incus are much less common.

The action of the intrinsic muscles of the middle ear may not be essential to the auditory process, but it is of value in the functioning of this chamber. The tensor tympani muscle, which is about 22 mm long, goes from the upper edge of the orifice of the Eustachian tube to the handle of the malleus. It brings the handle of the malleus inward, and it increases the tension on the tympanic membrane. It heightens the sensitivity of the ear to high frequencies and may also protect the ear from excessive amplitude of vibrations. The muscle is relaxed during silence. If the tympanic membrane is slack, movements of peripheral portions of the membrane will not affect the handle of the malleus. Transfer of energy from the drum to the malleus involves a tensing of the drum. The muscle is innervated by the tensor tympani branch of the trigeminal nerve.

The stapedius muscle, which runs from the posterior tympanic wall to the posterior surface of the neck of the stapes, pulls the stapes laterally and puts the oval window under tension. This is a protective function. The muscle is innervated by the facial nerve.

Some points should be brought out about the developmental anatomy of the middle ear. The gill-arch system of aquatic vertebrates is deeply involved in providing the evolutionary material, and the embryology roughly recapitulates the evolution. We have described the formation of the gill arches earlier in the text, and some pertinent facts are emphasized below.

When vertebrates took to land and the elements of their respiratory gill system were no longer necessary, the parts became transformed into useful derivatives including the auditory structures. Thus, in man the middle ear and the Eustachian tube are derived from the first pair of lateral pharyngeal evaginations called pouches, with a small contribution from the second pharyngeal pouches. These pouches originate from the embryonic germ layer called entoderm. In fishes each pouch would have pushed laterally to fuse with the corresponding medially directed ectoderm of the arch. Their fusion and the subsequent dissolution of the intervening plate would have produced a branchial groove, or gill slit. In man the first and second pouches dilate, and they reach the outer ectoderm only fleetingly. The proximal stalk of each of these pouches narrows at approximately the second month, and this narrowed region forms the Eustachian tube, which gradually elongates. The dilated distal pouch is the forerunner of the middle ear chamber on each side.

Posteriorly located skeletal parts of the first and second arches form the auditory ossicles. In lower vertebrates the malleus and incus are drawn into the construction of the upper and lower jaws, but in mammalian and human embryology they are removed from their chewing function and come to serve for sound transmission. The second (hyoid) arch produces hyomandibular and hyoid pieces. It is the former which attaches the jaws to the skull in fishes, but in amphibians, reptiles, and birds it forms the columella, which carries sound impulses across the middle ear. In mammals the hyomandibular piece produces the stapes, which is the evolutionary homologue of the columella.

The middle ear and the Eustachian tube make their first appearance in the higher, anuran orders of amphibians. The Eustachian tube is variably developed in reptiles, and it is a bony structure in birds. Mammals below man generally have a wide and patent tube, and, as in man, the tube tends to be differentiated into bony and cartilaginous sections.

THE INNER EAR

The inner ear in its embryology is derived from a placode, or thickened plate, of ectoderm which early in development sinks below the

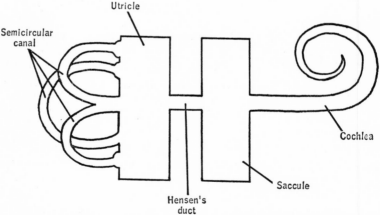

Fig. 13–6. The vestibule of the inner ear and its diverticula. Diagrammatic.

surface on each side to form an otic pit. This pit deepens to a vesicle from which all structures of the membranous labyrinth develop.

The internal ear grows as a labyrinthine series of membranes into the petrous portion of the temporal bone. The membranes proliferate into the temporal bone as a cast into a mold. The central or entrance section of this structure is the vestibule. The membranous vestibule divides to a saccule and utricle which remain connected by Hensen's duct. From the utricle three semicircular canals develop. Since these are organs of equilibrium and not of hearing, they will not be discussed further.

From the saccule there sprouts out a lagena, later called the cochlea, which contains the receptors of hearing. The membranous cochlea becomes a spiral structure by developing approximately two and one-half turns. The diagrams herein show the membranous cochlea lying within the bony cochlea. A fluid called perilymph develops in the bony cochlea, while endolymph forms within the membranous cochlea. The membranous structure is known as the scala media, or cochlear duct, and the surrounding bony cochlea is subdivided to a scala vestibuli and scala tympani. The scala media is separated from the scala vestibuli by

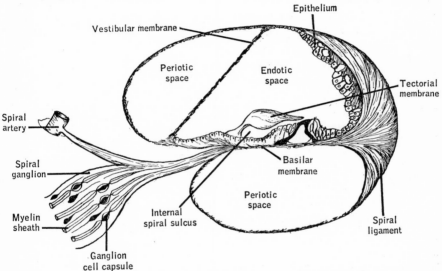

Fig. 13–7. The internal ear in section to show its membranes and the auditory nerve.

Reissner's membrane and from the scala tympani by the basilar membrane.

In diagrams of the cochlea, its long axis is usually drawn as vertical with the scala vestibuli lying above the scala tympani. The cochlea is actually a flattened cone with a central core called the modiolus. Around this core a hollow spiral tube about 32 mm long makes two and one-half turns. The apex of the cochlea faces forward and laterally, while the base goes backward and medially. The scala vestibuli is placed anteriorly and the scala tympani posteriorly, with the scala media between. Spiral canals in the modiolus transmit blood vessels and the cochlear nerve fibers. The base of the bony cochlea opens into the vestibule, into the round window, and also into the perilymphatic duct to make connections with the subarachnoid space.

In its spatial relationship the saccule connects with the medial wall of the middle ear. On this wall the oval window is adjacent to the scala vestibuli, and the round window is adjacent to the scala tympani.

In function the middle ear bones vibrate, and the footplate of the stapes thrusts against the oval window, which transmits the incident pressure to the perilymph of the scala vestibuli. Since the bony labyrinth is inextensible, the waves travel a variable length up the scala vestibuli and then down the scala tympani to terminate in the membrane of the round window. The latter is thrust back into the middle ear, and equilibrium is restored. Whether the pressure waves will travel up the scala vestibuli all the way to its apex (helicotrema) depends upon the frequency of the tones. Low tones approach the apex, whereas high frequency vibrations short-circuit the length of the cochlea and cross at the basal end, producing local vibrations of the basilar membrane during their passage from the scala vestibuli to the scala tympani.

As explained later, the place of deformation of the basilar membrane is the crux of auditory analysis in the inner ear. At any frequency of sound a given sector of the membrane vibrates more strongly than other sectors. Very high frequencies produce resonance pressure nodes near the base of the cochlea, while intermediate frequencies excite the membrane at about the middle of the cochlea. These points are called the resonant nodes for such frequencies. The position of resonance on the membrane is determined primarily by the fibers of the basilar membrane. The greater elasticity of the basal fibers plus the small inertia of the fluid at the base determine the fact that high-frequency sounds will be resonated at the base. This fact accords with the principle that the frequency of vibration varies directly with the elastic coefficient of the system and inversely with the inertia of the system. High fluid inertia and a lower elastic coefficient at the apex of the cochlea bring about resonance of low tones there. The position of resonant nodes on the basilar membranes is approximately known for each frequency (Guyton, 1956).

The round window is of considerable importance because the retrograde elastic thrust of its membrane into the middle ear allows pressure equalization within the inner ear. Any rigidity of this membrane has been claimed, controversially, to hinder the vibration of the relatively incompressible perilymphatic fluid and thus impair hearing. Theoretically, there are other ways of escape for the pressure variations in the inner ear. The round window is not importantly concerned with the forward conduction of sound waves into the inner ear, although even this view is controversial.

The Vibrating Membranes. The fluid-pressure vibrations in the perilymph excite the production of electrical potentials in the organ of

Corti. This organ is situated upon the basilar membrane, and it is bathed by the endolymph of the scala media. It is built up as a series of arches, or pillars, arranged in series along the length of the basilar membrane. Supporting cells and sensory hair cells lie between these arches. The hair cells contain hairs, or cilia, which project from their free surface. There is a row of inner hair cells on one side of the inner rod, which is a limb of the arch, and there are several rows of outer hair cells on the side of the outer rod, which completes the arch. A colloidal semifluid tectorial membrane rests upon the hair cells. At their basal ends the

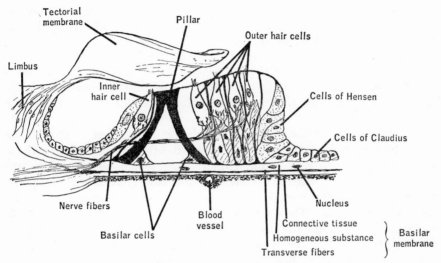

Fig. 13–8. A histological view of a section of the organ of Corti.

cells are connected with the terminal twigs of nerve fibers which combine to form the main bundle of the cochlear nerve.

When the stapes vibrates, there is evidence that the basilar membrane vibrates correspondingly. How the vibrations are transmitted to the hair cells is uncertain. They may be carried through the rods forming the arches of Corti and agitate the endolymph of the scala media. This activity may in turn excite the hair cells by way of their cilia, that project up into the endolymph. There is no proof that this is actually the manner of transmission.

Excitation of the hair cells probably produces the discharges called cochlear potentials, or microphonics. It also produces acoustic nerve potentials. These potentials will be considered later.

Another membrane of uncertain significance is the vestibular (Reissner's) membrane. It separates the scala vestibuli from the scala media.

The vestibular membrane may have no part in transmitting vibrations into the scala media, although it has been said to function in this way for certain frequencies. Guyton (1956) states that it is too weak to resist the passage of sound waves from the scala vestibuli to the scala media. Each time that the fluid impinges upon the membrane, the structure moves along with the fluid. The result is a forward movement of the endolymph of the scala media. Because of this the membrane may be ignored in auditory function. Perhaps it serves only to separate the fluids of the scala vestibuli and scala media. The need for fluid separation is obscure.

The tectorial membrane in the scala media may act as a damper to suppress excessive and continued vibrations, or possibly it may be activated by the stapes and in turn stimulate the hair cells (Kostelijk, 1950). The actual roles played by the tectorial and vestibular membranes are uncertain. Even the stimulating function of the basilar membrane is not conclusive, despite its known response to vibrations of the perilymph. It has been said that the movements of the basilar membrane may be infinitesimal.

The vibrations of the tectorial membrane have been studied in an effort to explain how the hair cells excite the free nerve endings. These cells may be stimulated through their hairs, which project freely into the scala media. There is a view that the hair cells are mechanically vibrated against the tectorial membrane, and the latter in turn stimulates the hair cells. They may conceivably be stimulated by fluid in agitation between themselves and the tectorial membrane. Von Békésy (1951) states that there is no valid evidence that the tectorial membrane is concerned significantly with the sense of hearing.

Neuroanatomical Pathways. Jungert (1958) reviews the central auditory pathways in the brain stem and inferior colliculi.

The auditory pathways use a succession of four neurons from the cochlea to the temporal cerebrum. The first-order neurons are in the modiolus, where they form the spiral ganglion of the cochlea. There are about 25,000 to 29,000 such fibers, and they originate on the internal or external hair cells. They leave the temporal bone through the internal meatus. The fibers seem to be systematized in that tones are transmitted by different groups among them according to the sound frequencies. Spatial orientation occurs within the auditory nerve.

The first-order neurons enter the ipsilateral dorsal and ventral cochlear nuclei in the upper medulla and pons. Many second-order neurons from both nuclei cross over within the trapezoid body, and some or all of these neurons synapse with the contralateral cells of the superior olivary nucleus of the pons. Other second-order neurons rise ipsilaterally and eventually cross over and end in the inferior colliculus, a lower auditory center. All the second-order ascending tracts are said to reach the lateral lemniscus.

Third-order neurons ascend in the lateral lemniscus to another auditory center called the medial geniculate body, which is in the posterior part of the thalamus. The final auditory radiation rises to Heschl's convolution located in the superior temporal (anterior transverse) cerebral

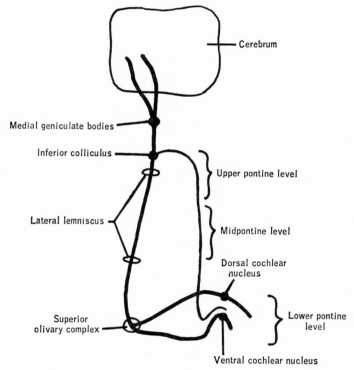

Fig. 13–9. Diagrammatic view of the auditory tract to show the neurons and centers involved.

convolution. Because possibly 50 per cent of the nerve fibers travel upward ipsilaterally from the cochlear nuclei, the impulses from each ear reach both the right and left cerebral cortex. Therefore, the removal of one temporal lobe does not cause deafness in either ear. There is a factor of dominance, however, and the removal of the dominant temporal lobe impairs associations and decreases the ability to interpret the meaning of sounds, despite the persistence of sound reception.

In the process of impulse transmission from ear to brain, the number of nerve impulses progressively decreases. This decrease indicates that the temporal cortex is not concerned with all auditory processes. The lower nuclei perhaps act as filters which adjust the impulses and relay only certain ones to the cerebrum. These lower centers are also relay nuclei which can send adjusted impulses to other bodily areas for quick adaptive responses to sound. The medial geniculate bodies of the thalamus may be able to generate a crude consciousness of the various qualities of sound. This possibility is suggested by the ability to perceive intense sounds after the removal of both primary temporal cortices.

The medial geniculates appear to be systematized, in that each point on the organ of Corti has a corresponding point there. Also the geniculates may have a systematized projection upon the ipsilateral temporal cortex. Local destruction of the geniculates can be followed by localized destruction in the temporal cortex. This is a logical extension of the place-mechanism theory of hearing (Fulton, 1955), in which the pitch heard depends upon the area of the cochlea stimulated and which cells in the cerebrum are activated.

THE PHYSICAL NATURE OF SOUND

Sound is produced by vibrating bodies of various kinds which set up a disturbance in an elastic medium, usually air. Sound will not travel in a vacuum.

The air particles vibrate back and forth in the nature of rapid periodic or pendulum-like swings. The disturbance activates the successive particles of the medium by progressive transmission, but each particle does not significantly change its own final position.

Sound waves are said to be longitudinal, which means that the particles of the medium oscillate back and forth in the direction in which the waves are traveling. This distinguishes sound from light waves. The latter are transverse, which implies that the particles of the medium oscillate at right angles to the direction in which the waves are traveling.

The velocity of the sound waves is dependent upon the properties of the medium and is independent of other parameters of sound. All sounds in air, regardless of their pitch, loudness, or quality thus travel at about 1,100 feet per second, and this prevents auditory confusion for perceiving different tones.

Sounds are pure or complex. The former type is simple. The latter is composed of two or more pure tones.

A pure tone has a given wavelength, frequency, and intensity. The wavelength is the length of a given wave emitted. It is measured, for example, as the distance between the crest of one wave and the crest of the successive one or as the distance between any two corresponding points in the two waves.

The frequency of a pure tone is the number of waves passing a given point in a given time. The longer the wavelength, the less the number of waves which will travel past an observer in a given time; the frequency is inversely proportional to the wavelength. The unit of time is usually 1 second, and one speaks of so many repetitive cycles of vibration as the number of cycles per second. We shall relate frequency to pitch in discussions to follow.

A point may be made about the use of symbols for cycles per second. In the older physiological literature, dv/sec (double vibrations per second) was a common expression because of the employment of tuning forks. The terms c/s and cps are in common use today, and many investigators prefer the latter.

The frequency is not the same as the velocity of a wave. Velocity implies the distance traveled by the wave in a given time.

Frequency should be differentiated from intensity. The latter refers to the maximum displacement of a vibrating body. The term displacement does not indicate a deviation in only one direction from a position of rest. The sound vibrations are oscillatory movements involving opposite phases in a cycle, and they are described as simple harmonic motions. The motion of a pendulum to the left and right of a position of rest is simple harmonic vibration. The displacement is the distance of the body from the resting point at a given time. The position of maximum displacement is called the amplitude, and it is measurable in linear units such as inches or centimeters.

Intensity may be determined by the frequency as well as by the amplitude of sound. We shall refer to intensity later in more detail and relate it to the psychological sensation called loudness.

The attributes of a pure tone described above hold also for complex tones. The latter possess in addition the factor of quality, which is dependent upon the established frequencies and their relative intensities.

The distinction between tones and noise arises in complex tones. In tones, the frequencies have well-defined mutual relationships. The lowest frequency is the fundamental, and it generally determines the pitch sensed.

If the sound waves are not regular and periodic, noise rather than tone is produced. Noise may be defined as an unwanted sound or one to which no definite pitch can be assigned. It is a waveform having a number of frequencies combined in a random manner. The waveform is compounded from pure tones, and the elements of the total waveform can be differentiated by harmonic analysis. The distinction between noise and tone is frequently a matter of psychology and training. Even physically, the distinction between degrees of periodicity and complexity may be a relative one.

Noise and tone are simultaneously emitted in speech. The relatively pure tones are vowels, which are normally of laryngeal origin. The sounds that are largely noise include the voiceless consonants, such as s or к, which originate in the organs of articulation.

The reader is referred to Wise et al. (1941) for a brief exposition of the physics of speech. See also Gray and Wise (1946), Fletcher (1953), Sataloff (1957), Travis (1957), and Van Riper and Irwin (1958).

In listening to ordinary speech, one may easily differentiate the fundamental tones and a series of higher tones, which are overtones of the fundamental. If the overtones have frequencies two, three, four, five, etc., times that of the fundamental, i.e., integral multiples of the fundamental, they may properly be called harmonics (as well as overtones). The term partial is used for both the fundamental and its overtones. In a fundamental of 100 cps and an overtone of 200 cps, the fundamental is the first partial and 200 cps is the second partial (or first overtone). The partial is the segmental vibration, and the overtone is the sound resulting from segmental vibration above the first partial.

Fig. 13–10. Diagrammatic displacement of a string vibrating as a whole, in halves, and in thirds.

The simplest but not necessarily the correct and current explanation of the origin of the complex waveform in speech is that the vocal folds are behaving as a set of vibrating strings. In accordance with this simplified assumption, the fibers of the vocalis muscles of the folds vibrate not only as a whole but also in separate localized groups. This action simultaneously produces sounds of different frequencies. If a string, as a model, vibrates as a whole, the wave produced is a fundamental note. If each half vibrates, the first overtone is produced. If each third vibrates, the next overtone is produced. In these instances the wavelength decreases from 1 to ½ to ⅓, whereas the frequency increases reciprocally from 1 to 2 to 3.

The tympanic membrane of the ear responds unselectively to the whole waveform, but in the classical resonance theories the internal ear may differentiate fundamentals and overtones through sympathetic vibration, or resonance. In this early concept an elastic body is set into vibration by movements in the medium if its own inherent frequency of movement, or natural period, corresponds with the frequency of the sounded body. Structures on the basilar membrane may act as a series of selective resonators. Views on this matter are presented below.

THEORIES OF HEARING

The outstanding psychological characteristics of sound are pitch, loudness, and timbre. Other sensations include density, volume, and time. In physics there are sound parameters, or dimensions such as frequency, intensity, and others.

The Perception of Pitch. Most theories concerning the function of the inner ear have emphasized the perception of pitch (von Békésy and Rosenblith, 1951). Pitch is a consciousness of the highness or lowness of tones.

In the resonance theory, emphasized by Helmholtz (1863), the analysis of sound, especially for pitch perception, is a function particularly of the cochlea rather than of the cerebrum. The basilar membrane is considered to contain a series of transverse fibers, or resonators, whose natural periods correspond with the range of frequencies in the audible spectrum. These resonators set up a peripheral action to which respective hair cells respond. Low tones are analyzed at the apex and high tones at the base of the membrane. For a compound wave a given region responds to the fundamental and other regions to the overtones. The brain becomes conscious of pitch by localizing the area of stimulation on the basilar membrane. Modern investigators disagree about whether the transverse fibers or other structures are selectively stimulated.

Pitch in the original resonance concept is a psychological sensation corresponding to the physical dimension of frequency. In the modern versions these dimensions are differentiated in that frequency can be regarded as the number of incident sound waves reaching the ear in a given time, whereas pitch is the tone as perceived. In high intensities there can be a relative change in pitch without a change in frequency, so that these two parameters of sound are not always in correspondence.

One of the many objections to the resonance theory has been that the basilar fibers are embedded in a homogeneous ground substance which binds them into a continuous structure and prevents them from vibrating separately as a selective series of resonators. The conception of maximum stimulation has been proposed to meet this objection to the resonance view. Sound activates not only the basilar fibers in tune with it but also and less forcibly the fibers on each side of the tuned resonators. A given set of fibers vibrates maximally, and others vibrate progressively less as their distance increases from the central disturbance. Only the vibrations of maximal amplitude effectively stimulate the nerve endings and become associated with the discrimination of pitch.

Helmholtz stated that the segments of the basilar membrane could be brought into vibration only when the tension in the transverse direction greatly exceeded the tension in the direction of their length. However, von Békésy asserted that the basilar membrane has no tension and acts like a gelatinous layer and also that the tension in a transverse direction is no different from that in a longitudinal direction. These objections could seriously weaken one of the cardinal tenets of the resonance theory.

A paradox exists in the resonance theory, in that the cochlea seems to possess both high selectivity and almost critical damping. These qualities are antagonistic, since a critically damped system loses its characteristic frequency, and this effect exerted upon a set of such systems does away with their functioning as a harmonic analyzer (Kostelijk, 1950).

There are theories that treat the cochlea as a hydrodynamic system in an elastic tube. These views have the advantage that the cochlea can act as an analyzer and obtain maximum displacement despite critical damping. Resonance is disregarded. A wave traveling along the basilar membrane sets up a local pressure maximum which is the stimulus for the organ of Corti. Helmholtz believed that the pressure pulse is propagated not as traveling waves but as a mass movement where all parts of the moving fluid are in about equal phase. A mass movement was said to characterize the windows and the fluid between them.

Wever (1949) discusses theories which have gradually evolved, such as place and frequency theories. The reader is also referred to Kostelijk (1950). The place theories are subdivided to resonance and nonresonance (wave) theories. The frequency theories are subdivided into telephone (nonanalytic) and pitch (analytic) types. Wever accepted elements of the place and frequency views in helping to synthesize a resonance-volley theory.

If any view held rigidly that the frequency of impulses in each nerve fiber increases to discriminate pitch, the theory would be weakened by the fact that an auditory nerve fiber can follow the frequency of stimulus only up to 900–1,000 cps. The Wever and Bray resonance-volley theory attempted to explain transmission of higher frequencies by postulating rotational activity of individual fibers at higher frequencies. A bundle of fibers delivers a volley of impulses at a higher frequency than is possible for one fiber. At a given frequency one group of fibers might respond to every second pulse, and the remaining fibers might respond to the alternate ones. At higher frequencies a group of fibers could respond to every third, fourth, or successively higher wave. High frequencies can have synchronous volleys fired by dividing all the available fibers into progressively smaller squads. Galambos and Davis (1943) estimated about 400 cps as the point at which fiber rotation begins. The smaller the squads, the more the volleys must decrease in size, and there is some evidence to bear this out (Fulton, 1955). One objection to the volley theory is that the secondary and tertiary neurons of the auditory path follow the stimulating frequency even less well than do the primary neurons, and the central auditory areas may follow the frequency with even less success. Above 3,000–4,000 cps, rotation of fibers becomes inadequate to explain sound transmission.

Wever and Bray in 1930 performed an experiment which was eventually used to support modified resonance ideas. Their work brought about the important discovery of the electrical activity of the cochlea. The voice, as spoken into the ear of an anesthetized cat, and pure tones up to 20,000 cps were reproduced after the impulses were led off the cochlea, amplified, and sent into a loudspeaker.

The Wever-Bray phenomenon at first seemed to substantiate a telephone theory in which the basilar membrane acting as a diaphragm was following the high-frequency 20,000 cps impulses. The Helmholtz resonance view appeared to be untenable except for the lower frequencies, since the auditory nerve did not have a refractory period brief enough to allow it to conduct the higher frequencies. The intrinsic operations occurring in the nerve were made doubtful, because the high frequencies were reproduced, although for a brief period, even after the death of the experimental animal. Because the phenomenon did later disappear after death, Wever and Bray concluded that it was biological in nature.

Two processes are involved in the explanation, (1) a cochlear response and (2) the VIIIth nerve response. In the former, electric cochlear potentials (microphonics) are generated, according to Davis and his coworkers, through conversion of pressure vibrations in non-nervous structures to electrical impulses, perhaps as a summation of the output of the hair cells. This is analogous to a piezoelectric effect, and these impulses may be recorded from any tissue, such as the round window. Cochlear potentials are said by some workers to represent the form in which the stimulus is received and altered by the peripheral auditory machinery.

Cochlear microphonics should not be confused with the electrical action potentials that arise in the acoustic nerve. Both result from sound waves activating the cochlea, and the cochlear microphonics can mask the action of the acoustic nerve potentials unless suitable instrumental detection is enlisted. The microphonics are artifacts which precede the true action potentials, although it has even been contended that they are the stimulus for the nerve endings on the hair cells. In more acceptable theories the hair cells are said to liberate a chemical mediator, such as acetylcholine, which activates the true acoustic potentials. The cochlear microphonic potentials are still of obscure significance, and they may be incidental by-products of activity. They have been studied intensively, however, in auditory physiology, since they indicate that sound has stimulated the organ of Corti. They are also useful in localizing the site of a lesion in the cochlea. The microphonics can reproduce the frequency and form of the sound waves that stimulate the cochlea, and they are an important tool to measure cochlear function during life.

Davis (1957) has summarized the current status of the biophysics of the inner ear. He discusses four kinds of electrical phenomena occurring in the cochlea. The AP is the action potential associated with nerve impulses. The EP is a positive endocochlear potential and a negative intracellular potential found in all excitable cells. The CM is the cochlear microphonic, or alternating current response, said to originate from stimulation of the hair cells. The SP is a summating potential, which is a positive or negative change in the magnitude of the endolymphatic potential.

The reader is also referred to von Békésy (1956), who has done monumental work in the physiology of hearing.

The hypothesis that chemical mediators may stimulate the nerve fibers has the advantage that the latent period of the nerve impulses can be explained. A latency of 0.7 milliseconds or more showed by the auditory nerve impulses has been an objection to the view that the electrical potential stimulates the nerve. In the chemical theory the latency expresses the time needed for some substance to cross the cell membranes and excite the nerve fibers. The mediator is possibly acetylcholine. This substance could also be the mediator between the hair cells and the sensory nerve fibers.

The place theories have shed some light on the problems left unanswered by other viewpoints. The salient features of a place theory are now reviewed.

There are perhaps as many as 29,000 individual basilar fibers in the basilar membrane. The same number of nerve fibers travel from the hair cells above the basilar fibers into the spiral ganglion of Corti. These fibers in turn enter the cochlear nuclei of the brain stem. Each area on the basilar membrane connects with a given area in the cochlear nuclei. The neurons retain their relative positions, and the stimulus pattern is possibly carried through to higher levels of the brain.

The incident sound waves are said to stimulate a specific area of the basilar membrane. The vibrations of the basilar membrane will have a maximum at some region even though a large segment of its length can be thrown into vibrations by a pure tone. The nerve fibers originating from the region of maximum response will discharge at maximum level, and the pitch is then sensed through evaluation of the maximum level. Alteration of the pitch implies shifting in the locus of the point of maximum along the basilar membrane. In the event that there is enough intensity to a tone probably the whole basilar membrane responds. This kind of theory supports the resonance view that the cochlea can separate sounds into the individual frequencies of the complex waveform.

Place theories in themselves only partly explain sound analysis; for example, pitch is altered by a change in intensity. In the Wever-Bray theory low tones are represented by frequency, high tones by place, and other tones by a combination of frequency and place.

In the Wever and Lawrence volley theory all tones affect the entire cochlea, but high tones have their maximum effect at the base and low tones at the apex. The form of the patterns determines pitch, in that high tones give sharp, peaked curves and low tones give broad, sloping curves. Intensity is said to depend upon the voltage output of each hair cell, and this output varies with the amplitude of output at a given place.

In the space-time pattern theory of Fletcher (1953) the pitch is sensed not only by its place of maximum stimulation on the cochlea but also by the time pattern transmitted to the cerebrum. Time is more important for low tones and place for high tones. The time pattern in the air is translated to a space pattern on the basilar membrane; the space pattern upon reaching the brain produces similar right and left cerebral patterns, and the time of maximum stimulation in each patch of structures involved on the basilar membrane is detectable. Thus, in binaural hearing four space patterns are produced in the brain, and each carries some sort of time pattern. Fletcher holds that the recognition of the changes of these patterns accounts for all the phenomena of hearing. The space-time pattern theory explains loudness by the number of nerve impulses reaching the brain each second and also by the extent of the stimulated patch on the basilar membrane. The length of the stimulated patch produces a definite size for the portion of the brain excited. This delineation in turn gives a sensation of extension or volume.

There is a body of theory which denies the selective action of the basilar membrane. The Rutherford telephone theory (1886) asserted that the membrane vibrates as a whole, as the diaphragm of a microphone, and that the differentiation of the various frequencies of the waveform is not a resonance property of the cochlea. Pitch was said to depend upon the frequency of the impulses transmitted over each auditory nerve fiber and received by the auditory centers. Wrightson (1918) proposed what is essentially a telephone concept in his modification of Rutherford's contentions. The telephone theories have suffered from the knowledge that there is no close relation between sound frequency and action currents in the acoustic nerve.

As a general statement, the crude response to pitch is perhaps made peripherally, whereas the finer discrimination is a function of the cerebrum.

The Perception of Loudness. The parameter called loudness is considered a psychological attribute of sound, related to the physical dimension of intensity. It describes the strength of the sensation, i.e., soft or loud.

Loudness has some correlation with the amplitude of the sound wave. Intensity is roughly synonymous with amplitude. When the incident sound waves have greater intensity, as evidenced by their amplitude, the number of nerve impulses increases. The total number of nerve impulses generated, however, is determined by the general activity of structures in the cochlea.

Frequency as well as amplitude influences the loudness of a sound. As the frequency of nerve impulses increases, the sound becomes louder. If a nerve fiber from the basilar membrane is stimulated at low frequency, the sensation is one of a weak sound, whereas stimulation of the same fiber at high frequency produces a louder sound. It may be well to point out that the frequency of the nerve impulses is not necessarily the same as the frequency of the incident sound.

Loudness appears to depend not only upon the intensity of the waves but also upon the frequency of the nerve impulses. It also depends upon the number of nerve fibers involved in carrying the impulses, although the numerical relations are not simple. Finally, it involves subjective judgment. Loudness from the standpoint of speech production depends upon the volume of the vibrations of the vocal folds, and it may possibly bear a proportionality to the breath used.

Although loudness increases with the intensity of a pure tone, a given intensity may still sound much louder near the mid-point of the audible range of frequencies than at very high or very low frequencies.

A digression will now be made into the physical meaning of intensity. Intensity involves the flow of energy (in ergs) carried by the sound waves through a unit area (sq cm) in a unit time (sec). It is arbitrarily measured in bels or more conveniently in decibels (0.1 bel or db). The larger unit, or bel, is the logarithm of the ratio of the energy of two sounds. The logarithm is used to avoid large numbers. The bel (and also the decibel) state by what ratio one value is greater or lesser than another. For example, a sound is 1 bel greater than another if its energy is 10 times greater than the other (or the logarithm of the ratio is 1); a sound of 3 bels (30 decibels) is 1,000 times greater in power.

The following equations show the quantitative relationships of the number (N) of bels and decibels.

$$N_{bel} = N_b = \log \frac{\text{energy of sound described}}{\text{energy of reference sound}} = \log \frac{E_1}{E_2}$$

$$N_{db} = 10 \log \frac{E_1}{E_2}$$

Fortuitously, 1 db is approximately the least discernable difference in loudness from the subjective standpoint.

Any pure tone has a definite intensity as well as frequency. If a reference level is taken as zero db for the intensity of the faintest sound audible to normal ear, then the intensity of lively speech is perhaps as high as 60 db. Ordinary speech is a mixture of sounds of various intensities, and the weaker sounds may be about 30 db less than the stronger ones.

Gray and Wise (1946) describe intensity differences as follows. If very loud speech is 60 db greater than a very soft whisper and if the number of db is 10 times the logarithm of the numerical ratio between these two intensities, then the logarithm itself is 6, or the corresponding number is 10^6 (1 million). That is, very loud speech is 1 million times greater than a soft whisper. If we arbitrarily ascribe a value of zero to the power of average speech, then very loud speech has a power of plus 20 db, weak speech minus 20 db, and a whisper minus 40 db.

Judson and Weaver (1942) consider the definition of intensity in terms such as the average speech power, or the totality of all speech sound energy emitted in a complete speech divided by the total time for that activity. They note an estimate of 15 microwatts for the average speech power of the average person in this country. This estimate rises to 1,000 in extremely loud speech and falls to 0.001 microwatts in soft whispering. The greatest range of intensity one would expect would vary from 0.01 to 5,000 microwatts, which would correspond to a range of about 60 db. Houssay (1955) states that the whole range of intensities perceptible to the human ear is expressed by 120 db.

Fletcher (1953) makes an interesting comment about the minute energy output of speech in his statement that, " . . . it would take 500 people talking continuously for a year to produce enough energy to heat a cup of tea." The low speech power is nevertheless measurable electronically with calibrated microphones and vacuum-tube amplifiers.

The power of speech is described not only as the average speech power (above) but in several other ways. Thus, the mean speech power is the average speech power over a period of 0.01 seconds; the instantaneous speech power is the rate of radiation of the sound energy at any instant; the peak speech power is the maximum value of the instantaneous speech power in a given interval; the syllabic speech power is the maximum value of the mean speech power attained when a syllable is spoken, and it is indicative of the energy given to the syllable; and the phonetic speech power is the maximum value of the mean speech power for a vowel or consonant being spoken, and it indicates the relative power of diverse speech sounds.

The methods of measuring speech intensity are reviewed by Steer and Hanley (1957). It is noted that such terms as sound power and sound pressure are analogous to sound intensity, since the same frame of reference is used to evaluate all three concepts, despite different methods to investigate them. Since the terms are mutually convertible and since intensity is the most commonly used term, the latter is the one most often discussed and emphasized.

The Perception of Quality. A distinct parameter of sound is its quality, or special nature, called timbre. This quality is determined by the frequency, strength, and number of partials present. Musical instruments might be indistinguishable if only their fundamental tones were sounded, and this is true for the voice. Timbre is associated with the complexity of the waveform. Two identical sounds of the same fundamental pitch may have unlike waveforms.

The auditory mechanism can discriminate the separate simple tones of a complex waveform, provided the sound is neither very intense nor has many overtones. A trained person can differentiate all the instruments in an orchestra and even all the notes sounded at one time. This power is referred to as the analytical capacity of the ear.

The timbre of the voice sounds is related to the vibrations of the vocal folds, the size and shape of the air column, and the texture (tenseness and tonus) of the pharyngeal walls.

The qualities called consonance and dissonance are explainable through processes occurring in the basilar membrane. The pleasant sensation of a musical chord arises when the frequencies of simultaneous tones have simple mathematical ratios to one another and their overtones are in mutual support. In this instance the basilar membrane is said to display discrete nodes of activity at regular intervals while other areas along it are quiescent. In discordance the sounds do not support one another and produce generalized activity along several areas of the basilar membrane with fewer discrete nodes. Such diffuse stimulation of the cochlea along with irregular beats between tones produces a sensation of noise instead of consonance.

Beats result from summation and interference of sound waves. For example, if two tones with similar but not identical frequencies, such as 2,000 and 2,003 cps, reach the ear simultaneously, then the sound perceived may be periodically strengthened and weakened. The result is pulsations, or beats. Reinforcement occurs when the sounds reach the ear in the same phase, and a mutual weakening occurs when they are in opposite phases.

It is known that a pure tone may sound differently to different individuals (Fowler, 1947). This is a result of anatomical variations. Cochleas are not identical, and the same is true for the higher centers. No one knows what the exact quality of a sound is in another person.

Pitch, loudness, and timbre are not the only parameters of sound.

Volume and time are some others (Erickson, 1926). Volume implies massiveness, or the filling of space by sound, and it is a subjective rather than a physical measure of the extensiveness of the incident sound. Rather than being dependent upon a specific mechanism for its production, it is a function of pitch and intensity, varying with the amplitude and approximately inversely with the frequency, or pitch (Osgood, 1956). The volume increases with increasing areas of stimulation of the cochlea. Loudness is closely related to volume but not synonymous in cause or effect.

Time is involved in the psychological interpretation of sound. It is expressed in the duration of tones and also in the frequency and duration of the pulses between tones.

Van Riper and Irwin (1958) discuss the factor of time in relation to such phenomena as the sound duration, the time qualities of the syllable, the time values of the pause, the sound unit, and the word. They have coined certain terms in this connection. Pitch/time is the judgment of the frequency of vocal fold vibrations. Loudness/time is a quality judgment of the incident sound intensity at a given time, and it is related to complex laryngeal mechanisms. Quality/time is the listener's perception of the frequencies and their relative intensities, and it, too, is a complex function of several laryngeal mechanisms.

SOUND LOCALIZATION AND MASKING

There is an auditory perspective which consists of recognizing the direction of sound. The time of arrival in each ear is an important determinant. Ordinarily, the ear which first receives the sound makes us localize the sound on the corresponding side. When both ears are simultaneously excited, the source seems to be in the median plane of the listener. If a sound is heard with greater intensity in one ear, we also tend to localize it on the corresponding side.

In continuous sounds of low pitch the phase of the waves is important. We have already noted that movements of a sound wave resemble those of a pendulum. The particle of air vibrating is displaced in one direction, then returns and becomes displaced in an opposite direction. Finally it returns to its resting position. Sound waves are localized in the median plane when they arrive in both ears in the same phase. If they reach the ear in different phases, we localize the sound where the crest of the wave arrives first.

A sound lateral to the ears is more easily localized than one from above. Also, intermittent sounds are more easily localized than continuous ones.

The location of the brain centers for finding sound direction is uncertain. Because of the rapidity of the reactions, the centers are said to be in the brain stem. Nuclei therein are also involved in responsive eye and general body movements.

The masking effect of sound is obvious in trying to interpret conversation in noisy surroundings. When two tones are sounded together, one may raise the threshold of the other. The effect is measurable in decibels. The closer the tones coincide in pitch, the greater is the masking effect. Also, two tones reaching the same ear are more likely to produce masking of one than if such tones arrive at opposite ears.

The decrease in the neural response to one sound by simultaneous stimulation with another is linked with the refractory period of nerve fibers. A second tone produces impulses in fibers whose refractory states are such that the first tone does not get through. Apparently the stimuli are competing for the same fibers. It is of interest that although action potentials show masking, the cochlear microphonics summate (add) the impulses. This fact reveals a basic difference in the nature of these two varieties of current.

The perception of the distance of sounds is another attribute of auditory function. This property depends partly upon previous experience with intensity values at given distances and, to a small extent, upon the fact that distant sounds change their quality through reflection and refraction.

The eventual interpretation of the message received by way of the ear depends upon a combination of processes, one involving perception of the incident sound waves and the other based upon the listener's previous knowledge of the language. The perception of the sound waves is probably not based upon the absolute value of a factor such as the frequency or intensity but upon the associative relationships among such physical quantities.

THE BIOLOGICAL SIGNIFICANCE OF SPEECH SOUNDS

A system of sounds is available as language in man, and it is also used as a primitive code of communication in animals. There are vast possibilities of variation because of such differences as occur in the pitch of tones, in the patterns of overtones, in the great range of noises of varied pitch, and in the changes in volume.

Most vertebrates produce no noise. The large class of fishes is dumb except for a few species. The development of voice has been closely dependent upon the emergence of animals from an aquatic to a terrestrial existence.

Many animal sounds are purposeless, such as those resulting from movement of limbs. Some sounds, such as sneezing, are not for communication. In time, purposeless sounds may have become biologically adaptive and eventually used for social communication.

Sound in animals is used primarily for its survival value, as in offense, defense, food, and sex. It is generally the male who calls to the female in courtship phonation. Animals also use calls to keep together or to signal impending danger.

Many parts of the animal body have been put to use to produce sound. Some insects rub one part of the integument against another. The porcupine rattles its quills. The transmission of the most complicated messages, however, makes use of parts of the respiratory apparatus. The development of the vocal folds in mammals becomes the most efficient adaptation.

Sound can be produced with a fairly simple vocal mechanism. However, the presence of an adequate phonating structure is not enough for meaningful sound production. Animals with similar structures may be contrastingly vocal and mute. An animal such as the rabbit uses its larynx only in extreme circumstances, screaming, for example, when struggling against an enemy or subjected to severe stress. A deer or giraffe is notably silent but not because of laryngeal defection. The use of sound may be tied up with intelligence, the free use of the extremities, and the manner of life.

Sound and language in animals may be more related to the degree of development of the brain than to the structure of the larynx. Charles Darwin had the view that the higher apes have no speech because they lack sufficient intelligence. Darwin's view has been contested on the basis of animal experimentation. The voice has been studied particularly in the chimpanzee. Keleman (1948), after such an anatomical study, concluded that a hypothetical animal with a human brain and chimpanzee larynx could not produce any other phonetic effect than that animal now does. A human variety of speech would fail in spite of the animal's rich scale of phonetic possibilities.

The primitive sense organ for sound was probably a vibration receptor, such as the lateral line organ of fishes. Sounds of very low pitch seem to be sensed in fishes.

APPLIED ANATOMY AND PHYSIOLOGY

Informational Feedback. Fry (1957) discusses the dependence of speech upon hearing through natural feedback controls. In any speech sequence the information concerning the progress and bodily effects of the sound transmission is simultaneously relayed to the brain of the sender, and such information is used to control subsequent speech and adjunctive activity. The main servo-mechanism is the auditory feedback, although there are in addition tactual and kinesthetic circuits. Much of this information is stored in memory circuits, and the speaker can draw upon this in future speech activity. Informational feedback will also enable him to control speech movements even in the temporary absence of the auditory feedback.

Fatigue. All sense organs are subject to fatigue. The ear has the power of rapid recovery from fatigue in spite of continuous stimulation. High tones in particular increase the duration of fatigue. A common measurement is to contrast the intensity threshold of a tone which has been sounded continuously for some time with the resting threshold.

Prolonged stimulation by noise produces general bodily disorders such as an increase of the energy required for cardiac and respiratory activity, a jump in the metabolic rate, and psychological disturbances (Houssay, 1955).

Very high sound frequencies known as supersonics can cause severe damage to many animal cells or even the death of the animal. The chief cause of death is cavitation. This process involves the appearance of submicroscopic bubbles in tissue fluids, and the pathological effects are immediate.

Fatigue should not be confused with another auditory property called adaptation. When stimulation begins, the rate of the nerve discharges is high but decreases rapidly. As seen in the electrical responses of single nerve fibers, the voltage (spike height) also decreases. There is thus an adaptation in both rate and amplitude, and it is similar to adaptation in other varieties of sensory fibers.

Hearing Loss. The usual range of hearing is roughly from 20 to 20,000 cps, but the upper limit decreases with age. In normal speech, frequencies from approximately 250 to 4,000 cps are readily differentiated.

The intensity of a sound is another factor which determines whether it will be perceived. Even when we speak at a fairly uniform intensity, certain speech sounds are more easily heard. Every sound is linked by its method of phonation and resonation with a certain speech power. For a table of the relative phonetic powers of the speech sounds in order of strength, consult Akin (1958). The frequency region in which the greatest energy of each of the speech sounds lies is also given in the table.

Deafness as a term is confusing in that it may imply hearing deficits covering a wide range of intensities, perhaps from a small 15 db loss to a total loss at the 100 db level. More descriptive terms have come into usage. A loss that is innately restorable or subject to correction by prosthetic means is a hypacusis. People who are hard of hearing may be described as being mildly or moderately hypacustic.

If a person has a more profound loss or an ear-nerve disorder which can not be restored to a reasonable level of hearing, the term anacusis applies. When the defect is central and includes psychogenic types and the aphasias, the term dysacusis is applicable.

A loss of hearing that is less than 15 db may be considered to be within the normal range of hearing speech sounds. Low intensity sounds may be hard to hear when the loss is between 15 and 30 db. The difficulty in hearing conversation increases when the hearing loss exceeds 30 db. Between a loss of 45 to 60 db the individual is generally incapable of ordinary speech communication. Beyond 65 db the hearing loss is severe.

In the past literature, deafness was classified into two or three major types. The reader should consult standard works in otology for details.

External and Middle Ear Deafness. This category includes conduction-transmission disorders. In the external ear, auricle deformation, impacted wax, and otitis from infections may cause hearing loss. In the middle ear, blocked Eustachian tubes are frequent. This blockage may be caused by enlarged adenoids or by infections. The absorption of air in the middle ear decreases sound transmission. In otitis media, resulting from infection, the products of inflammation may rupture the drum membrane, and the scar tissue produced in healing may decrease the responsiveness of the drum and cause deafness.

Rohan (1957) reviews the history of the attempts to make artificial tympanic membranes. These devices are particularly applicable in chronic suppurative otitis media. In 1640 Marcus Banzer attempted to close the perforated eardrum with a disk of pig bladder fixed to the end of an ivory rod. Interest waned during the early twentieth century and is now being revived. One device is dried human amniotic membrane, but it falls off too easily and it is readily infected. Polyethylene lamellae are more easily sterilized, are more resistant, and can be cut into any shape. To keep the lamellae in place, the natural cerumen plus electrical forces may suffice. Rohan states that Pigmentum Matiche Compositum (BPC) has given the best results. Mawson (1958) has found skin grafting to be fairly satisfactory for repairing defective drum membranes. The problem is chiefly one of maintaining the blood supply.

Another large problem is otosclerosis, in which the stapes become fixed in the oval window. In the Lempert or fenestration technic, a new window into the internal ear is constructed so as to short-circuit the stapes (Jackson and Jackson, 1945; Lempert, 1950; Lewis, 1958). The operation is not indicated if the nerve endings are destroyed. Kos (1957) discusses technics to correct hearing loss resulting from otosclerosis, and he compares the procedure of stapes mobilization (Rosen, 1953) with that of fenestration. He states that fenestration is still the cornerstone of modern otosurgical methods and that it can improve the hearing in many patients in whom the stapes mobilization technic fails. The latter may succeed where hearing losses do not fall within the levels essential to successful fenestration, and it could partly restore hearing when the nature of the loss cannot be improved by resorting to fenestration. McKenzie and Rainer (1957) review the Rosen operation for stapes mobilization in otosclerosis, and they emphasize certain advantages that it has over the fenestration technic, including the possibility of normal hearing. Goodhill (1957) comments on his own modification of the stapes mobilization operation.

The emphasis given here to the stapedial-mobilization surgery for otosclerotic deafness stems from the fact that it restores hearing through normal physiological routes. Rosen approached the stapes through the external auditory canal, and he produced a fracture of the bony otosclerotic area, which had ankylosed the footplate of the stapes to the bony margin of the oval window. The tympanic membrane, which was resected, was then replaced.

Internal Ear Deafness. This type of deafness includes perceptive disorders, such as lesions in the organ of Corti and in the efferent cochlear nerve. The auditory receptors may be damaged congenitally or from explosive noises, trauma, and infections. The cochlea and cranial nerve VIII may be involved in syphilis and meningitis. Tumors also can destroy nerve fibers. Drugs, such as streptomycin, may be toxic to the static labyrinth and to the VIIIth cranial nerve nuclei. Decreased acuity of hearing is also a complication of the aging process. Refer to Lewis (1958) for a brief review of nerve (perception) deafness.

Ménière's disease is a perceptive deafness in which the pathological process affects chiefly the cochlea and the saccule, with increased pressure in the labyrinth. There may be vertigo, tinnitus, nausea, vomiting, nystagmus, and variable hearing loss.

Ruedi (1954) has reevaluated the role of vitamins in the ear, and has suggested that vitamin A acts as it does in the adaptation machinery of the retina. He had successful results in treating perception deafness with vitamin A. This vitamin also increased the tolerance for potentially traumatic noise.

Central Deafness. This type of deafness involves the auditory tract and the cerebral endings in the auditory cortex. A tumor may grow on the auditory nerve and produce spreading degeneration.

Hearing Tests. The development of audiometry (Saltzman, 1949) was stimulated by the earlier inadequate testing methods, and it is turning the measurement of auditory acuity into a fairly exact science. The audiometer is an important diagnostic instrument to provide intensities at controlled frequencies of sound. It evaluates the auditory sensitivity within the audible range of frequency as a function of the intensity of sounds.

Intensity is conveniently measured in decibel units. The decibel, as already stated, is the logarithmic ratio of the intensity of two sounds. It may be thought of as the smallest change of intensity that is perceptible.

The audiometer consists essentially of an electronic oscillator which generates pure and constant tones whose frequency and intensity can be varied over a large range. The output of the oscillator is fed to an earphone connected to the system. The intensity of each tone can be increased or decreased at will from the zero level. For instance, if the intensity must be increased 20 db above normal for audibility, then the hearing loss for that tone is 20 db. Approximately ten tones covering the auditory range are tested to find the hearing loss for each tone in each ear.

The subject is seated comfortably in a quiet room to avoid apparent hearing loss, especially for the lower tones. The earphone is placed directly over the ear canal. (A special instrument is pressed against the mastoid for bone conduction.) The subject signals with a nod of his head or by raising a finger if he perceives the sound.

In a routine examination with the older audiometers, the frequency control may be set at 1,024 cps, which is the middle of the tone range. The response at this frequency has been said to be most accurate and least variable in the scale. These frequencies are based on a musical notation, i.e., that middle C is 256 cps. However, in working with frequency it has been found more convenient to use a scale based upon multiples or submultiples of 1,000, as the physicists do.

A reasonably loud signal is presented at an intensity based upon the apparent hearing loss. The intensity is decreased in steps of 5 to 10 db until no response is elicited. The intensity is then increased until the tone is heard. The procedure is repeated, and a uniform response is obtained several times for each frequency. This level is then recorded as the hearing threshold of the frequency tested. Loss of hearing is expressed either in decibels or in per cent of normal for each tone.

The examination is continued for frequencies such as 512, 256, and 128 cps. Then the higher frequencies should be tested from 2,048 on. Newer audiometers begin usually no lower than 125 cps and run up in multiples thereof, as 250, 500, 1,000 cps, etc.

The audiometric curve is constructed by marking a point for each threshold determination on a chart called an audiogram. Frequencies are read on the abscissa and intensities on the ordinate. A cross is used as a symbol for the left ear and a circle for the right ear. For each ear the points found are connected by straight lines.

For evaluating an individual's ability to hear speech, there is one area in the audiogram which generally indicates whether he can get by, with difficulty, or whether he cannot undertake normal social intercommunication. This region is between 1,024 and 2,896 cps (or 1,000 and 3,000 cps in the newer audiometer) with less than 40 db hearing loss. Speech is usually accomplished at 7 to 15 feet at 40 to 60 db above threshold. A 40-db loss eliminates all but the loudest speech except at close range.

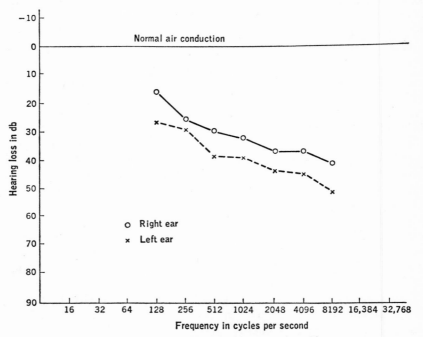

Fig. 13–11. Audiogram with older type of machine.

Some clinicians use comparative audiograms for serial examination of changes in auditory acuity. These audiograms may indicate a trend and are useful in prognosis.

One of the directions of audiometry is to make the process of taking thresholds, difference limens, etc., automatic by giving the patient control of the stimulus. He presses a button as long as he hears or can discriminate the tone, and he releases the button when the tone is not perceptible to him. There are other automatic audiometers which involve pairing a sound with a light or a picture.

Conditioning audiometry, using the Pavlovian pairing of two stimuli, is also gaining wide acceptance, particularly for the detection of malingerers; such methods are sometimes useful with small children, since they do not require the voluntary cooperation of the patient.

A screening procedure for children has been suggested by House and Glorig (1957), in which testing is done only at 4,000 cps, on the assumption that most children with a hearing loss are defective at that frequency.

Some practical although approximate tests of hearing are outlined below. Students working in pairs could do these as a laboratory exercise. For a more detailed account of hearing tests refer to Ballenger (1947), and Watson and Tolan (1949). Many workers are now con-

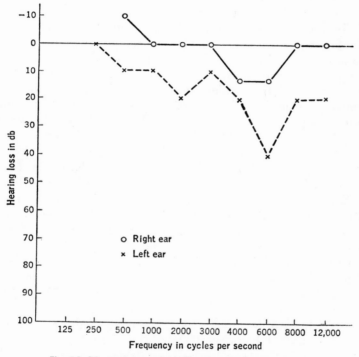

Fig. 13–12. Audiogram based on the newer metric scale.

vinced that the older approximate tests have little or no place in modern diagnosis (Jackson and Jackson, 1945). Pure tone audiometry of both air and bone condition and also tests using word lists to evaluate speech reception are in current vogue.

Formal methods of testing speech reception can require a large investment in equipment. For this reason some clinicians use tests with the spoken voice. The whisper is often used for uniformity. In whispering, only the residual air should be used. In this method the subject is at one end of a quiet room, and he directs his test ear toward the examiner while he closes the other ear with his index finger. The examiner approaches the subject until the correct answers to the whispered speech are elicited, and this distance is measured. The other ear is similarly tested. Under the stated test conditions, the average person may not hear the whisper beyond 20 feet.

If the room is too short, the examiner may turn his back to the subject. If this distance is still too short, the subject should turn his open ear to the opposite wall. Each of these variations may be assumed to indicate an increment in distance of about one-third.

Another method is the watch-tick test for checking the audibility of a limited frequency. It is used by immediate contact with the ear or mastoid, by approaching the ear, or by placing the watch between the teeth and finding the ear that senses it more acutely.

There are drawbacks to watch-tick tests or to those using the whispered or spoken voice. In such tests there is no measurement of the loudness or pitch of the incident sound. The reception of the sound is significantly influenced by the acoustical qualities of the test room. The procedures have more value in screening than in diagnostic evaluation.

The Weber test compares the bone conduction of both ears to find whether a monaural defect has a neural or obstructive cause. A sounded 256-cps tuning fork is placed in the mid-line upon the vertex, forehead, teeth, or chin. The subject is asked to state in which ear he hears the fork better. If he hears it more clearly in the diseased ear, the bone conduction is greater in that ear, and a conduction type of deafness exists. If he hears the sound better in the normal ear, the hearing defect of the diseased ear is of the perception type.

In the Rinne test, the duration of bone conduction is compared with that of air conduction for each ear. The shank of a vibrating 512 cps fork is placed against the subject's mastoid until it is no longer sensed, then the prongs are held about an inch lateral and broadside to the external ear. If the ear is normal, the fork is heard about twice as long by air as by mastoid bone conduction. If air conduction equals bone conduction, then both air and bone conduction are generally shortened in duration. However, air conduction suffers more, and a perception or mixed type of deafness is present; this result is called a negative Rinne.

In the Schwabach test, forks such as 512, 1024, and 2048 cps are successively used. The fork is sounded, and the time is recorded until the subject can no longer hear the sound. The shank of the vibrating fork should be placed on the subject's mastoid, and the test should be repeated on the mastoid of the examiner (whose hearing should be normal). In conduction deafness the sound through the cranial bones persists longer than normal. Equal decrease in both air and bone conduction, as compared to that in a normal individual, indicates perception deafness.

The data obtained from any of these tests can be evaluated with more accuracy by an audiometer.

Tests may be performed for the limits of pitch sensibility. With a series of low frequency tuning forks used in succession, one is found that is at the threshold of hearing (about 16–20 cps). For the high frequencies (16,000–22,000 cps) several instruments are available, such as the Galton whistle (Edelmann's), the monochord, or the audiometer. Most of the audiometers stop at 12,000 cps, however.

The audiometer does not test over-all hearing activity. To do this, word lists and sentence tests have been set up. These tests measure the ability to understand speech. They evaluate functions adjunctive to speech interpretation, such as sentence intelligibility, capacity to identify words, sound discrimination, and tolerance for loud sounds. The Speech Reception Threshold Test (Hirsch, 1952) measures the threshold intensity of speech at which the subject discriminates half the test matter given. Another variety of test gives, by magnetic tape or phonograph, P-B lists of phonetically balanced one-syllable words, or spondee disyllable words with equal stress on each syllable. The intensity of speech in db required by the subject to hear 50 per cent of the words is subtracted from the intensity needed by normal individuals; the result obtained is the score. Not all these tests are at the 50 per cent level. Berry and Eisenson (1956) devote a section to the manner of testing children with speech retardation, and they briefly list spondee and phonetically balanced words used in current auditory tests.

Tests of hearing loss in the infant and the very young child meet special obstacles, and they are still imperfectly developed. Startle responses from loud noises have been used. The nature of the brain waves by electroencephalography has also been studied (Marcus and Gibbs, 1949). Although uncertain, the psychogalvanic skin response (Hardy and Pauls, 1952) is available. Somewhat older children can be tested by the speech audiometer which, unlike the pure-tone audiometer, delivers a live voice at controlled intensities (Bangs and Bangs, 1952).

Rehabilitation. Rehabilitation of the patient with hearing loss involves many methods and skills, depending upon the specific case. Treatment but not diagnosis involves technics which are not commonly those of the physiologist. One physiological approach to therapy implies the development of latent stretch or proprioceptive reflexes in the patient. When the reader observes a speaker, he must learn to feel the sound vibrations. In another method called speech reading, the reader talks in unison with the speaker to get the muscular sensation of different words. This muscle-feeling or kinesthetic approach often succeeds. Other factors enter, of course, such as the development of attitudes and the concentration upon the rhythm and emphasis of words.

If a child does not hear spoken words, he does not learn to talk. One method of instruction is to have the patient place his fingers on the instructor's larynx and try to reproduce the same feeling in his own. This method is for vocalization only.

An experimental form of visible speech has been developed by recording an analysis of speech somewhat similar to the analysis done by the ear (Potter et al., 1947). The sound patterns which are visible can be read and are theoretically interpretable for visual hearing. The sound spectrograph (Prestigiacomo, 1957; Steer and Hanley, 1957) has been used to translate the sound by spreading out the dimensions of speech so that they are visible to the eye as they are audible to the ear. Visible records are made of the frequency, intensity, and time analysis of short samples of speech, and the record displays conspicuously the variations of vocal resonance with time.

One application of the method, which has yet to be realized, is in the education of the deaf. The machinery, developed by the Bell Telephone Laboratories, could conceivably make the telephone available to the totally deaf through the visible portrayal of speech sounds.

Among the other methods of rehabilitation one should take into account the possibility of training and utilization of residual hearing ability and the acquisition of a means of communication. The latter may involve hearing aids, lip reading, and the social and psychological retraining of the patient.

Hearing aids are devices used in impaired hearing to raise the intensity of the incident energy of sound. The loudness of sound is controlled by minimizing air losses between the transmission source and the subject and by carrying electrically amplified sounds into the ear.

In developing hearing aids, mechanical devices such as cupped hands and ear trumpets were first employed. In the electrical field, the midget vacuum tube and then the transistor circuits have come into existence. They are especially suitable for conduction deafness. These electronic aids are amplifying devices powered by minute batteries. Sound is translated into electricity by a microphone, and the electric impulses are sent through an amplifier to a small air transmitter and through a fitted lucite ear piece placed in the external ear or else to a vibrator allowing bone conduction through the mastoid process. Air conduction is more efficient, since 30 to 40 db of sound are lost in transmission through the skull. However, the bone conduction is better in some patients. Also, air terminals are not desirable in the presence of any middle ear infections. In most cases the instrument is fitted to one ear, although binaural terminals are sometimes helpful.

The patient with nerve deafness has more difficulty with a hearing aid because of the annoying effect of an abnormally rapid increase in the loudness of ordinarily just-audible tones, a phenomenon called recruitment. Hearing aids should be selected by employing pure-tone audiometer readings and speech receptive tests. The hearing aid may benefit those with losses up to perhaps 85 db, although its gain provides only partial compensation. A patient with a 50-db loss and a 30-db external gain still retains a 20-db handicap, but he has sufficient hearing for normal social activity.

SUMMARY

The ear develops as a fusion of internal, middle, and external parts. In comparative anatomy, living vertebrates exist with only the internal ear or with only the internal and middle ear present. The human embryo recapitulates these transitional stages.

The external ear localizes sound vibrations and transmits them to the drum membrane. The latter vibrates like the diaphragm of a microphone. The middle ear amplifies the vibration through its chain of ossicles. The Eustachian tube allows optimal transmission by equalization of the pressure inside the middle ear with that of the atmosphere. The internal ear contains the auditory receptors upon the organ of Corti.

The hair-cell receptors differentiate the fundamentals and overtones partly through sympathetic vibration, or resonance. To analyze and transmit frequencies above perhaps 400 cps, there may be rotational activity of individual fibers, in which groups of fibers fire in volleys. The specific place of stimulation upon the basilar membrane produces a maximum excitation at that area, and pitch is sensed through cerebral evaluation of the maximum level.

Loudness is sensed from the frequency and intensity of the waves; there is also a dependence upon the number of nerve fibers involved.

Quality, or timbre, is determined by the frequency, strength, and number of overtones present.

The localization of sound is linked with the intensity and phase of the waves and the differential time of arrival in the ear. Masking is dependent upon the refractory period of the nerve fibers which have previously been excited.

Hearing loss and tests of auditory acuity are discussed.

GLOSSARY

abdominal aponeurosis The conjoined tendon of the oblique and transverse muscles on the abdomen.

abscess A localized mass of pus walled off in a cavity produced by disintegrating and defensive cells.

abscissa The horizontal section of a mathematical graph as contrasted with the vertical axis, or ordinate.

acetylcholine The mediator of nerve impulses in parasympathetic nerves, in preganglionic sympathetics, and in cerebrospinal fibers.

acinus 1. A small lobule of a compound gland. 2. The air sac of the lung. 3. The glandular type may have a narrow lumen in contrast to the free lumen of the alveolus.

acoustic impedance The buffering effect of the air in the middle ear against sudden, large pressure changes or loud low-frequency sounds.

acromegaly Chronic enlargement of the bones and soft parts of the hands, feet and face due to excessive secretion of growth hormone of the anterior pituitary.

action current A transmitted electric current set up in active tissue, the active part being electronegative.

adenoids The hypertrophied pharyngeal tonsil. Luschka's tonsil.

adiadochokinesis A failure in timing of muscle impulses to the appropriate muscles, so that activities such as pronation vs. supination or flexion vs. extension are interfered with.

adipose tissue A variety of connective tissue serving preferentially for the deposit of fat cells.

adrenalin A hormone secreted by the medulla of the adrenal gland, technically called epinephrine.

adrenergic Designating sympathetic nerves which secrete a mixture of adrenalin and nor-adrenalin.

adrenogenital syndrome The situation in which the female shows excessive secondary sexual characteristics of the male because of hyperadrenal activity.

afferent Coming in, as opposed to efferent or going out. May be sensory or nonsensory.

affricative A speech sound that begins with a stop and ends with a

319

fricative. For example, CH as in church begins like T and ends like
SH.

afterdischarge   A series of repetitive responses from one afferent stimulus. May be due to central reverberating circuits.

agnosia   Failure to recognize objects in general.

agonist   A muscle whose action is opposed by another muscle called its antagonist.

alexia   Failure to comprehend the written word.

all-or-none   Pertaining to the general property of nerves and muscles whose individual fibers react maximally or remain inactive.

alveolar   1. Pertaining to an alveolus, or tooth socket. 2. Referring to the air sac of the lung.

alveolus   1. The socket of a tooth. 2. The air sac of the lung. 3. The acinus of a gland.

ambilaterality   No marked dominance of either hand or other ordinarily unilateralized structure.

amphiarthrosis   A somewhat movable joint in which the opposing structures are connected by disks of fibrocartilage. Ordinarily there is no joint cavity.

amplitude   The distance from crest to trough in a given wave. The amount of contraction and expansion as represented by the deviation of the curve from the base line.

anacusis   A profound hearing loss or ear-nerve disorder which is not restorable to a reasonable level of hearing.

analytical capacity of the ear   The capacity to differentiate all the distinct qualities or frequencies in a complex waveform.

anastomose   To join with one another, as blood vessels do. Noun is anastomosis.

androgens   Male sex hormones.

aneurysm   A sac resulting from the dilatation of the walls of a blood vessel and filled with blood.

angular gyrus   An area near the junction of the occipital, parietal, and temporal lobes in which the brain synthesizes many diverse impulses to integrated concepts.

anlage   The embryonic region in which evidence of a structure first appears.

anomaly   A marked deviation from the normal.

anoxia   State without oxygen. The more usual state is hypoxia, or a given degree of oxygen lack.

ansa hypoglossi   A U-shaped nerve loop on each side of the neck, formed by a branch of the hypoglossal nerve joining with branches from the first few cervical nerves.

anterior poliomyelitis   Inflammation of the ventral horns of the gray matter of the spinal cord.

aphasia A defect in symbolization of objects. Defective expression in speech, writing, or signs. Failure to comprehend spoken or written language.

apnea Suspended respiration, usually from washing out of carbon dioxide from the blood.

aponeurosis A broad flat tendon investing muscles or connecting muscles with the structures they move.

areolar tissue A variety of connective tissue in which bundles of elastic and inelastic fibers produce an open meshwork in the ground substance.

articulation 1. A joint. 2. The enunciation of words and sentences.

articulators Valves to stop the exhaled air completely or to narrow the space for its passage.

aryepiglottic folds Bilateral folds of tissue that help form the upper opening of the larynx. They extend from the epiglottis to the arytenoids.

astasia Loss of steadiness. Motor in-coordination with inability to stand.

asthenia Loss of muscle force. Asthenic is the adjective.

ataxia Irregularity of muscle action due to faulty timing and coordination of muscle agonists and antagonists. A drunken-like gait. Asynergia.

athetoid movements Aimless, slow, twisting movements and facial grimaces considered to be release phenomena and referable to basal ganglia disorders.

atresia Absence or closure of a normal aperture.

atrophy A wasting away of a cell, tissue, or organ through a decrease in protoplasm. A diminution in size.

audiometer An instrument to measure auditory sensitivity within the audible range of frequency as a function of the intensity of sounds.

auditory perspective The recognition of the direction of sound.

average speech power The totality of all speech sound energy emitted in a complete speech, divided by the total time for that activity. Expressed in microwatts.

axillary Pertaining to the armpit.

axon A process of a neuron that transmits the impulse away from the neuron cell body.

basal ganglia Subcortical nuclei relaying impulses through the extrapyramidal tracts. The term includes the caudate, putamen, globus pallidus, and the amygdaloid nuclei.

basal metabolism The lowest energy expenditure in the waking state compatible with life. Better called standard metabolism.

basilar membrane A membrane of the inner ear which supports the organ of Corti.

beats Throbs, or pulsations, resulting from the summation and interference of sound waves.

bel The logarithm of the ratio of the energy of two sounds.

Betz cells Large pyramidal cells in one or more of the layers of the principal motor area of the gray matter of the cerebrum.

bifid Split into two parts.

bifurcate Divide into two parts.

bolus A cohesive, sticky mass of food prepared for swallowing by the salivary glands and by the action of the tongue and palate.

brachial Pertaining to the arm.

brain stem The midbrain, hindbrain, and medulla not including the cerebellum.

branchial (visceral) arches Bars of cartilage on each side of the neck of the fetus which in evolution served as a framework for the blood vessels (aortic arches) and gill-breathing apparatus of water-living vertebrates.

branchial pouch A pocket-like finger thrust out bilaterally in the throat of the fetus from the entodermal lining of its digestive tract. In fishes these pouches meet inpushing ectodermal pockets from the body surface to produce gill slits between each skeletal gill arch.

breathiness The escape of unvocalized air so that the voice sounds as if a whisper were added to the tone.

Broca's area Area 44 in the frontal lobe of the cerebrum in the left inferior frontal convolution. Originally said to control the formation of words.

Brodmann's areas Discrete small regions generally in the neocortex of the cerebrum which are given numerals.

bronchiole A fine division of the arborized bronchial tree. It has no serosal capsule, and the muscular layer is exposed.

bronchus One of the two sections into which the trachea has divided.

buccal cavity The irregular space between the teeth and the cheeks. Distinct from the oral cavity, which is bounded externally by the teeth.

buccal whisper Accumulation of air in the mouth and pharynx which is used instead of that ordinarily expelled from the lung passages.

bulbar palsy A paralysis due to destruction of motor cells in the medulla oblongata. Poliomyelitis. Progressive bulbar paralysis.

carious Pertaining to decay, or caries, of a bone or tooth.

carotid sinus A dilatation at the beginning of the internal carotid artery which is stimulated by changes in blood pressure.

celiac plexus A great, paired ganglionated neural mass just under the diaphragm which receives the vagus and splanchnic nerves and distributes these fibers to visceral structures.

cerebral palsy A special paralysis affecting control of the motor system, due to lesions in various parts of the brain. A result of birth injury or prenatal brain defects.

cerumen Ear wax from sebacious gland secretion.

chest pulses Rapid-breath pulse movements produced by costal muscles.

choanae The posterior pair of nasal openings, which lead into the pharynx. Singular is choana, or posterior naris.

cholinergic Designating parasympathetic nerves which secrete acetylcholine.

chondrification Transformation into cartilage.

chorea A convulsive nervous disease displaying involuntary and irregular jerky movements. An example is St. Vitus's dance.

choreiform movements Aimless and abruptly changing movements and facial grimaces possibly referable to disorder of the corpus striatum. A release phenomenon.

cilia Minute hairs on the free borders of cells which move in synchronism and propel materials in a given direction.

cinefluorography Moving pictures made by fluoroscopy.

cineradiography The making of moving pictures by X rays.

clavicular breathing Raising the clavicle and sternum excessively during inspiration.

cochlear microphonics A piezoelectric effect in the cochlea, where pressure vibrations in nonnervous as well as nervous structures can be converted into electrical impulses. These microphonics simulate the true action potentials generated in the hair cells and transmitted to the auditory cortex for hearing.

collagen A protein occurring in bones, cartilage, and white fibrous connective tissue.

collaterals Shunts or side branches.

colliculi The paired superior and inferior colliculi are nuclei in the dorsal midbrain which collectively comprise the corpora quadrigemina. The superior pair are lower visual centers, and the inferior pair are lower auditory centers.

colloidal Pertaining to basic particles, such as those of proteins, etc., whose size is between that of large particles (like sand) held in suspension and microscopic particles of molecular size. Because of relatively large particle size, colloidal solutions are cloudy.

commissure A fiber or fibrous tract connecting the right and left sides of the nervous system.

conditioned reflex   Behavioral learning by associating an indifferent or unlearned stimulus with a stimulus which ordinarily evokes a given reaction.

congenital   Existing at or before birth. Not necessarily hereditary.

consonance   A pleasant sensation which results when the frequencies of simultaneous tones in a musical chord have simple mathematical ratios to one another and their overtones are in mutual support.

conus elasticus   The lateral section of the cricothyroid membrane, whose free border forms the vocal ligament, or platform for the construction of the vocal folds.

copula   A median ventral swelling on the embryonic tongue formed by fusion of the paired hyoid branchial arches. The copula forms the root of the tongue.

cornified   1. Changed to tissue resembling horn. 2. Epithelium converted to a stratified squamous type.

corpus callosum   A great white band of commissural fibers connecting the right and left cerebral hemispheres.

corticofugal   Directed outward or away from the cortex.

cretin   An individual with congenital lack of thyroid secretion, associated with hyponormal physical and mental development.

cricopharyngeal sphincter.   A sphincter of the esophagus or an esophageal section of the inferior constrictor muscle. Also called the cricopharyngeus muscle or the pinchcock at the lower end of the pharynx.

crus   The stalk or leg of any structure. Plural is crura.

crusotomy   Bilateral interruption of the pyramidal tracts in the crura of the midbrain.

cul-de-sac   A blind pouch, or hollow diverticulum, of the main passage.

cybernetics   The study of regulatory mechanisms including governors, thermostats, feedback and reverberating circuits.

cyst   A normal or abnormal sac containing fluid or a semisolid.

damping   A lessening of the incident energy. In damping of partials in resonating cavities, the energy of some of the tones is selectively absorbed by soft surfaces or neutralized by opposing movements in the same space.

decibel   A quantitative unit of sound intensity bearing a logarithmic relationship to the amplitude of the sound. One tenth of a bel.

deciduous   Temporary. The first set of teeth.

decorticate   Pertaining to animals with their cerebral cortex surgically removed.

decussate   The crossing over of nerve fibers to the other side of the central nervous system.

deglutition Swallowing.

dementia paralytica Chronic result of syphilis, showing progressive mental deterioration and generalized paralysis. General paresis.

demulcent An agent which protects and soothes a surface.

dendrite A short but extensively branched set of processes of a neuron. It receives impulses and sends them to the neuron cell body.

dentine The chief substance of a tooth. It surrounds the pulp and is covered by enamel on its exposed part, or crown.

desquamation Sloughing off of tissue cells.

diaphragmatic breathing Protrusion of the anterior abdominal wall with each inspiration. Abdominal breathing, as contrasted with costal breathing seen more in the female and characterized by activity predominantly of the ribs.

diarthrosis A freely movable joint having a joint cavity.

dichotomize Split into two.

digastric triangle. A triangular space in the lateral aspect of the neck, bounded above by the mandible, anteroinferiorly by the anterior belly of the digastric muscle, and posteroinferiorly by the posterior belly of the digastric muscle.

diphthong 1. Two contiguous vowel phonemes in the same syllable. 2. A vowel sound that ends so unlike its beginning that it requires two letters to represent it adequately.

dissonance An inharmonious combination of musical sounds in contrast with consonance.

diverticulum An offshoot of the main chambers or tube.

dominance, cerebral The implication that most or all neurally regulated functions will be governed by one hemisphere.

dura mater The outermost sheath of the three sheaths, or meninges, covering the brain and spinal cord.

dysacusis Hearing defect which is central in origin, including psychogenic types and the aphasias.

dysarthria Imperfect articulation in speech.

dyslalia Disorders of articulation in which sounds are improperly produced, replaced by others, or else entirely lacking.

dysphonia plicae ventricularis The condition in which the false vocal folds phonate in place of the true folds.

edema Excessive collection of tissue fluid in locations such as in the spaces around the cells, causing swelling or dropsy.

elastic tissue Connective tissue having a predominance of yellow elastic fibers.

electrical vocal tract A device to synthesize vowel sounds simulated to be natural.

electroencephalogram An electrical record of brain waves occurring normally and abnormally. Action currents are the source of the waves.

electromyography The testing of action potentials from muscles.

eleiden A substance similar to keratin, occurring in the cells of the stratum lucidum of the skin.

emollient A softening or soothing agent.

encephalization The shifting in evolution of important functions to the cerebrum.

eosinophile A variety of white blood cell susceptible to staining with acid dyes. Acidophile.

ergometer A device to measure mechanical output or work done.

esophageal speech Speaking by expelling air trapped in the esophagus through the adducted surfaces of the cricopharyngeal sphincter or pseudoglottis.

estrogens Female sex hormones derived from the follicles containing the ova, or eggs, within the ovary.

etiology Cause or origin of a disease.

eunuch A castrated male.

eunuchoid Having the major characteristics of a eunuch. Functionally but not organically a male castrate.

eupnea Quiet, normal breathing.

Eustachian tube The auditory tube, or channel, connecting the middle ear with the pharynx.

evaginate To grow outward. Opposed to invaginate, or to grow inward.

eversion A turning outward. Opposed to inversion, or a turning inward.

exteroceptor Sense organ, such as pressure and other receptors, located on the surface of the body.

extrapyramidal tracts A loose system of nerve fibers ultimately controlled by the premotor cortex working through the basal ganglia. Fibers not pyramidal which help regulate postural and mass movements of voluntary muscles.

exudate Waste products in solution to be excreted from the blood to the kidney, skin, etc. To be distinguished from a transudate, which is a fluid that normally crosses cell membranes for vital purposes.

facies The expression of the face.

fascia Fibrous connective tissue covering the body just below the skin; also covering the muscles and certain organs.

fasciculus Mixed nerve tracts running together in the white matter. A cluster of muscle fibers.

fauces The opening between the mouth and the pharynx.

fenestration The Lempert operation, in which a new window is made into the internal ear to short-circuit the stapes.

fibrillar Containing threads, or fibrils.

fibrocartilage An elastic cartilage whose matrix contains an abundance of white fibrous tissue.

fibrous membrane Fibrous connective tissue that connects adjacent structures or forms capsules around organs.

fissure of Rolando A vertical groove in each cerebral hemisphere situated externally between the frontal and parietal lobes.

fissure of Sylvius A deep external groove at the side of each cerebral hemisphere just above the temporal lobe.

fistula A deep ulcer which may lead into an internal hollow organ.

flaccidity A state of marked hypotonus of muscles.

fluoroscopy Examination of deep structures by X rays, using a fluorescent screen covered with crystals of calcium tungstate.

formant frequencies Resonant frequencies.

fossa of Rosenmüller A deep pocket in the upper part of the nasopharynx on each side of the opening of the Eustachian tube.

frequency The number of waves passing a given point in a unit time, usually 1 second.

fricative A noise produced by forcing air through an opening, as in F, V, S, etc.

funiculus A column within the dorsal, lateral, or ventral regions of the white matter of the spinal cord.

galvanic current A direct current as contrasted with an alternating current.

gametogenesis Development of the sex cells to a sperm or an egg within the testis or ovary.

ganglion A collection of nerve cell bodies lying outside the brain or spinal cord. The dorsal root ganglion contains the cell bodies of afferent neurons.

general senses Those senses from the general body, such as pain, heat, cold, touch, and proprioception. To be distinguished from the special senses of taste, smell, vision, and hearing.

gestalt An action not isolated but part of a pattern involving relationships with a whole.

gingiva The gum. Plural is gingivae.

gingivitis Inflammation of the gums.

globus pallidus The interior, or the lenticular nucleus, of a basal ganglion called the corpus striatum.

glossitis Inflammation of the tongue.

glycogenolysis The breakdown of glycogen, or animal starch, into simpler products, the end product being the sugar, dextrose.

goiter Enlargement of the thyroid gland, visible as a swelling in the front of the neck.

gonadotropic hormones Chemicals which control puberty, lactation, growth of the sexual tract, and the secondary sexual characters.

granuloma A tumor composed of granulation tissue, which is connective tissue involved in the healing of wounds.

gravid Pregnant.

gyrus A hill, or convolution, of the cerebral cortex, as opposed to sulcus, or depression.

hamulus Any hook-shaped process. The pterygoid hamulus is a paired process of the pterygoid bone.

hard palate The bony front part of the partition which separates the oral and nasal cavities.

harelip A congenital defect of the upper lip in which a cleft occurs because the structures forming the lip do not fuse.

harmonics In sound, the overtones which are integral multiples of the fundamental tone, i.e., having frequencies 2, 3, 4, 5, etc., times that of the fundamental.

Haversian canals Freely intercommunicating canals of the compact tissue of bone. They contain blood vessels and nerves.

hematoma A mass, or tumor, containing blood that has come out of its vessel.

hemilaryngectomy Surgical removal of one-half of the larynx.

hemiplegia Paralysis of one side of the body.

Heschl's convolution An auditory projection terminal in the superior temporal gyrus of the cerebral cortex.

hiatus A gap or fissure.

hirsutism Excessive hairiness, especially in the female.

hoarseness A rough, harsh quality of the voice that is relatively low in pitch.

homologue The evolutionary descendant of a previous structure.

hormone A chemical messenger formed in a ductless gland and delivered through the blood stream to target organs.

humerus The bone of the arm.

hyoid bone A U-shaped bone in the neck, acting as support for the tongue root above and as a suspension for the larynx below.

hypacusis A hearing loss that is innately restorable or else correctible by prosthetic devices.

hyperkinesia Excessive movement.

hyperplasia An abnormal cell division or cell multiplication in a given structure.

hypertrophy A pathological increase in the size of an organ due to an increase in protoplasm.

hypophysectomy Surgical removal of the pituitary gland.

hypoplasia Faulty or incomplete development.

hypophysis cerebri The pituitary gland, which is an endocrine organ extending downward from the diencephalon of the brain.

hypothalamus An area of the diencephalon forming the floor and part of the lateral wall of the third ventricle. It includes the infundibulum, mammillary bodies, neurohypophysis, and tuber cinereum.

hysteria A psychoneurosis involving poor control of acts and emotions, anxiety, excessive self-consciousness and self-concern, and simulation of many diseases.

ideomotor area A cerebral area, usually unilateralized, anterior to the angular gyrus. It is a quick and automatic selector of words needed in an appropriate sequence for conversation.

impedance, vocal The quantitative resistance to the transmission of air, to the flow of an alternating current, or to other vibratory phenomena.

incisive foramen A funnel-shaped aperture centrally located in the hard palate just behind the incisor teeth. It opens into paired incisive canals which transmit the descending palatine artery and the nasopalatine nerve.

inertia A resistance to a change in the state or position in space of a body.

inflammation A reaction of tissues to injury, involving heat, pain, redness, swelling, and variable loss of function.

inguinal Pertaining to the groin.

innervation The distribution of nerves to a structure.

integument Outer surface of the body. Skin in man.

internuncial neuron An associative or connecting neuron between afferent and efferent neurons. A type-II Golgi cell restricted to the gray matter of the brain or cord.

interstitial Situated in the interspaces of a tissue. Between the cells.

intrapulmonic pressure The pressure in the lungs and air passages. Pulmonary pressure.

intrathoracic pressure The pressure in the thorax outside of the pulmonary spaces. Intrapleural pressure.

involute To regress.

ipsilateral Conduction of impulses on the same side, as opposed to contralateral conduction in which the fibers cross over.

irritability The capacity of protoplasm to react to a stimulus.

keratinization Making a tissue horny by deposition of a protein called keratin.

labial Pertaining to the lips. Noun is labium, plural is labia. In phonetics it implies involvement of lip articulation, as P, V, M.

labiodental Pertaining to the lips and teeth. The lower lip touches the upper front teeth, as in F or V.

lacrimal Pertaining to the tears and the system for lubricating the eyeball surface.

lamella A thin plate, as of bone.

laryngitis Acute or chronic inflammation of the larynx, with dryness and soreness of the throat, hoarseness, cough, and painful swallowing.

laryngitis sicca Chronic inflammation of the larynx, with dryness of the mucosa.

laryngocele An abnormal air sac connecting with the laryngeal cavity. It produces a tumor-like mass seen externally on the neck.

laryngoperiscope A self-illuminating laryngoscopic mirror.

laryngoscope An instrument for visual examination of the larynx.

larynx The voicebox, or musculocartilaginous organ with a mucous lining extending from below the hyoid bone to the top of the trachea.

lemniscus A fiber tract within the central nervous system. The lateral lemniscus carries up auditory impulses. The medial lemniscus transmits pressure, pain, heat, cold, taste, temperature, and other impulses.

lisping A disorder of the sibilant (hissing or whistling) consonants. s and z are particularly affected, and TH is substituted.

lobotomy Disconnection of lobes of the cerebral cortex from the remainder of the brain. Frontal and temporal lobotomies are examples. Surgical excision of a lobe is lobectomy.

localization, cerebral Association of specific bodily functions with definite areas of the cerebral cortex.

loudness An intensity dimension of hearing dependent upon the amplitude of the incident sound waves and also upon the number and the frequency of nerve impulses.

lower motor neuron The anterior horn cells of the brain and spinal cord and their axonal nerve fibers to the effectors.

lumbodorsal fascia A combined lumbar and dorsal aponeurotic fascia in the middle of the back, for attachment of several posterior muscles.

lumen Cavity or space. Plural is lumina.

lymph A colorless fluid derived from the blood, acting chiefly to drain wastes from the tissue cells and bring such wastes back to the blood.

lymph nodes. Glands or filtering stations for microorganisms, placed at strategic areas along the lymphatic vessels. They produce lymphocytes.

lymphadenitis Inflammatory reaction in lymph glands.

lymphopenia Reduction in the count of the white blood cells called lymphocytes.

macrostomia Excessively large and wide mouth caused by incomplete fusion of the mandibular and maxillary processes. Contrasted with microstomia, or tiny mouth and astomia, or no mouth.

male climacteric Cessation of sexual activity and regression of secondary sexual characters in the male.

medial longitudinal fasciculus An extension into the brain stem of the anterior and lateral ground bundles on each side of the spinal cord.

mediastinum The central area of the thorax between the lungs and their pleural investments.

Ménière's disease Deafness, dizziness, and ringing in the ears associated with nonsuppurative disease of the otic labyrinth.

meningitis Inflammation of the meninges, or coverings, of the brain and cord.

mesenchyme Connective tissue of the embryo. A part of the mesoderm which forms connective tissue, blood vessels, and lymphatics.

metabolism The sum total of the energy exchanges occurring in the body at a given time.

mimetic Pertaining to simulation. Also applies to muscles of expression.

modality A separate sense, such as hearing or vision. Experiences in a given modality can be arranged in a continuum.

modiolus The central pillar, or columella, within the cochlea.

modulate To alter the voice adaptively during speech. To vary the tone volume.

monaural Designating one ear, as contrasted with binaural, or both ears.

mucoperiosteum Periosteum with a mucous surface.

mucopurulent Containing both mucus and pus.

mucous Resembling mucus, which is a viscid secretion that covers mucous membranes.

mucous membrane Epithelium upon a basement membrane with a subcutaneous tissue. It lines canals and cavities, such as the Eustachian

tube and alimentary canal, which communicate with the external
air.

myelin   The inner fatty covering of a typical neuron; medullary sheath.

myoneural junction   A specialized area or motor end plate between a
nerve and a muscle.

myotome   An embryonic muscle block.

myxedema   An abnormal hypothyroid condition in an adult, characterized by retardation of vital processes.

nasality   Too much or too little nasal resonance.

nasal resonance   The normal resonance added by the nasal passages to
the tone.

natural period   The inherent power of a vibrating body to go into free
oscillation with regard to frequency.

neoplastic   Pertaining to a new and abnormal growth, such as a tumor.

nerve impulse   The disturbance propagated along a nerve fiber, probably electrochemical in nature.

neuralgia   Pain expressed along the course of one or several nerves.

neuritis   Inflammation of a nerve.

neuroblasts   Embryonic cells which produce neurons.

neurogenic   Seated in the nervous system.

neuron   A nerve cell. The basic unit of structure and function of the
nervous system.

noise   A complex sound having many frequencies not in mutual
harmonious relation. A "white noise" contains all frequencies in the
sound spectrum.

nucleus of the tractus solitarius   An ending nucleus of the facial, glossopharyngeal, and vagus nerves. The nucleus extends the whole length
of the medulla on each side. The nucleus is especially concerned
with taste.

obturator   A plate which closes an opening.

occiput   Back of the head. Occipital region. The basiocciput is the basal
section of the occipital bone.

occlusal   Pertaining to closure with reference to the chewing surfaces
of molar and bicuspid teeth.

odontoblast   A connective tissue cell which produces the outer surface
of the dental pulp contiguous to the dentine.

olfaction   Smell.

ontogenetic   Embryological.

optimum pitch   The general level of pitch in an individual at which he
can best emit rich, full, and resonant tones.

orthodontic Pertaining to the prevention and correction of irregular teeth and malocclusions.

otitis media Inflammation of the middle ear.

otosclerosis Appearance of spongy bone in the capsule of the auditory labyrinth.

ovariectomy Surgical removal of the ovaries.

overtone A multiple of the fundamental, which is the lowest frequency tone for a vibrating structure.

palatography Making graphic records of the movements of the palate in the process of speaking.

palatopharyngeal sphincter The levator veli palatini and superior pharyngeal constrictor muscles, acting to narrow the passage between the nose and pharynx.

palliate To relieve symptoms.

palpate To obtain knowledge of a structure from touch and pressure.

papilla A pimple, or nipple-shaped elevation. Plural is papillae.

parameters Dimensions. Arbitrary constants whose values characterize the quantitative expressions into which they enter. Pitch and volume are parameters of sound.

paranasal sinuses Cavities in the interior of skull bones, all of which drain into the nose.

parasympathetics The cranial or sacral part of an involuntary or autonomic nervous system, the other part of which is sympathetic or thoracolumbar.

Parkinson's disease Paralysis agitans. A disorder of the basal ganglia in which release phenomena occur, such as tremors, postural inadequacies, and hypertonicity of muscles.

partial A fundamental and its overtones. A segmental vibration. In a fundamental of 100 cps and an overtone of 200 cps, the fundamental is the first partial and 200 is the second partial (or first overtone).

Passavant's cushion The highest part of the superior constrictor muscle of the posterior pharyngeal wall. The pterygopharyngeal muscle fusing posteriorly with superior constrictor muscle fibers.

past pointing The inability to bring a finger to a predesignated mark unless the eyes are kept open.

patent Open.

pendulous Loosely hanging.

perception A consciousness that is the result of a complex pattern of stimulation plus the effect of experience and attitudes. This is in contrast to a sensation which is very dependent upon specific sense-organ stimulation.

perichondritis Inflammation of the perichondrium.

perichondrium The white fibrous tissue sheath covering the surface of cartilage.

periosteum The fibrous membrane that ensheaths a bone.

phagocyte A scavenging cell that ingests other cells or microorganisms. Macrophages; polymorphonuclear leucocytes.

pharyngitis Inflammation of the mucous membrane and deeper tissue of the pharynx.

pharyngomaxillary fossa A space forming each lateral boundary of the retropharyngeal space.

pharyngostome Window into the pharynx.

pharynx The throat, or pouch-like structure between the base of the skull and the sixth cervical vertebra. It is a common digestive and respiratory passageway.

phase A given stage in a cycle. For example, in a 60-cycle alternating current, each phase is $\frac{1}{120}$ second.

phasic activities Voluntary isolated movements of skeletal muscle.

phoneme A family of speech sounds.

phrenicectomy Surgical division of the phrenic nerve. Phrenectomy.

phylogenetic Pertaining to phylogeny. The evolution, or ancestral history, of a race or group.

physiological breathing Respiration for gas exchange without reference to speech. Biological breathing.

piezoelectricity Electricity produced by mechanical pressure. It is seen in crystals which are compressed along certain axes.

pitch A qualitative dimension of hearing related to the highness or lowness of tones and correlated with the frequency of the sound waves making up the stimulus. Higher frequencies yield higher pitches.

place theory In hearing, pitch is associated with a place in the basilar membrane where maximal activation occurs.

placode A plate of ectoderm which, in the embryo, indicates the anlage of an organ.

pleural cavity A potential space in the double-walled sac surrounding and enclosing each lung.

plexus A network of nerves or of veins.

plosive A sound involving oral closure followed by abrupt opening through air pressure with the posterior nasal and other openings obstructed. A stop.

pneumograph An instrument to visualize respiratory movements on a kymographic drum or other recording device.

polyp A smooth growth from a hypertrophied mucous surface. It is attached by a stalk.

pons A bridge in the ventral hindbrain connecting the cerebrum, cerebellum, and medulla.

postcentral convolution A region in the parietal cerebral cortex posterior to the fissure of Rolando and encompassing the somesthetic area.

precentral convolution A region of the cerebral cortex anterior to the vertical fissure of Rolando and above the horizontal fissure of Sylvius, encompassing the principal motor area.

preganglionics Neurons that connect the autonomic system with the brain or spinal cord. The postganglionics leave the primary autonomic ganglion and travel toward the visceral effector.

prevertebral fascia The anterior part of the great vertebral fascia, which encloses the vertebral column and its muscle masses.

primordia Original structures. Anlages.

progesterone Female sex hormone derived from the corpora lutea within the ovary.

prognathic Marked projection of the lower jaw.

prognosis The probable course and outcome of a disease.

projection area A region on the cerebral cortex where a function is localized.

propositional speech The communication of meanings, as contrasted with the expression of feelings.

proprioceptor Sense organ for detecting the position and spatial relations of a muscle, located in the muscles or tendons.

prosthetic Pertaining to artificial organs, parts, and devices.

prosthodontist Prosthetic dentist, who makes appliances and substitutes for oral structures.

protoplasm The material of the body cells which displays the properties of life.

protract To push forward, as contrasted with retract, or pull backward.

pseudostratified epithelium Epithelium which appears to consist of two or more layers but does not. It enters into the lining of the upper respiratory tract where it has goblet cells and cilia to catch and remove dust.

pterygoid processes Paired medial and lateral wing-like processes of the sphenoid bone, which project down from the bone like a pair of legs. Between the lateral and medial processes is the pterygoid fossa.

pterygomandibular raphe A tendinous structure between the buccinator and superior pharyngeal constrictor muscles. It gives origin to the middle part of both muscles. The pterygomandibular ligament.

pterygopalatine fossa A space deeply located in the facial bones just below the apex of the eye socket.

puberty The period of reproductive and associated mental and physical maturation in either sex.

putamen The outer part of the lenticular nucleus of a basal ganglion called the corpus striatum.

pyramidal tract The corticobulbar and corticospinal fibers passing from the motor cerebrum to the nuclei of cranial and spinal nerves. The upper motor neuron which regulates voluntary motion.

pyriform sinus A depression on each side of the larynx external to the aryepiglottic folds.

ramus A branch of a vessel or nerve. Also a section of a bone. Plural is rami.

raphe A line of union between the members of a bilaterally symmetrical structure.

reflex A fundamentally involuntary response to an afferent stimulus.

refractory period The time of depressed irritability during the activity of a protoplasmic structure.

register, vocal An arbitrary division of the range of pitch in music, such as head and chest registers.

reinforcement Increase in the intensity of the incident vibrations. It occurs for laryngeal vibrations when supraglottic air vibrates in tune with one or more partials of the incident wave.

Reissner's membrane The vestibular membrane of the cochlea which separates the scala vestibuli from the scala media. Its functions are speculative.

resonance 1. The vibrant sound of ordinary speech as contrasted with dull or flat sound. May imply sound intensification by transmission of the vibrations to a cavity. 2. Sympathetic vibration.

resonant nodes The place on the basilar membrane excited by the sound waves.

resonator An instrument that intensifies sounds.

reticular formation The central core of the brain stem.

reticuloendothelial system Cells in different organs showing a common phagocytic behavior toward dyes.

retrograde Directed backward or in a course contrary to the usual direction.

retropharyngeal space The region behind the pharynx which is subdivided to four potential spaces: peripharyngeal, parapharyngeal, postvisceral, and prevertebral. The space is also called the retropharyngeal fascial cleft.

rhinencephalon The smell brain, or discrete cell bodies on the cerebral cortex. The archipallium. Distinguished from the nonolfactory neocortex.

rhinitis A symptom complex in which nasal secretions are increased and the nasal mucosa is swollen.

rhinolalia aperta Excessive nasality of voice through undue patency of the posterior nares.

rhinolalia clausa A nasal quality of the voice from excessive closure of the nasal passages.

Rinne test The duration of bone conduction is compared with that of air conduction for each ear, using a tuning fork.

roentgenography The study of X rays.

rostrum A beak, such as the beak of the sphenoid bone. Rostral may indicate the cranial as opposed to the caudal end.

sacculus An upward, hollow projection from the roof of the ventricle of Morgagni.

sarcoplasm Muscle protoplasm.

Schwabach test The shank of a vibrating tuning fork is placed on the patient's mastoid until no longer heard, then placed on the examiner's mastoid. The results are recorded in plus or minus seconds.

sebacious glands Glands which secrete an oily lubricating fluid called sebum.

secondary palate The final palatal structures which complete the floor of the nasal cavity and the roof of the mouth.

secretion A substance put out by any gland and serving a useful purpose, as distinguished from an excretion.

selective permeability The quality of a cell membrane which allows only certain substances to cross in or out of it.

sensation A change in awareness or consciousness resulting from a discrete sensory stimulation.

sepsis Infection.

sequelae Results of an action or disease.

seromucinous Partly serous and partly mucous. Also called seromucous.

serous Resembling serum in physical consistency. Watery.

serous membrane Connective tissue lining any of the major splanchnic or lymph cavities. Peritoneum, pleura, pericardium.

sigmatism Incorrect, difficult, or excessive use of the s sound.

singer's nodules Fibrous nodes between the anterior third and middle of the vocal folds. Screamer's nodes.

sinus A cavity, recess, or hollow space. It may contain air or fluid.

soft palate The mobile and muscular posterior sections of the partition between the nasal and oral cavities, and between the mouth and pharynx.

somatic Pertaining to the body. Also implies voluntary as contrasted with autonomic.

somesthetic area Discrete areas on the parietal cerebral cortex including areas 3, 1, 2, 5, and 7 for three-dimensional reasoning about projected sensations, such as pain, hot, cold, and muscle sensation.

sonant   1. Voiced or having sound. 2. A sound which in itself makes a syllable or subordinates to itself the other sounds in the syllable.

sound spectrograph   A machine to obtain visible records of the frequency, intensity, and time of samples of speech.

spasticity   A state of marked hypertonus of muscles.

speculum   An instrument for bringing into view a bodily passage or chamber.

speech defect   A significant deviation from an assumed normal speech pattern, or a deviation which significantly interferes with communication.

speech deviation   Any demarcation from an assumed normal speech pattern.

speech stretcher   A device to play back speech sounds at a changed utterance rate, without changing the original pitch.

sphenopalatine foramen   A space between the orbital and sphenoid processes of the palate bone. It goes from the pterygopalatine fossa into the superior meatus of the nose. It carries sphenopalatine vessels, nasopalatine nerves, and superior nasal nerves.

sphincter   A muscle arranged around an opening to constrict or dilate the passageway. May be smooth or skeletal muscle.

splanchnic   Pertaining to the abdominal viscera.

spirometer   An instrument to measure the volumes of air respired under many conditions. The data are in the science of spirometry.

spondee   Two equally accented syllables.

stapes mobilization   A method to treat otosclerosis by exposing the lenticulocapitular joint and applying instruments on parts of the stapes. The method preserves and uses the middle ear bones and does not change the structure of the external or middle ear.

stenosis   Narrowing of a duct or canal.

stereognosis   Three dimensional reasoning about an object by means of touch, pressure, and muscle sensibility. Opposed to astereognosis or agnosia.

stimulus   Any change in the internal or external environment which can elicit a response or protoplasmic change.

stomodeum   The embryonic anlage of the mouth. The ectodermal portion that indents.

stratified squamous epithelium   This lining has several layers to withstand wear and tear, but the depth of cells prevents them from functioning in absorption and secretion. Flat cells.

stretch reflex   Myotactic or proprioceptive reflex. The feedback of information from muscle receptors concerning the tensions of these muscles and the adaptive change in the tone of the same muscles.

stridency A harshness for tones of high pitch. Any creaking sound.

stridor A harsh and high-pitched respiratory sound often heard in an acute laryngeal obstruction.

stroboscope An instrument to analyze the successive phases of the movements of a structure.

stuttering Repetitious speech, as compared with stammering, or hesitant speech.

styloid process A downward projecting spur from the temporal bone serving for the origin of muscles and ligaments.

superciliary Pertaining to the region of the eyebrow. The arch is the visible prominence.

supersonics High-frequency sound waves above 20,000 cps.

suppressor areas Regions of the brain that can inhibit motor activity.

suppurative Producing pus.

surd A voiceless consonant.

suture The line of union of adjacent cranial or facial bones.

sympathectomized Designating the removal of the thoracolumbar or sympathetic section of the autonomic nervous system.

symphysis A line of fusion between bones that were originally separate. Example is pubic symphysis.

synapse Synaptic junction, or physiological but not physical contact, between the axon of the preceding neuron and the dendrites of the successive neuron. A one-way valve for electrochemical impulses.

synchondrosis A joint in which the bones are joined by fibrous or elastic cartilage.

syndesmosis A fixed joint between bones whose opposing surfaces are joined by fibrous tissue.

syndrome A symptom complex which is the total of the signs of any morbid condition.

synergism State of cooperation with another agent such that the total action is greater than the single ones. Synergy.

synovial membrane A membrane lining the interior of the capsule surrounding a freely movable joint and capable of secreting a watery or synovial fluid to lubricate the joint surfaces.

systemic Pertaining to the general blood stream.

tachycardia Excessively fast pulse rate.

tectorial membrane A membrane within the scala media, spreading like a lid over the organ of Corti. It may possibly act to dampen after-vibrations of the auditory hair cells.

tegmentum The upper covering of the crura cerebri, or cerebral stalks. The upper and larger portion of the two major portions of each cerebral stalk.

tendon A connective tissue band which connects a muscle with a bone.

tetanus A fusion of discrete individual muscular contractions. The verb is to tetanize. The condition is usually normal.

tetany A disorder involving generalized intermittent muscular contractions and muscle pain. Often caused by hypoparathyroidism and calcium deficiency.

thalamus A part of the forebrain, or diencephalon, containing many nuclei which principally mediate and adjust impulses arriving from discrete sense organs below. A center of crude consciousness.

throatiness A guttural quality in which the voice seems to fall back into the throat and become harsh and raspy.

thymus A gland in the front part of the neck or in the upper mediastinum which may be endocrine and which, if enlarged, can mechanically affect speech.

thyroglossal duct A duct of the embryo extending from the posterior area of the tongue to the thyroid gland. The vestigial opening after birth is the foramen cecum.

tic A habit spasm. A twitching, as of the face.

timbre The quality of sound. The differentiation of tones of a given pitch in different instruments or sources.

tinnitus Ringing sensation in the ears.

tongue-tied Designating an adherent tongue with too little mobility, tied too closely by the frenulum to the floor and sides of the mouth.

topical Pertaining to a localized area.

topically Locally. On a particular region.

torpid Sluggish.

torus tubarius The projecting posterior lip of the Eustachian tube in the pharynx. The Eustachian cushion.

trachea The windpipe extending from the pharynx to the bronchi.

tracheostomy Making a window in the trachea to insert a cannula.

tracheotomy Making an opening into the trachea.

transillumination Examination of the interior of a cavity by an intense beam of light directed into it from outside its walls.

trapezoid body A decussating group of fibers in the hindbrain which represents the second order of neurons of the auditory tract. These fibers transmit impulses from the cochlear nuclei to somewhat higher auditory relay centers.

tremor An involuntary trembling.

tussive Pertaining to or caused by a cough.

ultimobranchial bodies Diverticula of the fourth branchial pouches or derivatives of the fifth pouches. They are surrounded by the lateral lobes of the thyroid gland and may completely atrophy.

upper motor neurons The neurons of the pyramidal or corticospinal tract, traveling down to the anterior horn cells of the spinal cord.

upper premotor neurons The axons of neurons having an ultimate origin in the premotor cortex and relayed as extrapyramidal fibers through the basal ganglia.

uvula A cone-shaped structure projecting downward from the center of the free lower border of the velum.

vagal centers Individual cell bodies of axons belonging to the afferent and efferent systems of the vagus nerve. The term embraces the dorsal nucleus, the nucleus ambiguus, and also the jugular and nodose ganglia.

vallecula 1. Any depression. 2. A pair of depressions between the lateral and median glossoepiglottic folds.

vasoconstriction The narrowing of the bore, or lumen, of a blood vessel, as opposed to opening, or vasodilation.

vasomotor Pertaining to nerves which control the diameter of blood vessels, and therefore the blood pressure.

velopharyngeal mechanism The machinery of the velum and pharynx to partition the phonated air properly between the oral and nasal passages, thus providing appropriate resonance.

velum The lower portion of the soft palate that hangs down like an incomplete curtain.

ventricle of Morgagni The middle division of the internal laryngeal chambers.

ventricular ligament The framework of the false vocal folds or the free border of the quadrangular membrane.

vertex The crown or top of the head. A summit or apex.

vesicle A small sac, or bladder, containing fluid.

vestigial A remnant of a more functional structure in racial evolution.

virilism 1. Masculinity. 2. The development of masculine traits in the female.

viscera Internal soft organs in the body cavities. Singular is viscus.

vital capacity The largest volume of air that can be put out in a forced expiration after the deepest inspiration. The respiratory capacity.

vocal ligament The skeleton and medial part of the vocal fold. It represents the free border of the conus elasticus.

volley theory Wever and Bray's modified frequency theory in which the stimulus frequency is represented in fiber bundles of the auditory nerve acting somewhat independently so that higher frequencies are represented by a composite volley.

volume Massiveness, or the filling of space by sound. A subjective sensation.

Waldeyer's ring A discontinuous ring of tonsillar masses that surrounds the entrance to the oropharynx.

Weber test A tuning-fork test to compare the bone conduction in both ears, for evaluating conduction vs. perception deafness.

Wernicke's area An auditory center in the left superior temporal gyrus and the adjacent part of the middle temporal gyrus. Its destruction may involve failure to understand the spoken or written word.

zygomatic arch The prominent bone of the side of the face, or cheek, produced by the zygomatic process of the temporal bone fusing anteriorly with the zygoma, or malar bone.

BIBLIOGRAPHY

Akin, Johnnye: *And So We Speak: Voice and Articulation*, Prentice-Hall, Inc., Englewood Cliffs, N.J., 1958.

Anderson, V. A.: *Training the Speaking Voice*, Oxford University Press, New York, 1942.

Ardran, G. M., F. H. Kemp, and L. Mannen: "Study of the Alterations in the Lumen of the Larynx During Breathing and Phonation," *British J. Radiol.*, 26:497–509, 1953.

Asherson, N.: "Large Cysts of the Epiglottis: A Classification and Case Records," *J. Laryng. & Otol.*, 71:730–743, 1957.

Ballenger, H. C.: *A Manual of Otology, Rhinology and Laryngology*, 3d ed., Lea & Febiger, Philadelphia, 1947.

Bangs, J. L., and T. E. Bangs: "Hearing Aids for Young Children," *Arch. Otolaryng.*, 55(5):528–535, 1952.

Barbara, D. A.: *Stuttering*, The Julian Press, Inc., New York, 1954.

Bastian, H. D.: *The Brain as an Organ of the Mind*, Kegan Paul, Trench, Trubner & Co., London, 1880.

Batson, Oscar V.: "The Cricopharyngeus Muscle," *Ann. Otol. Rhin. & Laryng.*, 64:47–54, 1955.

Berry, M. F., and J. Eisenson: *Speech Disorders*, Appleton-Century-Crofts, Inc., New York, 1956.

Bloomer, H. H.: "Speech Defects Associated with Dental Abnormalities and Malocclusions," in L. E. Travis (ed.), *Handbook of Speech Pathology*, Appleton-Century-Crofts, Inc., New York, 1957.

Bocock, E. J., and R. W. Haines: *Applied Anatomy for Nurses*, E. and S. Livingstone, Ltd., London, 1955.

Bogert, B. P., and G. E. Peterson: "The Acoustics of Speech," in L. E. Travis (ed.), *Handbook of Speech Pathology*, Appleton-Century-Crofts, Inc., New York, 1957.

Boies, L. R.: *Fundamentals of Otolaryngology*, 2d ed., W. B. Saunders Company, Philadelphia, 1955.

Borden, R. C., and A. C. Busse: *Speech Correction*, F. S. Crofts & Co., New York, 1929.

Bosma, James F.: "Deglutition: Pharyngeal Stage," *Physiol. Rev.*, 37:275–300, 1957.

Brain, Russell: *Diseases of the Nervous System*, 5th ed., Oxford University Press, London, 1955.

Broca, Paul: "Remarques sur le Siège de la Faculté du Langage Articulé suive d'une Observation d'Aphémie," *Bull. et mém. Soc. Anat. Paris*, 36:2me série, 331, August, 1861.

Bryngelson, B.: "Sidedness as an Etiological Factor in Stuttering," *J. Genetic Psychol.*, 47:204–217, 1935.

Bucy, Paul C.: "Is There a Pyramidal Tract?" *Brain*, 80:376–392, 1957.

Calnan, J.: "The Error of Gustav Passavant," *Plast. & Reconstruct. Surg.*, 13:275–289, 1954.

Campbell, C. J., and J. A. Murtagh: "Electrical Manifestations of Recurrent Nerve Function," *Ann. Otol. Rhin. & Laryng.*, 65:747–765, 1956.

Carmody, Francis J.: "An X-ray Study of Pharyngeal Articulation," *Univ. of California Pubs. in Modern Philology*, University of California Press, 21(5):377–384, 1941.

Carrell, J. A.: "A Comparative Study of Speech Defective Children," *Arch. Speech*, 1:179–203, 1936.

Carroll, John B.: *The Study of Language*, Harvard University Press, Cambridge, Mass., 1955.

Cates, H. A., and J. V. Basmajian: *Primary Anatomy*, 3d ed., The Williams & Wilkins Company, Baltimore, 1955.

Cecil, R. L., and R. F. Loeb: *Textbook of Medicine*, W. B. Saunders Company, Philadelphia, 1955.

Charcot, J. M., and A. Pitres: *Etude Critique et Clinique de la Localization Matrices*, Librairie Felix Alcan, Paris, 1883.

Cleary, James A.: "On the Ary-epiglottic Folds," *Ann. Otol. Rhin. & Laryng.*, 63:960–979, 1954.

Conley, J. J., F. DeAmesti, and M. K. Pierce: "A New Surgical Technique for the Vocal Rehabilitation of the Laryngectomized Patient," *Ann. Otol. Rhin. & Laryng.*, 67(3):655–664, 1958.

Converse, J. M.: "The Cartilaginous Structures of the Nose," *Ann. Otol. Rhin. & Laryng.*, 64:220–229, 1955.

Conway, Herbert: "Report to the American Association of Plastic Surgeons of Vitamin Therapy for Cleft Lip," *Scope Weekly*, 3(28):3, 1958.

Cracovaner, A. J.: "Endoscopy in Paralysis of Vocal Cords," *Arch. Otolaryng.*, 60:154–157, 1954.

Curry, R.: "Two Simplified Technics for Synchronized X-ray, Sound Recording and Cathode Ray Oscillographic Studies of Speech," *Rev. Scient. Instr.*, 8:382–385, 1937.

———: *The Mechanism of the Human Voice*, Longmans, Green & Co., Inc., New York, 1940.

Davidson, Morris: "Abscesses of the Retropharyngeal Space in Adults," *Laryngoscope*, 59:1146–1170, 1949.

Davis, H.: "Psychophysiology of Hearing and Deafness," in S. S. Stevens (ed.), *Handbook of Experimental Psychology*, John Wiley & Sons, Inc., New York, 1951.

———: "Biophysics and Physiology of Inner Ear," *Physiol. Rev.*, 37:1–49, 1957.

Dejerine, J.: *Anatomie des Centres Nerveux*, J. Rueff, Paris, 1901, vol. II.

———: "L'Aphasie Sensorielle: Sa Localization et sa Physiologie Pathologique," *Presse méd.*, 14:437–439; 453–457, 1906.

Diamond, Moses: *Dental Anatomy*, 3d ed., The Macmillan Company, New York, 1952.

Doty, R. W., and J. F. Bosma: "An Electromyographic Analysis of Reflex Deglutition," *J. Neurophysiol.*, 19:44–61, 1956.

Dunbar, F., and L. G. Rowntree: *Psychosomatic Diagnosis*, Paul B. Hoeber, Inc., New York, 1943.

Eggston, A. A., and Dorothy Wolff: *Histopathology of the Ear, Nose and Throat*, The Williams & Wilkins Company, Baltimore, 1947.

Eisenson, Jon: "Aphasia in Adults"; "Correlates of Aphasia in Adults"; "Therapeutic Problems and Approaches with Aphasic Adults," in L. E. Travis (ed.), *Handbook of Speech Pathology*, Appleton-Century-Crofts, Inc., New York, 1957.

Erickson, C. I.: "The Basic Factors in the Human Voice," *Psychol. Monographs*, 36:82–112, 1926.

Faaborg-Andersen, K.: "Electromyographic Investigation of Intrinsic Laryngeal Muscles in Humans," *Acta physiol. scandinav.*, 41, Suppl. 140:1–149, 1957.

Fairbanks, Grant: *Voice and Articulation Drillbook*, Harper & Brothers, New York, 1940.

—— and E. M. Green: "A Study of Minor Organic Deviations in Functional Disorders of Articulation 2. Dimensions and Relationships of the Lips," *J. Speech & Hearing Disorders*, 15:165–168, 1950.

—— and B. Bebout: "A Study of Minor Organic Deviations in Functional Disorders of Articulation 3. The Tongue," *J. Speech & Hearing Disorders*, 15:348–352, 1950.

—— and M. V. Lintner: "A Study of Minor Organic Deviations in Functional Disorders of Articulation 4. The Teeth and Hard Palate," *J. Speech & Hearing Disorders*, 16:273–279, 1951.

Farnsworth, D. W.: "High-speed Motion Pictures of the Human Vocal Cords," *Bell Lab. Record*, 18:203–208, 1940.

Fink, B. R., and M. Basek: "The Mechanism of Opening of the Human Larynx," *Laryngoscope*, 66:410–425, 1956.

Fletcher, Harvey: *Speech and Hearing in Communication*, D. Van Nostrand Company, Inc., Princeton, N.J., 1953.

Fowler, E. P.: *Medicine of the Ear*, 2d ed., Thomas Nelson & Sons, New York, 1947.

Freedman, A. O.: "Diseases of the Ventricle of Morgagni," *Arch. Otolaryng.*, 28:329–343, 1938.

Freund, E. D.: "Voice and Breathing," *Arch. Otolaryng.*, 67:1–7, 1958.

Froeschels, Emil: *Twentieth Century Speech and Voice Correction*, Philosophical Library, Inc., New York, 1948.

——: *Dysarthric Speech*, Expression Company, Magnolia, Mass., 1952.

—— and A. Jellinek: *Practice of Voice and Speech Therapy*, Expression Company, Boston, 1941.

Fry, D. B.: "Speech and Language," *J. Laryng. & Otol.*, 7:432–452, 1957.

Fulton, John F.: *A Textbook of Physiology*, 17th ed., W. B. Saunders Company, Philadelphia, 1955.

Furstenberg, A. C., and J. E. Magielsk: "A Motor Pattern in the Nucleus Ambiguus; Its Clinical Significance," *Ann. Otol. Rhin. & Laryng.*, 64:788–793, 1955.

Fymbo, L. H.: "The Relation of Malocclusion of the Teeth to Defects of Speech," *Arch. Speech*, 1:204–216, 1936.

Galambos, R., and H. Davis: "The Response of Single Auditory-nerve Fibers to Acoustic Stimulation," *J. Neurophysiol.*, 6:39–57, 1943.

Garde, Edouard: *La Voix*, Presses Universitaires de France, Paris, 1954.

Gillilan, L. A.: *Clinical Aspects of the Autonomic Nervous System*, Little, Brown & Company, Boston, 1954.

Gisselsson, Leonard: "Dislocation of the Larynx," *Laryngoscope*, 60:117–120, 1950.

Goldstein, Kurt: "Ueber Aphasie," *Schweiz. Arch. f. Neurol.*, 19:3–38, 1926.

————: *Aftereffects of Brain Injuries in War*, Grune & Stratton, Inc., New York, 1942.

————: *Language and Language Disturbances*, Grune & Stratton, Inc., New York, 1948.

Goodhill, Victor: "Pathology, Diagnosis and Therapy of Deafness," in L. E. Travis (ed.), *Handbook of Speech Pathology*, Appleton-Century-Crofts, Inc., New York, 1957.

Gottlober, A. B.: *Understanding Stuttering*, Grune & Stratton, Inc., New York, 1953.

Grant, J. C. B.: *A Method for Anatomy*, The Williams & Wilkins Company, Baltimore, 1944.

Gray, G. W.: "Speech Sound Formation," in L. E. Travis (ed.), *Handbook of Speech Pathology*, Appleton-Century-Crofts, *Inc.*, New York, 1957.

———— and C. M. Wise: *The Bases of Speech*, Harper & Brothers, New York, 1946.

Gray, Henry: *Anatomy of the Human Body*, 26th ed., Ed. by C. M. Goss, Lea & Febiger, Philadelphia, 1954.

Greene, M. C. L.: *The Voice and Its Disorders*, The Macmillan Company, New York, 1957.

Guild, S. K.: "Elastic Tissue of the Eustachian Tube," *Ann. Otol. Rhin. & Laryng.*, 64:537–545, 1955.

Guilmette, C. A.: *Vocal Physiology*, Charles C. Pearson, Concord, N.H., 1877.

Guyton, A. C.: *Textbook of Medical Physiology*, W. B. Saunders Company, Philadelphia, 1956.

Hafford, A.: "A Comparative Study of the Salivary pH of the Normal Speaker and the Stutterer," *J. Speech & Hearing Disorders*, 6:173–184, 1941.

Hagerty, R. F., M. J. Hill, H. S. Pettit, and J. J. Kane: "Posterior Pharyngeal Wall Movement in Normals," *J. Speech & Hearing Res.*, 1:203–210, 1958.

Hahn, E. F.: *Stuttering—Significant Theories and Therapies*, Stanford University Press, Stanford, Calif., 1943.

————, C. W. Lomas, D. E. Hargis, and D. Vandraegen: *Basic Voice Training for Speech*, McGraw-Hill Book Company, Inc., New York, 1952.

Hardy, W. G., and M. D. Pauls: "The Test Situation in PSGR Audiometry," *J. Speech & Hearing Disorders*, 17(1):13–24, 1952.

Head, H.: *Aphasia and Kindred Disorders of Speech*, The Macmillan Company, New York, 1926, 2 vols.

Heffner, R. M. S.: *General Phonetics*, The University of Wisconsin Press, Madison, Wis., 1950.

Henderson, I. F., and W. D. Henderson: *Dictionary of Scientific Terms*, D. Van Nostrand Company, Inc., Princeton, N.J., 1949.

Henschen, S. E.: "On the Functions of the Right Hemisphere of the Brain in Relation to the Left in Speech, Music and Calculation," *Brain*, 49:110–123, 1926.

Hilger, J. A.: "Otolaryngologic Aspects of Hypometabolism," *Ann. Otol. Rhin. & Laryng.*, 65:395–413, 1956.

Hirsch, I. J.: *The Measurement of Hearing*, McGraw-Hill Book Company, Inc., New York, 1952.

Holinger, P. H., and K. C. Johnson: "Congenital Anomalies of the Larynx," *Ann. Otol. Rhin. & Laryng.*, 63:581–606, 1954.

Hollender, A. R.: *The Pharynx*, Year Book Publishers, Inc., Chicago, 1953.

Hollinshead, W. H.: *Anatomy for Surgeons*, Paul B. Hoeber, Inc., New York, 1954.

Holmes, F. L.: *A Handbook of Voice and Diction*, F. S. Crofts & Co., New York, 1946.

Hopp, E. S.: "The Development of the Epithelium of the Larynx," *Laryngoscope*, 65(7):475–499, 1955.

—— and H. F. Burns: "Ground Substance in the Nose in Health and Infection," *Ann. Otol. Rhin. & Laryng.*, 67:480–490, 1958.

Hough, J. N.: *Scientific Terminology*, Rinehart & Company, Inc., New York, 1953.

House, H. P., and A. Glorig: "New Concept of Auditory Screening," *Laryngoscope*, 67:661–668, 1957.

Houssay, Bernardo A.: *Human Physiology*, 2d ed., McGraw-Hill Book Company, Inc., New York, 1955.

Huber, J. F.: "Anatomy of the Mouth," *Clin. Symposia, Ciba*, 10(3):67–94, 1958.

——: "Anatomy of the Pharynx," *Clin. Symposia, Ciba*, 10(4):117–128, 1958.

Hudgins, C. V., and R. H. Stetson: "Relative Speed of Articulatory Movements," *Arch. Neerl. Phon. Exp.*, 13:85–94, 1937.

Husson, R.: "Etude des Phénomènes Physiologiques et Acoustiques Fondamentaux de la Voix Cantée," *Disp. edit. Rev. scientifique*, Paris, pp. 1–91, 1950.

Jackson, Chevalier: *Peroral Endoscopy and Laryngeal Surgery*, The Laryngoscope Company, St. Louis, Mo., 1915.

—— and L. J. Jackson: *Diseases of the Nose, Throat and Ear*, W. B. Saunders Company, Philadelphia, 1945.

Jackson, Willis: *Communication Theory*, Butterworth Scientific Publications, London, 1953.

Jenkins, George N.: *Physiology of the Mouth*, Blackwell Scientific Publications, Oxford, 1954.

Johnson, W., J. J. Curtis, C. W. Edney, and J. Keaster: *Speech Handicapped School Children*, Harper & Brothers, New York, 1956.

Jones, W.: "Nature of the Soft Palate," *J. Anat.*, 74:151, 1949.

Judson, L. S., and A. T. Weaver: *Voice Science*, Appleton-Century-Crofts, Inc., New York, 1942.

Jungert, Stig: "Central Auditory Pathways in the Brain Stem and Inferior Colliculi," *Acta oto-laryng., Suppl.* 140:182–185, 1958.

Kantner, Claude E., and Robert West: *Phonetics*, Harper & Brothers, New York, 1941.

Karlin, I. W.: "Stuttering—The Problem Today," *J.A.M.A.*, 143:732–736, 1950.

—— and A. E. Sobel: "A Comparative Study of the Blood Chemistry of Stutterers and Non-Stutterers," *Speech Monograph*, 7:75–84, 1940.

Keleman, George: "The Anatomical Basis of Phonation in the Chimpanzee," *J. Morphol.*, 82(2):229–256, 1948.

Keogh, C. A.: "The Neurology and Function of the Pharynx and its Powers of Compensation in Paralysis," *Ann. Otol. Rhin. & Laryng.*, 66:416–439, 1957.

Kodman, Frank: "Ventriloquism; An Area for Research," *Laryngoscope*, 65: 1065–1070, 1955.

Kopp, G. A.: "The Metabolism of the Stutterer as Evidenced by Biochemical Studies of Blood, Alveolar Air and Urine," doctoral dissertation, University of Wisconsin, Madison, Wis., 1933.

——: "Metabolic Studies of Stutterers," *Speech Monographs*, 1:117–132, 1934.

Kos, Clair M.: "Conservation of Hearing; Fenestration or Stapes Mobilization," *New England J. Med.*, 163:814–817, 1957.

Kostelijk, P. J.: *Theories of Hearing*, Universitaire Pers Leiden, Leiden, 1950.

Krieg, Wendell, J. S.: *Functional Neuroanatomy*, McGraw-Hill Book Company, Blakiston Division, New York, 1942.

Lassek, A. M.: "Human Pyramidal Tract; Numerical Investigation of Betz Cells of Motor Area," *Arch. Neurol. & Psychiat.*, 44:718–724, 1940.

—— and G. L. Rasmussen: "Human Pyramidal Tract; Fiber and Numerical Analysis," *Arch. Neurol. & Psychiat.*, 42:872–876, 1939.

LeJeune, F. E., and M. G. Lynch: "Review of the Available Literature on the Pharynx and Pharyngeal Surgery for 1954," *Laryngoscope*, 65(11): 1005–1031, 1955.

Lempert, J.: "Analytical Survey of Evolutionary Development of Fenestration Operation," *Ann. Otol. Rhin. & Laryng.*, 59:988–1019, 1950.

Lewis, D. K.: "Recent Contributions to the Study of Deafness," *New England J. Med.*, 259(4):169–178, 1958.

Licklider, J. C. R., and G. A. Miller: "The Perception of Speech," in S. S. Stevens (ed.), *Handbook of Experimental Psychology*, John Wiley & Sons, Inc., New York, 1951.

Lindsley, D. B.: "Emotion," in S. S. Stevens (ed.), *Handbook of Experimental Psychology*, John Wiley & Sons, Inc., New York, 1951.

Marcus, R. E., E. L. Gibbs, and F. A. Gibbs: "Electroencephalography in the Diagnosis of Hearing Loss in the Very Young Child," *Dis. Nerv. System*, 10(2):170–173, 1949.

Marie, Pierre: "La Troisième Circonvolution Frontale Gauche ne Joue Aucun Role Spécial dans la Fonction du Langage," *Semaine méd.* 26:241–247, 1906.

——: "Que Faut-il Penser des Aphasies Sous-corticales (Aphasies Pures)?" *Semaine méd.*, 26:493–500, 1906.

Martin, H.: "Esophageal Speech," *Ann. Otol. Rhin. & Laryng.*, 59:687–689, 1950.

Mawson, S. R.: "Myringoplasty," *J. Laryng. & Otol.*, 73:56–66, 1958.

McBurney, J. H., and E. J. Wrage: *The Art of Good Speech*, Prentice-Hall, Inc., Englewood Cliffs, N.J., 1953.

McCroskey, R. L. J.: "Effect of Speech on Metabolism: A Comparison between Stutterers and Non-stutterers," *J. Speech & Hearing Disorders*, 22:46–52, 1957.

McKenzie, William, and E. H. Rainer: "The Rosen Operation—Early Experience," *J. Laryng. & Otol.*, 71:655–666, 1957.

McLean, F. C.: "The Ultrastructure and Function of Bone," *Science*, 127 (3296):451–456, 1958.

Merritt, H. H., F. A. Mettler, and T. J. Putnam: *Fundamentals of Clinical Neurology*, McGraw-Hill Book Company, Inc., Blakiston Division, New York, 1947.

Meyers, Russell: "Physiological and Therapeutic Effects of Bilateral Intermediate Crusotomy for Atheto-dystonia (17 cases)," *Surgical Forum*, 6:486–488, 1955.

————: "Results of Bilateral Intermediate Midbrain Crustomy in Seven Cases of Severe Athetotic and Dystonic Quadriparesis," *Am. J. Phys. Med.*, 35: 84–105, 1956.

Michel, R.: "Die Bedeutung des Musculus Sternothyroideus für die Rahmenmodulation der Menschlichen Stimme," *Folia phoniatrica*, 6(2):65–100, 1954.

Milisen, Robert: "The Incidence of Speech Disorders," "Methods of Evaluation and Diagnosis of Speech Disorders," in L. E. Travis (ed.), *Handbook of Speech Pathology*, Appleton-Century-Crofts, Inc., New York, 1957.

Miller, G. A.: "Speech and Language," in S. S. Stevens (ed.), *Handbook of Experimental Psychology*, John Wiley & Sons, Inc., New York, 1951.

Mills, Charles: "Aphasia and the Cerebral Zones of Speech," *Am. J. M. Sc.*, 16:375–377, 1904.

Montreuil, Fernand: "Bifid Epiglottis: Report of a Case," *Laryngoscope*, 59:194–199, 1949.

Moore, G. Paul: "Motion Picture Studies of the Vocal Folds and Vocal Attack," *J. Speech & Hearing Disorders*, 3:235–238, 1938.

Moore, I.: "The So-called Prolapse of the Laryngeal Ventricle and Eversion of the Sacculus," *J. Laryng. & Otol.*, 37:265–274, 1922.

Morris: *Human Anatomy*, 11th ed., Ed. by J. P. Schaeffer, McGraw-Hill Book Company, Inc., New York, 1953.

Morrison, W. W.: *Diseases of the Ear, Nose and Throat*, Appleton-Century-Crofts, Inc., New York, 1955.

Moses, P. J.: *The Voice of Neurosis*, Grune & Stratton, Inc., New York, 1954.

Mosher, H. D.: "The Expression of the Face and Man's Type of Body as Indicators of His Character," *Laryngoscope*, 61:1–38, 1951.

Negus, V. E.: *The Mechanism of the Larynx*, William Heinemann, Ltd., London, 1929.

————: *The Comparative Anatomy and Physiology of the Larynx*, Grune & Stratton, Inc., New York, 1949.

————: "The Mechanism of the Larynx," *Laryngoscope*, 67:961–986, 1957.

————: "Tracheostomy," *Laryngoscope*, 67:1098–1112, 1957.

————, E. Neil, and W. F. Floyd: "The Mechanism of Phonation," *Ann. Otol. Rhin. & Laryng.*, 66:817–829, 1957.

Nelsen, Olin E.: *Comparative Embryology of the Vertebrates*, McGraw-Hill Book Company, Inc., Blakiston Division, New York, 1953.

Nielson, J. M.: *A Textbook of Clinical Neurology*, Paul B. Hoeber, Inc., New York, 1941.

O'Leary, J. L., and L. A. Coben: "The Reticular Core—1957," *Physiol. Rev.*, 38:243–276, 1958.

Orban, Balint, J.: *Oral Histology and Embryology*, 4th ed., The C. V. Mosby Company, St. Louis, Mo., 1957.

O'Rourke, J. T., and L. M. S. Miner: *Oral Physiology*, The C. V. Mosby Company, St. Louis, Mo., 1951.

Osgood, Charles E.: *Method and Theory in Experimental Psychology*, Oxford University Press, New York, 1956.

Palmer, M. F.: "Orthodontics and the Disorders of Speech," *Am. J. Orthodontics*, 34:579–588, 1948.

Parker, W. R.: *Pathology of Speech*, Prentice-Hall, Inc., Englewood Cliffs, N.J., 1951.

Patten, Bradley M.: *Human Embryology*, 2d ed., McGraw-Hill Book Company, Inc., New York, 1953.

Patton, F. E.: "A Comparison of the Kinesthetic Sensibility of Speech-defective and Normal-speaking Children," *J. Speech & Hearing Disorders*, 7:305–310, 1942.

Peele, Talmage L.: *The Neuroanatomical Basis for Clinical Neurology*, McGraw-Hill Book Company, Inc., New York, 1954.

Penfield, W., and T. Rasmussen: *The Cerebral Cortex of Man: A Clinical Study of Localization of Function*, The Macmillan Company, New York, 1950.

Perkins, W. H.: "The Challenge of Functional Disorders of Voice," in L. E. Travis (ed.), *Handbook of Speech Pathology*, Appleton-Century-Crofts, Inc., New York, 1957.

Peterson, G.: "Changes in Handedness in the Rat by Local Application of Acetylcholine to the Cerebral Cortex," *J. Comp. & Physiol. Psychol.*, 42:404–412, 1949.

Portmann, G.: "The Physiology of Phonation," *J. Laryng. & Otol.*, 71:1–15, 1957.

Potter, R. K., G. A. Kopp, and H. C. Green: *Visible Speech*, D. Van Nostrand Company, Inc., Princeton, N.J., 1947.

Pressman, J. J.: "Physiology of the Vocal Cords in Phonation and Respiration," *Arch. Otolaryng.*, 35:355–398, 1942.

———: "The Sphincters of the Larynx," *Tr. Am. Acad. Ophth.*, 57:724–737, 1953.

———: "Sphincters of the Larynx," *Arch. Otolaryng.*, 59:221–236, 1954.

——— and G. Kelemen: "Physiology of the Larynx," *Physiol. Rev.*, 35:506–554, 1955.

Prestigiacomo, A. J.: "Plastic-tape Sound Spectrograph," *J. Speech & Hearing Disorders*, 22:321–327, 1957.

Proetz, A. W.: *Applied Physiology of the Nose*, Annals Publishing Company, St. Louis, Mo., 1941.

Ranke, Otto F., and Hans Lullies: *Lehrbuch der Physiologie*, Springer-Verlag, Berlin, 1953.

Rasmussen, T., and W. Penfield: "Further Studies of the Sensory and Motor Cerebral Cortex of Man," *Fed. Proc.*, 6:452–460, 1947.

Raubicheck, Letitia: *Speech Improvements*, Prentice-Hall, Inc., Englewood Cliffs, N.J., 1952.

Ritzman, C. H.: "A Comparative Cardiovascular and Metabolic Study of Stutterers and Non-stutterers," *J. Speech & Hearing Disorders*, 7:367–373, 1942.

Robbins, S. D.: *A Dictionary of Speech Pathology and Therapy*, Expression Company, Boston, 1951.

Rohan, R. F.: "Artificial Tympanic Membranes: Old and New," *J. Laryng. & Otol.*, 71:605–615, 1957.

Rosen, S.: "Mobilization of Stapes to Restore Hearing in Otosclerosis," *New York J. Med.*, 53:2650–2653, 1953.

Ruedi, L.: "Actions of Vitamin A on the Human and Animal Ear," *Acta otolaryng.*, 44:502–516, 1954.

Russell, G. O.: *Speech and Voice*, The Macmillan Company, New York, 1931.

Rutherford, Burneice, R.: *Give Them a Chance to Talk*, Burgess Publishing Company, Minneapolis, Minn., 1956.

Saltzman, Maurice: *Clinical Audiology,* Grune & Stratton, Inc., New York, 1949.

Sataloff, Joseph: *Industrial Deafness,* McGraw-Hill Book Company, Inc., New York, 1957.

Saunders, J. B. de C. M., C. Davis, and R. Miller: "The Mechanism of Deglutition (Second Stage) as Revealed by Cine-radiography," *Ann. Otol. Rhin. & Laryng.,* 60:879–916, 1951.

Seltzer, A. P.: *Diseases of the Eye, Ear, Nose and Throat,* McGraw-Hill Book Company, Inc., New York, 1950.

Sharp, G. S., W. K. Bullock, and J. W. Hazlet: *Oral Cancer and Tumors of the Jaws,* McGraw-Hill Book Company, Inc., New York, 1956.

Sicher, H.: *Oral Anatomy,* 2d ed., The C. V. Mosby Company, St. Louis, Mo., 1952.

Soloman, Alan: "An Unusual Receptive Aphasia as a Manifestation of Temporal-lobe Epilepsy," *New England J. Med.,* 257:313–317, 1957.

Starr, H. E.: "The Hydrogen Ion Concentration of the Mixed Saliva Considered as an Index of Fatigue and Emotional Excitation, and Applied to a Study of the Metabolic Etiology of Stammering," *Am. J. Psychol.,* 33:374–418, 1922.

――――: "Psychological Concomitants of High Alveolar CO_2: A Psycho-biochemical Study of the Etiology of Stammering," *Psychol. Clin.,* 17:1–12, 1928.

Steer, M. D., and T. D. Hanley: "Instruments of Diagnosis, Therapy and Research," in L. E. Travis (ed.), *Handbook of Speech Pathology,* Appleton-Century-Crofts, Inc., New York, 1957.

Stetson, R. H.: *Motor Phonetics,* North Holland Publishing Company, Amsterdam, 1951.

―――― and C. V. Hudgins: "Functions of the Breathing Movements in the Mechanism of Speech," *Arch. Neerl. Phon. Exp.,* 5:1–30, 1937.

Stovin, J. S.: "The Importance of the Membranous Nasal Septum," *Arch. Otolaryn.,* 67:540–541, 1958.

Strong, L.: "The Mechanism of Laryngeal Pitch," *Anat. Rec.,* 63:13–28, 1935.

Timcke, R., H. von Leden, and P. Moore: "Laryngeal Vibrations: Measurements of the Glottic Wave," *Arch. Otolaryng.,* 68:1–19, 1958.

Townshend, R. H.: "The Formation of Passavant's Bar," *J. Laryng. & Otol.,* 55:154–165, 1940.

Travis, L. E.: *Speech Pathology,* Appleton-Century-Crofts, Inc., New York, 1931.

――――: "The Unspeakable Feelings of People with Special Reference to Stuttering," in L. E. Travis (ed.), *Handbook of Speech Pathology,* Appleton-Century-Crofts, Inc., New York, 1957.

Tremble, G. E.: "Hypertrophied Lingual Tonsils," *Laryngoscope,* 67:785–795, 1957.

Triboletti, E.: "Unusual Congenital Anomaly Involving the Larynx, Trachea and Esophagus," *New England J. Med.,* 258(20):1002–1003, 1958.

Trumper, H. A.: "A Hemato-respiratory Study of 101 Consecutive Cases of Stammering," doctoral dissertation, University of Pennsylvania, Philadelphia, 1928.

Van den Berg, J.: "Myoelastic-aerodynamic Theory of Voice Production," *J. Speech & Hearing Res.,* 1(3):227–244, 1958.

Van Riper, C., and J. V. Irwin: *Voice and Articulation,* Prentice-Hall, Inc., Englewood Cliffs, N.J., 1958.

Vogel, P. H.: "The Innervation of the Larynx of Man and the Dog," *Am. J. Anat.*, 90:427–447, 1952.

von Békésy, Georg: "Current Status of Theories of Hearing," *Science*, 123(3201):779–783, 1956.

—— and W. A. Rosenblith: "The Mechanical Properties of the Ear," in S. S. Stevens (ed.), *Handbook of Experimental Psychology*, John Wiley & Sons, Inc., New York, 1951.

von Mever, Georg H.: *The Organs of Speech*, D. Appleton & Company, New York, 1884.

Walter, H. E., and L. P. Savles: *Biology of the Vertebrates*, 3d ed., The Macmillan Company, New York, 1949.

Washburn, S. L., and D. Wolffson: *Anthropological Papers of Franz Weidenreich, 1939–1948: A Memorial Volume*, The Viking Fund, Inc., New York, 1949.

Watson, L. A., and T. Tolan: *Hearing Tests and Hearing Instruments*, The Williams & Wilkins Company, Baltimore, 1949.

Weisenburg, T., and K. E. McBride: *Aphasia*, The Commonwealth Fund, New York, 1935.

Weisskopf, A., and H. F. Burns: "The Ground Substance of the Nasal Turbinates," *Ann. Otol. Rhin. & Laryng.*, 67:292–304, 1958.

Wepman, Joseph M.: *Recovery from Aphasia*, The Ronald Press Company, New York, 1951.

Wernicke, C.: *Der Aphasische Symptomcomplex*, Breslau, 1874.

West, Robert: *Diagnosis of Disorders of Speech*, The College Typing Company, Madison, Wis., 1936.

——: "Recent Studies in Speech Pathology," *Proc. Am. Speech Correction A.*, 6:44–49, 1936.

——: "The Neurophysiology of Speech," in L. E. Travis (ed.), *Handbook of Speech Pathology*, Appleton-Century-Crofts, Inc., New York, 1957.

——, L. Kennedy, and A. Carr: *The Rehabilitation of Speech*, Harper & Brothers, New York, 1937.

——, M. Ansberry, and ——: *The Rehabilitation of Speech*, Harper & Brothers, New York, 1957.

Wever, Ernest G.: *Theory of Hearing*, John Wiley & Sons, Inc., New York, 1949.

Wiener, Norbert. *Cybernetics*, John Wiley & Sons, Inc., New York, 1948.

Williams, A. F.: "The Recurrent Laryngeal Nerve and the Thyroid Gland," *J. Laryng. & Otol.*, 68:719–725, 1954.

Williams, D. E.: Masseter Muscle Action Potentials in Stuttered and Nonstuttered Speech," *J. Speech & Hearing Disorders*, 20:242–261, 1955.

Winterstein, Hans: "Chemical Control of Pulmonary Ventilation," *New England, J. Med.*, 255:272–278, 1956.

Wise, C. M., J. H. McBurney, L. A. Mallory, C. R. Strother, and W. J. Temple: *Foundations of Speech*, Ed. by J. M. O'Neill, Prentice-Hall, Inc., Englewood Cliffs, N.J., 1941.

Woodburne, R. T.: *Essentials of Human Anatomy*, Oxford University Press, New York, 1957.

Yale, Caroline A.: *Formation and Development of Elementary English Sounds*, Metcalf Printing and Publishing Company, Northampton, Mass., 1946.

INDEX

Date Due